STUDIES IN ANCIENT TECHNOLOGY

VOLUME IX

STUDIES
IN ANCIENT TECHNOLOGY

BY

R. J. FORBES

VOLUME IX

WITH 48 FIGURES AND 8 TABLES

LEIDEN

E. J. BRILL

1964

PRINTED IN THE NETHERLANDS

CONTENTS

LIST OF ABBREVIATIONS USED IN THE TEXT

AAA	Annals of Archaeology and Anthropology (Liverpool)
AfO	Archiv für Orientforschung
AJSL	American Journal of Semitic Languages and Literatures
AL	D. J. Wiseman, The Alalakh Tablets (London, 1953)
Ant.J.	Antiquaries Journal (London)
AO	Der Alte Orient (Leipzig)
APAW	Abhandlung der Preussischen Akadamie der Wissenschaften
AR	J. H. Breasted, Ancient Records of Egypt (Chicago, Third Imp. 1927)
ARL	D. D. Luckenbill, Ancient Records of Assyria and Babylonia (Chicago, 1926)
ARM	Archives Royales de Mari (edit. G. Dossin e.a., Paris, 1950–)
BA	Beiträge zur Assyriologie
B.A.report	Report of the British Academy (London)
BK	see KB
Bab.Miz.	F. H. Weiszbach, Babylonische Miszellen
CAH	Cambridge Ancient History
CT	Cuneiform texts from Babylonian tablets, etc. in the British Museum
DP	Délégation en Perse, edit. J. de Morgan
Falkenstein	A. Falkenstein, Archaïsche Texte aus Ur (Leipzig, 1936)
HWB	Erman-Grapow, Handwörterbuch der aegyptischen Sprache
ILN	Illustrated London News
ITT	Inventaire des tablettes de Tello
JEA	Journal of Egyptian Archaeology (London)
JEOL	Jaarbericht Ex Oriente Lux (Leyden)
KAH	Keilschrifttexte aus Assur historischen Inhalts

KAR	Keilschrifttexte aus Assur religiösen Inhalts
KAVI	Keilschrifttexte aus Assur verschiedenen Inhalts
KB	H. H. Figulla - E. F. Weidner, Keilinschriften aus Boghazkoï
OLZ	Orientalische Literatur Zeitung (Leipzig).
PW	Pauly-Wissowa, Real-Encyclopädie der klassischen Altertumswissenschaft.
RA	Revue d'Assyriologie (Paris)
ŠL	Deimel, Šumerisches Lexikon (Rome)
Sethe Urk.	Urkunden des ägyptischen Altertums, edit. K. Sethe
VAB	Vorderasiatische Bibliothek (Leipzig)
YOS	Yale Oriental Series, Babylonian texts.

PREFACE

Continuing our previous vol. VIII of these Studies we now present a recast version of the chapters on copper and bronze, tin, arsenic, antimony and iron from our Metallurgy in Antiquity. Here again finality is impossible as we are in the midst of important research on ancient metal objects. As the previous volumes of this series this volume too is not meant to be more than a guide and an introduction to the subject for archaeologists and historians who want to understand more about the scientific and technical principles involved in working and shaping these metals and their alloys, by which Nature sets limits to the possibilities of the ancient craftsman.

Dr. J. Needham was so kind as to allow the author to quote verbatim the conclusion of his Development of Iron and Steel Technology in China.

Amsterdam, April 1963

R. J. FORBES.

CHAPTER ONE

COPPER

Our intended Discourse is now of *Venus* or
Copper (Geber, *On the Sum of Perfection*, XII)

1. *Introduction*

According to the definition of Geber copper is "a *Metallick Body*,
livid, partaking of a dusky *Redness*, ignible (or sustaining *Ignition*),
fusible, extensible under the *Hammer* but refusing the *Cupel* and
Cement".

But then this was in the Middle Ages when Albertus Magnus could
speak of "workers in copper in our parts, namely Cologne and Paris
and in other places where I have been and seen things tested by experience to investigate nature and characteristics of copper".

However, this scientific spirit was fairly recent, for even the Hellenistic alchemists had used copper only as a base-product for their
experiments. The Leiden papyrus, one of the earliest chemical papyri,
mentions the leukosis of copper. Sometimes copper is coloured to
imitate gold, this was effected by heating copper with a mixture of
powdered lead and gold. Ostanes invented a "divine water" to tinge
copper like gold, and the Transmutation series of Democritos, Hermes, Africanos, and Zosimos start with copper. Olympiodorus starts
the "work" by the treatment (*ergasiá*) of copper, and Stephanos by a
"battle between copper and mercury".

In alchemy copper is represented by the sign of the planet Venus.
Some have recognised this sign on Old Kingdom seals from Egypt,
but have been mislead by the sign *nefer*, beautiful. Others have derived
it from the well-known Egyptian *anch* (life) sign, but this too is ante-
dating a sign that belongs to Hellenistic astronomy.

Though copper figures in early chemistry and even in earlier magical
practices to some extent, it is far more important as the earliest useful
metal of mankind. For though the use of gold may have preceded
that of copper in some regions, the precious metal could not be fashioned into tools and weapons and its production had little influence on

early technology though the goldsmith's art was of great importance to later metallurgy. But copper production and working is the earliest branch of metallurgy, that art which has changed the face of Neolithic mankind. Has not Childe described the discovery of copper metallurgy as the most dramatic leap in the history of mankind? For it was with copper that early mankind learnt to experiment and to discover the astonishing changes that fire would work on these shining stones, the miraculous transformation of certain brightly coloured stones by fire into this metal and the possibilities that slumbered in this new kind of stone. Armed with this experience gathered in centuries of transition from Stone to Metal Age they attacked other stones, produced other metals, mixed metals or ores to get still more useful alloys and changed the face of the earth by applying the metals to art and industry.

2. *Native copper in the Pre-Columbian New World*

Copper occurs in the native state in many places in the world and as such it was first found and used by neolithic man. A good survey of the difference between the early native copper and the later copper industry can be had by a short glance at the stage of copper metallurgy in the New World by the time of its discovery by the whites (1).

One of the early students of the pre-Columbian North-American Indians, Schmidt, remarked already that copper was no more than a stone to these Indians, who at the time of the discovery of the New World were just settling down as semi-nomads and were only recently acquainted with agriculture. They collected native copper and treated it as any other stone. These facts led Schmidt to state that civilisation comes only with the Bronze Age and we have hardly any reason to speak of a Copper Age. In the United States of America near Lake Superior (State of Michigan) there are large outcrops of a ferrous sandstone which contains appreciable masses of native copper (1.3 to 1.4%) mainly in the form of dust, but also nuggets and lumps ranging from several pounds up to many tons occur. In the weathered outcrops of these strata big copper boulders had been found by the Indians and early travellers found that 'they had taken off every projecting point which was accessible by pounding with stone hammers or mauls, so that all the exposed surface was smooth". Modern mining has followed the stratum to a depth of 4000—5000' and by grinding, sieving and washing extracts a copper that is practically pure and contains only 0.15%

of silver, 0.002% of arsenic and 0.002% of antimony is obtained. Smelting and poling this copper yields a very pure product. It is now certain that the surface outcrops were worked by the pre-Columbian Indians. There are no early mines in our sense, they are just galleries or open-cuts to dig out nuggets, in some of which Phillips found nuggets of 99.4% purity. Remains of charcoal fires near the big boulders of Lake Superior and at other places show that the Indians used fire to

Fig. 1.
Huge copper nugget found near Lake Superior

detach pieces of copper-bearing rock, not for smelting. Other important copper finds were excavated in the burial mounds of the Mississippi plain. The "float" copper found in the neighbourhood is really carried by the ice masses from the strata of Lake Superior as far south as the mouth of the Ohio river and deposited there as native copper among the detritus of the rocks. The Indians used this native copper to make ornaments. The copper of these ornaments is very pure (usually 99.9% with traces of iron and silver), it can be distinguished with absolute certainty from imported copper of the earlier discoverers, which was seldom over 98% pure in that period and contained traces of nickel, cobalt, arsenic, antimony, sulphur, silver and iron. No piece of copper from the burial mounds of the Plains is either alloyed or smelted, every piece being hammered float copper. Their manufacture shows considerable skill and taste though they are of types closely related with stone tools. The Indians seem to have known only the malleability of native copper, they cut and trimmed it with stone tools and smoothed it by abrasion with stone. Most of the artefacts were made by that alternate hammering and heating which we call annealing. Casting was not practised as C. C. Willoughby of the Peabody Museum showed, whose work was continued by Wharton and West of the Milwaukee Museum, all the ancient artifacts could be reproduced by these simple means. Later investigations by Hurst, Larson and others have shown that the native copper was not in all cases Michigan copper, but that native copper of local origin was obtained in the south. Comparison of the data on the use of native copper by the North American Indians and the copper metallurgy of Chimu, Incas and Aztecs tend to show that Rivet was right in suggesting that copper metallurgy came to the Indians of the North American plains by way of the Caribbian islands from the north coast of South America (Colombia?).

We have discussed the latest evidence on the development of metallurgy (gold and copper) in South America, when we discussed the evolution of metallurgy in general (2) and we found that this originated on the south coast of Peru and spread to Ecuador, Colombia and Mexico, reaching the latter country but a few centuries before the Conquest (3). Hence the Aztects worked native copper at Zocutallan and Oaxaca and melted and cast it, and they also passed this art on to the Maya region. Sahagun reports that the Aztecs produced copper from ore and smelted it with three kinds of herbs to guarantee good copper production.

We know now that the Chimu started working copper and passed on the knowledge to the Incas, to whom we owe the exploitation of the deposits of Coro Coro. Barba says that in his time the Incas mined and smelted chalcopyrite at Cerro de Pasco, Colquijirca and Hualgayoc using small furnaces with natural draught as they did not possess bellows. At any rate if they could smelt copper this must have been a recent acquisition and perhaps introduced by the Spaniards for Helps and Prescott mention that they valued copper more than silver or gold at the time of the Conquest. A few modern analyses of Ecuadorian samples showed that they consisted of pure copper, while Mexican axes of the same type contained a small but natural percentage of tin. In both types of axes some process had been employed to harden the cutting edge, but there is no evidence against the hypothesis that the hardening was effected by hammering.

It would seem, therefore, that the New World did know the production of copper from ores, or may be they had learnt it shortly before or after the conquest. In the case of the Indians of North America it is certain that they were still in the Stone Age and treated their copper like stone, having no idea of its metallic qualities. This is also clear from the terms which Indians use for copper. The Algonquins call it

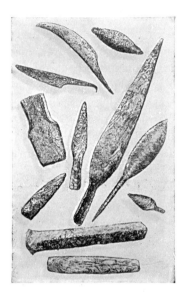

Fig. 2.
Implements fashioned from native copper by the American Indians
(after Andrée)

musquabik, e.g. "red stone", the Chippewas ozahwabhik, "yellow stone", the Zuni hi-we, "soft stone" and the South Californian Indians er-reck, "stone, also metal in general". Only a few like the Virginian Indians have a word for copper "Wassador", which is also used as a general term for metal.

True copper metallurgy, therefore, begins at smelting copper ores and casting native or smelted copper. Before discussing copper metallurgy we must describe copper ores and their distribution in the Ancient Near East and Europe as far as they were of importance to the Ancients.

3. *The copper ores*

The production of copper was greatly enhanced by the prominent part which electricity plays in modern life. More than 50% of the copper produced at present is used for electrical apparatus, wire, etc. Its malleability and toughness make this metal very suitable for coins and its small value as compared with gold and silver makes it eminently suitable as a material for small change. The greater part of the copper now produced is used in the form of alloys with other metals, many specific alloys have been developed for every special applications. Though pure copper and bronze formed the main materials in Antiquity, there existed already a tendency to develop special bronzes, etc. in later ages, especially in the Hellenistic and Imperial method. These alloys are very important in modern machine industry and armaments and they play a large part as bearing metals.

The most popular alloy is "copper-tin" which we call bronze; when alloys of copper and lead, antimony, etc. are made we usually speak of lead-bronzes, antimony-bronzes, etc.

Copper is very widely distributed in nature and is found in soils, waters and ores. *Native, malleable or virgin copper* occurs as a mineral, especially in the surface strata of deposits of copper and iron ores. In the upper workings of these deposits it is found in arborescent, dendritic, filiform, moss-like or laminar form. Small nuggets are frequent in the Ural mountains, larger lumps are found in Siberia, the Altaï and North-East Asia and Mexico, large boulders occur in the famous deposit of Lake Superior (Michigan).

We mention here only the principal *copper ores* (with their copper content):

Cuprite (red oxyde of copper, ruby ore), a copper oxyde,
    which occurs in small quantities only 88.8%
Malachite, a green (basic) carbonate of copper 57.3%
Azurite, a blue (basic) carbonate of copper, which should
    be clearly distinguished from lapis lazuli or lazulite. . . . 55.1%
Chrysocolla, a copper silicate, that is not identical with the
    ancient chrysocolla of Pliny and Theophrastus 36.0%

These ores together with native copper occur in the weathered surface outcrops of deeper strata of copper ores which belong to the second group of sulphides or copper-sulphur compounds:
Chalcocite (vitreous copper, redruthite, copper glance), a

copper sulphide 79.8%
Chalcopyrite (copper pyrites, towanite, yellow copper ore) a
    copper sulphide usually mixed with the sulphides of iron 34.6%
Bornite (purple copper ore, peacock ore), a rarer variety of
    chalcopyrite 55.5%
Covellite (indigo or blue copper), a less common copper
    sulphide 66.5%
Enargite, a compound of copper, sulphur and arsenic. . . . 48.4%
Tetrahedrite, a compound of copper, sulphur and antimony 52.1%
Fahlore, a compound of copper, iron, mercury and zinc sul-
    phides 30-48%

Nearly every copper mineral is distinguished by some bright hue, which made it very obvious to the ancient miner. It is certain that the earliest mining of copper ores started with the surface deposits of oxyde and carbonate ores. Many early exploited lodes must have been exhausted and many widely distributed deposits of ores of poor quality have left hardly any trace for the archaeologist. It is also certain that even in Antiquity the demand for copper grew already so great that deeper strata were mined and sulphide ores were worked. This may have been general practise in Roman times when nearly all the surface deposits within reach of the Romans had given out. The working of widely distributed pockets of surface ores with widely varying composition accounts for the many different systems of working the ores and the highly intricate methods. Only some of the older mines such as those at Mansfeld had larger ore bodies of a fairly constant composition. At present very poor but huge ore bodies are worked of a very constant copper content (from 0.85 to 6% but an average of 2%) where mass production has made the exploitation economical. Such are the modern ore bodies of Kazakstan, Chile and only in Katanga a richer ore of 6% of copper is worked. The figures for the copper content of the minerals given above are those of the pure minerals, if we take the gangue in account the ores worked by the ancients may have held something like 10—20% of copper, but patient selection and washing led to the working of very pure ores in the smelting furnaces by methods, which would of course be considered very uneconomical at present. At present the economy of working certain copper ores is often determined by other metals such as gold, silver, lead, zinc or rare metals.

Very little is known for certain about ancient copper mining (4).

The first to describe the bright coloured copper ores correctly was Theophrastus and of course these bright colours had led earlier miners to ore deposits. The Romans knew something about the connection between the oxides on the surface and the deeper sulphides for as Pliny says (5): "The early miners used to cease their operations when they came to alumen seeking no further, but the recent discoveries of the veins of copper below the alumen has removed this limit to their hopes". Biringuccio in the sixteenth century mentions the bright colour of the ore, the taste of water near the deposit and the micaceous fracture of the rocks as sure indications of ore bodies. Still the ancients knew several copper ores though they do not often distinguish them quite clearly.

Diosocorides mentions in his Herbal chrysocolla (our malachite!) and says: (6) "That of Armenia is the best very much ressembling leeks in ye colour, but that of Macedonia is ye second, then the Cyprian and of this the pure is chosen".

He also mentions chalcitis, which "is to be preferred if it looks like brass and is brittle being without stones and not old and moreover having somewhat long and glittering veins", but Pliny says: "The name chalcitis is given to another mineral from which copper is smelted. It differs from cadmea in that the latter is hewn from exposed rocks on the surface of the ground while chalcitis is mined from deeply-buried deposits. Again chalcitis is soft by nature, like condensed wool and crumbles quickly. Another point of distinction is that chalcitis contains three constituents copper, misy and sory to be described each in its proper place" and his following paragraphs (7) give vague descriptions of *chalcitis, misy, sory, chalcantos* (flowers of copper) and *melanteria*. There can be little doubt that some of Pliny's *chalcitis* may have been our chrysocolla, but that all of these products comprise the sulphide minerals of copper and iron and their alteration products, the latter including shoemaker's black or *chalcantum*. *Chalcitis* can be translated more or less as "weathered pyrites". Dioscorides also describes *misy*, which may be copperas (8). The *cadmea* described by Pliny is not only the zinc ore which we have already discussed (9) but often a mixture of copper and zinc ores either natural or artificial. Strabo (10) is more correct in applying the name *cadmea* to zinc ores only.

Pliny also describes *pyrites*: "The name is sometimes given to the millstone, because there is much fire in it; but there is another and more porous variety and yet another pyrites with a resemblance to copper. They assert, that the two kinds are found in the mines in the

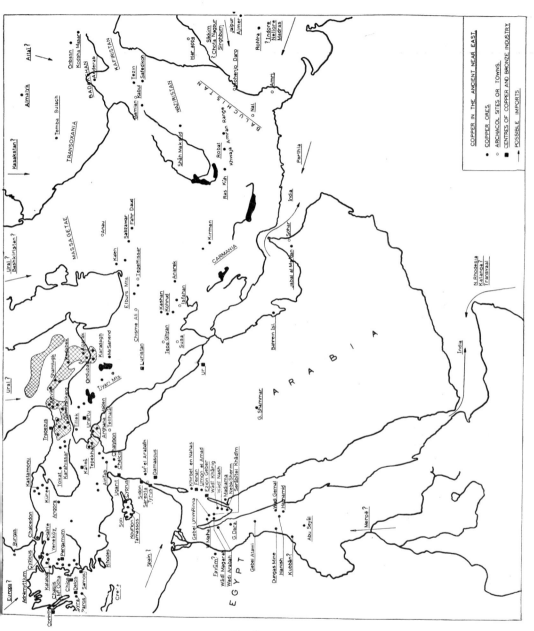

Fig. 3.
Map of the copper deposits in the Ancient Near East

neighbourhood of Acamas in Cyprus, one with the colour of silver (our marcasite!) and the other with the colour of gold (iron-copper pyrites!)" (11).

It is certain that every form of mining from open-cut mining to the driving of galleries into the mountainside to follow up the copper bearing strata was practised in Antiquity. But the details given on ancient mines are few and they should receive closer attention from younger generations of archaeologists. Fire-setting and other means were used to break up the rocks and stone tools were used upto the advent of iron as both copper or bronze tools are unsuitable for mining being either too soft or too brittle. In Sinai it was proved that stone tools remained in use until the Early Iron Age and it is the same in many other copper mines, especially those of Tirol and Salzburg which have been studied in detail (12). By washing, handpicking and crushing the ore was purified from the worthless gangue. Often the ores were immediately ready for use, especially as extraction was not very perfect in Antiquity and old slags have been retreated with profit in modern times, for instance in the copper districts of Spain.

As little is known about the ancient copper mines in the Near East. We have given only a few of the most important surface deposits in Fig. 3 mentioning those which are prominent in ancient literature or have some interest because of their situation amongst ancient sites. Many older deposits have given out or were cleared so well of their ores that they have escaped the often superficial investigation of travellers. Here again there is a lack of proper geological information which should be corrected as soon as possible.

4. *The copper mining districts of Antiquity*

There are several important copper deposits in *Egypt*, which have been enumerated and discussed by Lucas (13). The principal deposits occur in the peninsula of Sinai. In Wâdî Maghârah and Serâbît el-Khâdim the ore consists largely of malachite with a little azurite and chrysocolla, at Gebel Um Rinna of malachite as at Wâdî Malḥa and Wâdî Khârig. Wâdî Nasb and Sêh Baba contains large ancient slagheaps, along the plain of Senned azurite is found and in the hills west of the Nebk-Sherm plain malachite.

In Wâdî 'Arabah, east of Beni Suef in the eastern desert, chryso-colla occurs but it is doubtful whether it was mined in Antiquity. Chrysocolla occurs again at Gebel Dara and copper ores are found at Gebel Atawi and in the Dungash gold mine. Malachite occurs at Wâdî Gemâl and Hammamîd, the latter deposits showing shafts upto a depth of 80'. Malachite also occurs in the Sufr hills west of Jemsa and in Wâdî Sibrit, the slagheaps at Kubbân may originate from these mines. At Hamish chalcopyrite incrusted with blue copper compounds is found and at Abu Seyâl phyrrothite and copper sulphides with some chrysocolla.

Of these deposits the Sinai mines are by far the most important and practically the only source of Egyptian copper upto the XXI dynasty as we shall see. The Kubbân mines may have been exploited from the XIIth dynasty onwards but Abu Seyâl not earlier than the XIXth dynasty. Egyptian records mention no tributes of copper from the south. In the light of this information it is not probable that the Meroë mines mentioned by Strabo (14) existed before classical times. On the other hand graves in Nubia dating from pre-dynastic and Old Kingdom times contain copper objects, which may, however, have been imported from Egypt. Diodor (15) mentions these mines too.

In North Africa more than 60 mining sites have been discovered, which by their crude methods of working can hardly antedate the Arabs. Still Strabo says (16): "that there are also somewhere here in Massesyli (the present Algeria) copper mines", he probably refers to deposits near the modern Tenes. The mines of Maghreb (Morocco) (17) exported copper to the negroes though they had mines of their own in the Congo regions in the period of Al Bekrî (1050 A.D.), though nothing is known of any pre-Arab working.

It is very improbable that the deposits of practically pure carbonate ore of Hofrat en Nahas on the banks of the Bahr el Arab, a confluent of the Bahr el Ghazal in the Sudan were worked before the XIXth century. The copper mines in the Thebaïs mentioned by Diodor (18) can not be located.

The modern copper mines of Katanga and Northern Rhodesia and the deposits of Transvaal (Zoutpansberg, Ookiep) play no part in the supplies of the Ancient Near East, though they are most important in modern times.

Syria and Palestine have some deposits of more than local prominence, that are also mentioned by ancient authors (19). There are some vague references to copper mines in Palestine or close to its borders in the Bible (20). Lately Glueck (21) has described the important copper mines of Edom near Khirbet en Nahâs and Umm el 'Amad and its refineries both near the mines around Pheinan and at Ezion Geber that were

certainly of Solomonic date and may go back to the XVIIIth century
B.C. The deposits around Madiana in Midian contain malachite,
chrysocolla and pyrites, but it is not known for certain whether they
were worked in Antiquity. Pheinan is the Phinom mentioned by Eusebius (22) who states that there were copper mines in the Lebanon range
and Syria too.

Near the ancient centres of copper and bronze industry Sidon,
Tyrus and Sarepta we find the deposit of Mount al Araba'în near the
ancient Calchis (now Antschar) and the Lita river, a site probably to
be identified with the pre-classical Ķinnesrîn, which may be the mine
refered to by Eusebius. This district Riha near Damascus has been
identified with the Nuhašše of the Amarna letters and some authors
have tried to prove that the Hebrew word nechošeth for copper was
derived from this Nuhašše, the "copper-land", but this identification
can not be true as Knudtzon has proved beyond doubt that the kingdom Nuhašše was situated near Nii between Aleppo and the Euphrates (23). The region around Aleppo in North Syria has many copper
ores. Not only do they occur near Aïn Tab, Chirbet es Šamra and Wadi
Rwebe, where ore was dug at least in Roman and Byzantine times, but
in Roman times the district around Chalcis was called Chalcidice and
around Chalybon Chalybonitis. As Syria was always an important
centre of copper industry these mines may have been exploited in pre-
classical times.

Arabia is not very rich in minerals but apart from the copper ores
of Midian we find them at Gebel Shamar and in the Jabal al Ma'dan
in Oman near Sohar, which may have been the source of early Sumerian
copper, the Magan and Meluḫḫa of early texts. Some copper ores are
found on the Bahrein islands.

On the other side of the Persian Gulf Carmania was said to have
copper mines (24) which may have been near the present Kirman.
Mâsûdî mentions the copper from Oman, but not that from Carmania.

The ancient civilisation of Waziristan and Baluchistan discovered
by Aurel Stein and related to the Sumerians and the Indus civilisation
used copper and bronze freely but its sources are not yet known. Still
copper is found in the Râs Kûh and the Khwaja Amrân ranges. Slag-
heaps have been found near Shâh Ballaul and Robat.

These mines in *Baluchistan* may have formed the sources of the
Mohenjo Daro copper and bronze, but there are many other copper
districts in India proper. There are old workings in the Shan states,
Indore, Nellore, the Kistna district, Rupavati in Kathiawar, Ambra

Mata and Kumbaria in North Gujrat and in Nepal, though it is doubtful on other grounds that they were worked before Hellenistic times. There are rich outcrops in Merwâra Ajmer, Rohira in Sirohi state and in Jaipur (Chetri and Singhana). The Singhbum district (Mosaboni, Dhobani, Matigara) contains a fairly important copper industry; other deposits in the Orissa-Behar region are those at Chota Nagpur and Hazâribagh (Bengal). There are many other small workings in the south for instance in the Madras presidency and in Sikkim. Most of these deposits contain mainly pyrites and other sulphidic ores. Strabo mentions "Indian copper" (25) without any specification.

Afghanistan is rich in copper, many mines are mentioned by Hiuen Tsang. There are the mines of Shâh Maksud worked by Nadir Shah, other deposits at Safed Kûh (between Kabul and Kurram), at Tezin (east of Kabul) and the Shâdkani and Silwâtû passes.

In Eastern Turkestan there are mines near Onbash of the Musart river and at Kodscha-Masar on the Tisnaf river.

There are rich deposits in the Altai mountains at Ridder and other sites with ancient workings, while in Kasakstan there are the rich ore-bodies of Makain, Boschtschekul, Kounrad, and Dscheskasgan, which have been worked since 1930. A primitive but extensive copper industry was found at Temba Bulach in the Kizil Kum desert but its date is uncertain as that of the extensive "Chude pits" built and worked by the legendary Chudes which extend from the Altai mountains upto the Ural mountains but are particularly extensive near Abakansk on the Jenessei and on the banks of the Tscharysch a tributary river of the Ob. In Usbekstan there is an important ore-body near Almalyk. The Ural mountains contain very rich deposits at Pyschmin with 3—6% of copper and in Baschkiristan to the south the mines of Tanalyk, Bogomolowsk, Degtiarka and Bljawa. They were possibly the sources whence the Massagetae drew their copper (26). The ancient copper mines of Bamian near Kabul and in Kafiristan and the Paraponisus form the eastern extension of the belt of copper deposits which runs though Northern Persia upto the Caspian Sea and beyond to Transcaucasia. Ibn Hauqal mentions copper mines in Transoxania, but those on the eastern border of *Persia* were very important too, even in his times. There are the mines of Kal-SebZarre, Sabzawar and Fahr Daud near Meshed, Kaleh near Astrabad and in the Elburs mountains. The districts of Kashan, Kohund and Isfahan contain many important mines. The mines of Isfahan, Anarek and Bochara were the most important sources of copper for the Arabian Chalifs of the ninth century A.D., they paid no less than 10.000 dinars in taxes. There are easily reducible carbonates at Binamar and Pankaleh. In the North Mount Sahend and the Kara Dagh are extensions of the Transcaucasian deposits and probably the sources of Luristan copper. The deposits discovered in 1846 by Layard in the Ashishtha valley of the Tiyari mountains are often mentioned in Assyrian and Babylonian records. The Kara Dagh ores are rich in gold and silver too.

In *Caucasia* and *Transcaucasia* there are so many deposits that we could not possibly enumerate them in this short essay. The different copper districts have been described by Hančar (27), they have not been detailed on the map. The pyrites around Kedabek, Allaverdi and Shamlugk contains about 3.5% of copper, the ores near Sangesur upto 18%, the chalcopyrite and pyrites at Angarak upto 10%, the latter strata are covered by a fairly deep deposit of oxide and carbonate ore which contains laminar native copper. Native copper, covellin and chalcopyrite occur in the particularly rich ores of Chagali-Heliar where the copper content runs up to 25%. These Transcausacian deposits are continued into Turkey by the deposits of Artvin (Kuvarshane) with 7% of copper and the deposits of Gümüshkane and other Pontic districts in the famous ancient metallurgical centre of the Mossynoeci and Chalybes. Other continuations of the Transcaucasian deposits are the ores of Tillek and Arghana Ma'den both worked in Antiquity. The whole Armenian-Transcaucasian region and the Urartu of the foothills was most important as a centre of supply of Mesopotamian copper and there are plenty of traces of primitive mining and refining around the old deposits.

The copper mines of the Taurus region are old mines too, they are mentioned in Mesopotamian records and by Eusebius (28). Opposite the Cilician coast there is the island of *Cyprus*, from which copper derives its name. The copper mines of Cyprus are prominent in classical literature, they are mentioned by Homer and others (29). The old mines are near Tamassos, Amathus, Soli, Kurion and Krommyon near the edge of the andesite outcrops of the Troodos massif. At present these mines are still exploited, that is the strata on the north-west coast of the Morphu bay at Skuriotissa and Mavriuni, where 35.000 Tons of copper were produced in 1938.

The other deposits on the mainland of *Asia Minor* are far less important. There are several deposits on the mainland opposite to Samos where the inhabitants were clever bronze and copper-smiths according to Pliny and Pausanias (30). North of the ancient centre of bronze industry, Pergamum, there are several mines amongst others that of Cisthêne (31) Artemidorus states that the mine at Adramyttium was still in use at the time of Alexander the Great. The district to the south of the Lake of Marmora contains several copper deposits which are exploited at the present time. There was an ancient mine on the island of Kalki, the Chalcitis of Theophrastus (32) and Pollux off Chalcedon. Other deposits are known near Kastamonu and Tokat which do not seem to figure in ancient literature.

Ancient Greece was no copper-producing country and the small local deposits that are said to have existed near Sicyon and in Attika and Argolis seem to have been exhausted at a very early date. There are still small ore bodies on Syra and Paros. In Euboea copper ores of Mons Ocha and Aedepsos are mentioned but these are not confirmed by geological handbooks and it is held by many that Euboea had its fame as a copper-smithing country only ranking with Aegina and Rhodos or Delos (33), not as a production centre. On the other hand Strabo says: (34) "Above Chalcis is situated the Lelantine plain and in this plain was also a remarkable mine which contained copper and iron together (probably in the very common form of pyrites!) a thing is not reported as occuring elsewhere; now, however, both metals have given out".

In Macedonia copper ores occur and near the present Burgas (35) at Karabajir and Rosenbajir tools and slags of the La Tène period were found. The copper was probably shipped thence to the south by the Greeks who took other products from the Euxine.

Jugoslavia has some important deposits near Bor (Cuka Dulkan) and at Majdan Pek, mainly pyrites and chalcopyrite.

Italy had several copper mines which were mostly abandoned when the Spanish mines were opened in the Early Empire. Prominent amongst the Italian mines are those in Tuscany between Volterra and Populonia at Montecatini, Montanto and Monte Calve already exploited by the Etruscans (36). There are others in the Campiglia Marittima and pseudo-Aristotle seems to indicate these when he speaks of mines on the island of Elba (37) where there are no copper ores. In Sardinia there are the ores of Calabona and in Bruttium there was a mine near Tempsa of which Strabo says (38): "People say that Homer has in mind this Temesa not the Tamassos in Cyprus (the names are spelt both ways) when he says "to Temesa in quest of copper". And in fact, copper mines are to be seen in the neighbourhood, although now they have been abandoned". Then there are copper ores in Agordo in the Alps of which Pliny (39) says: "The next best kind of copper (after the Cyprian) was the Sallustian from the land of the Ceutrones in the Alps. This did not last long and was succeeded by the Livian from Gaul. Both names are derived from the owners of the mines, the friend and wife respectively of the emperor Augustus". And he continues: "Livian copper also gave out very quickly for very little is now found. To-day it is the turn of the Marian variety or Cordovan to give its alternative name". Indeed the copper deposits in France are very poor. There are some in Haute Savoie and the Aude Departement and also at Cabrières (Dépt. Hérault), Rozières (Dépt. Tarn) and Baiyory (Dépt. Basses Pyrenées). Most of these can hardly have had more than local importance, even in Antiquity.

The most important copper deposits in *Europe* both in Antiquity and at the present time are those of Spain and Portugal. The classical authors have long laudatory passages on these mines. This is what Strabo says (40): "But as for Turdetania and the territory adjoining it there is no worthy word of praise left to him that wishes to praise their excellence in this respect. Up to the present moment, in fact, neither gold, nor silver, nor yet copper, nor iron, has been found anywhere in the world in a natural state either in such quantity or of such good quality. But for the Turdetanians mining is profitable beyond measure because one-fourth of the ore brought out by their copperworkers is pure copper" and he mentions the copper and gold ores of Cotinae (Almaden?) (41). Pliny praises the Cordovan copper (42).

This Turdetania refers to the Rio Tinto ore body of the southern Sierra Morena. The provinces Almeria, Andalusia, Cordoba, Sevilla, Huelva, Estremadura and Asturias and Catalunia (Lérida) and the Portuguese districts over the southern border contain the valuable copper ores.

Germany has several important deposits in Sauerland and Siegerland of which Mansfeld and Rammelsberg are prominent. Other deposits near Salzburg and in Tirol, Styria and Carinthia were very important in the Late Bronze Age and Early Iron Age and are still exploited.

The English and Irish copper ores are practically exhausted. The main deposits of historical interest are found in Cornwall, Devon and Anglesey. Scandinavia and Finland have several deposits which, however, play no part in our story. They are the deposits of Aamdal, Evje, Sulitjelma and Röros in Norway, Falun and Boliden in Sweden and Orijärvi and Outokumpo in Finland.

5. *Smelting and refining copper*

Over 50% of the world production of copper is now used in the electrical industry, 9% in the automobile industry and 11% for building and architectural purposes. Though the electrical industry uses mainly pure copper it is generally used in the form of alloys of which those with tin (bronze) and zinc (brass) are prominent. The centre of the world's copper production has shifted considerably. Thus, for instance between 1831 and 1840 England produced 49% of the world's production, from 1861-1870 Chile came first with about 44% and in 1891-1900 the United States were prominent with 52%. At present three rival regions compete for the first place, the United States producing 25.8%, Chile 17.6%, Canada and Rhodesia together 28.9%, the Belgian Congo (Katanga) 6% and Russia 5%, minor production centres being Cyprus, India and Australia. As the Russian mines are mostly located in the Ural or east of these mountains, it can be said that European production is no longer prominent as it was of old. With the shifting of the production centre other types of deposits were attacked and this meant new production methods no longer based on working small bodies of varying composition but large ore-bodies of constant though much lower copper content are now worked. New methods such as concentration of the ore by flotation, furnace treatment, combination of roasting and smelting in the convertor process and hydrometallurgical treatment and electrical refining have been introduced. Of late there has been a tendency to return to older methods as the copper produced by modern mass methods, more especially by the convertor process, was not always of the quality required and this made refining more costly.

The refining processes discovered in Antiquity were very gradually developed until the Middle Ages and except for a few minor changes then it can be said that even upto the beginning of the twentieth century there was this same slow development directed to obtain a greater recovery of metal from a given quantity of ore. From Roman times to the days of Biringuccio and Agricola the main struggle was the perfection of the method of dry extraction of copper from sulphide ores, after this period heat economy by better and larger apparatus came to the fore.

Before the new methods were introduced and exploitation of enormous ore-bodies of comparatively uniform comoposition and electrical refining completely changed the face of copper metallurgy one had to distinguish the treatment of two types of ores.

The first type of ores, the *oxides, carbonates and silicates*, could be refined in principle by heating and reduction of the ore with charcoal or wood with the help of blast air in some suitable type of furnace, after which treatment the crude copper was refined.

This treatment formed the second stage only of the production of copper from the second type of ores, the *sulphides*, because in this case many impurities which had a bad effect on the quality of the copper produced had to be eliminated first. These noxious impurities were mainly sulphur, arsenic and antimony.

Fig. 4.
Roasting copper ores (Agricola)

The first stage of copper production from sulphides was *roasting* the ore. This roasting consisted of calcination of the ore in heaps or furnaces, it is now effected in special roasting furnaces as the sulphurous gases involved are now recovered to serve for the production of sulphuric acid. This roasting is necessary to remove as early as possible the arsenic and antimony compounds present in the ore and the greater part of the sulphur, it requires little fuel as the process developes sufficient heat to maintain the roasting until the end.

The second stage is the *smelting of the roasted ore* to a mixture of copper and iron sulphides known as "copper matte" or "coarse metal", which contains only little arsenic, antimony and silica. This is effected by smelting with charcoal in a shaft furnace, at present of course coke is taken instead of charcoal being the modern substitute to the far more expensive ancient fuel. This stage is often combined with the next one, the *smelting of the coarse metal* with charcoal (coke) and siliceous fluxes. These fluxes consist of quartz in the form of lumps or pebbles and it serves to take away the iron oxyde present, to form a slag with these and other basic slagging compounds and by covering the smelting product saves it from oxidation, which though not important in this stage is a most important function in later stages when the smelting product is pure copper liable to absorb oxygen and to form copper oxide in the heat. The smelting of the coarse metal does not yet produce pure copper, but purifies the copper sulphide formed during the second stage. The coarse metal usually contains 30—40% of copper, the smelting product 65—75%. It is called "blue metal" when more or less iron is still present, "pimple metal" if richer in copper or "fine metal" ("white metal") if it consists of comparatively pure copper sulphide (German Kupferstein: matte). In the case of very rich pyrites with a high copper content it is possible to skip the second stage and to proceed at once from the first to the third stage. Another method of achieving the same result is mixing the sulphides with carbonate or oxide ore.

At this stage the blue metal would be a product that could be economically transported and traded, but usually it is refined on the spot. This production of matte is at present achieved in reverbatory furnaces which, however, were unknown in Antiquity.

The fourth stage, the *resmelting of the blue metal*, is usually achieved in a shaft-furnace (or in a modern blast-furnace or reverberatory furnace) again with charcoal and fluxes and with the aid of blast air. Now the remaining iron sulphide oxidizes and the iron oxide formed combines with the flux to form slag. The blast air further oxidizes the sulphides present and the sulphur escapes in the form of sulphurous gases, the charcoal present reduces the copper oxide formed to copper. Apart from the copper and slag produced a small quantity of unreduced matte forms an intermediary layer in the furnace and it is returned to the third stage. The copper produced is called "coarse copper" or "blister copper" and contains about 95—97% of copper with the following impurities: gold, silver, iron, lead, arsenic, antimony, nickel, cobalt, zinc and tin in varying quantities but in too large a percentage to use this copper as such. The coarse copper also called "black copper" (Schwarzkupfer) is then refined. Some of the impurities

like gold and silver are valuable, sometimes even dominate the economy of copper production in such a way that they are the real cause
for the treatment of the copper ores and copper itself only a by-product.
On the other hand black copper is an easy form of copper to transport
and to trade and it did form an object of early trade as many of the slabs
or cakes of copper found in classical and pre-classical times are no
other than black, unrefined copper, to be refined by the local smith.

The fifth stage, *refining the black copper*, requires considerable skill.
The undesirable impurities are removed by a combination of oxidation,

Fig. 5.
Roasting copper matte (Agricola)

slagging and volatilisation. The black copper is heated and oxidized
by blast air, agitation of the molten metal being aided with iron rabbles.
This "flapping" is continued until about 6% of copper oxide is formed
in the molten metal. At that moment the iron, zinc, tin and cobalt and
the traces of sulphur are almost completely removed in the slag, the
"sett copper" produced contains the silver and gold present in the ore
as well as traces of arsenic and nickel. It is now necessary to reduce the
copper oxyde present (which would only embrittle the copper and
render it useless). This is effected by "poling", that is forcing green
logs or trees under the molten metal. The wood reduces the oxyde
formed and the product is called "tough pitch copper". This last step
is very delicate as it is easy to refine the copper too long, causing the

copper to absorb the gases evolved by the wood and producing "over-poled" copper. The refined copper is now from 98 to over 99.5% purity dependent on the percentage of precious metals present.

As we shall see it is quite possible that the Romans understood the principle of refining by "poling", but in earlier ages refining was certainly conducted by melting the black copper with charcoal over a crucible or in a charcoal fire with blast air.

If the percentage of precious metals is worth while extracting the black copper is alloyed with lead and the alloy liquated. *Liquation,* an important process for the refining of lead, is effected by heating the leadbearing alloy between the melting point of lead (which is low) and that of the alloying metal (in this case copper with a high melting point). The lead then sweats from the alloy and at the same time extracts those impurities that are very soluble in lead among which the precious metals are prominent. The extracted copper can then be refined as described above. Complicated as this procedure may seem, it will be seen as we work our way back down the ladder of ages that each of the stages described is essential and can not be left out. It will be clear that what could be accomplished forty years ago in five stages could not be achieved by the earlier metallurgist in so short a time; he had to use either more stages and therefore a still more complicated flow sheet or else he had to sacrifice efficiency and extract a smaller percentage of the copper present in the ore and leave more copper in his slags, etc. In fact, if the earlier processes may seem simpler they were so at the expense of efficiency. Now if we turn to the processes known to Agricola (1550 A.D.) we find that he already treats sulphides as fully as we should wish. He mentions different forms of initial roasting and afterwards describes methods of crushing and washing the ore. This crushed and roasted ore is then again roasted, washed with water to remove the sulphurous acid formed, crushed and reroasted until it has undergone seven roastings. Then follows smelting in a shaft-furnace with open hearth so that the black copper produced, the matte and the slag constantly flow from the furnace in this fore-hearth to a second one in which slag and matte can be removed from the black copper after cooling somewhat. The shaft-furnace allows constant refilling and it is an improvement on earlier furnaces. Now Agricola states that all ore whether copper-coloured, lead-coloured, malachite, azurite, brown or black is smelted in the same furnace, that silica is added as a flux and that after three smeltings, the product is broken up and roasted three times to be resmelted to give black copper. Only the malachite and azurite give black copper after just one smelting. For liquation of gold and silver the black copper is alloyed with the lead in a special furnace (Frischofen) and liquated in another (Saigerofen), the lead separated (Saigerblei) and the remaining copper (Kienstöcke) refined. The liquated copper is then heated without melting in a special furnace to remove the remaining lead in the form of lead oxyde. This process is called "Darren" and the refined copper bars ("Darrlinge") are now melted in a special furnace (Garherd) with

Fig. 6.
Liquation of crude copper

charcoal and blast air over the surface of the molten metal, which is pooled after the slag has been removed. The refined copper is called "Garkupfer" by Agricola (43).

His contemporary, Biringuccio, does not describe the earlier stage of these complicated methods very clearly but he goes in for more details when he comes to the refining of copper (44).

An earlier handbook, the *Mittelalterliches Hausbuch* of 1480, gives the earliest picture of a complete copper refinery. Here we see a shaft furnace with a forehearth in which the ore after roasting and crushing is smelted, the matte is then enriched in a second shaft furnace, the black copper alloyed with lead in a "Frischofen" and the alloy liquated in a fourth furnace (Saigerherd) by surrounding the blocks with glowing coals. The copper is refined in a "Darrherd" and a "Garherd" in the way of later generations except that no current of blast air is pictured in the last furnace to slag the traces of impurities, which is no doubt a mistake of the artist.

Going back to the tenth century A.D. we find a short description of the production of copper (45) from a special lead-bearing malachite or oxydised copper ore. After handpicking it is roasted "like lime" (chapter LXII) whereby "the ore does not lose its colour but only its hardness and then can be crushed". It is now smelted in a furnace at

Fig. 7.
Smelting copper in Old Japan (After Gowland, Metals)

fairly low temperature with blast air and the liquated lead flows off with the gold and silver. The copper is collected and Theophilus now goes on to describe the refining in a crucible. He fills a iron, clay-coated crucible with copper and charcoal, embeds the whole in charcoal and heats the crucible with blast air, part of which blows over the surface of the crucible. If after heating long enough the molten copper collects in the crucible, some ashes of coal are thrown in and by stirring with a piece of wood the slag is made to adhere to the ashes and can be skimmed off. The copper is then poured out and hammered. If it is still brittle, refining should be repeated, if it remains "healthy" it is cooled in water. This description is always thought to contain the earliest reference to poling.

We now reach the classical authors who are not very clear in their

descriptions of the refining of copper. Galen gives a short description
of the smelting in a shaft furnace with charcoal and blast air. Pliny
does not mentions the washing and crushing of the ore or its roasting,
etc. before the alloying with lead-bearing fluxes and most of his passages
refering to the refining of copper are very muddled. It is at least clear
that charcoal, sometimes of special plants, was used to smelt copper
ores (46). Täckholm (47) points out that Dioscorides (48) describes
a "two-storied" furnace working with blast-air, which may be the type
that Pliny describes in rather a loose way (49). A furnace depicted on
a vase in the British Museum is very similar to this Cyprian type. The
Berlin vase reproduced by Jahn does not depict a smelting furnace as
formerly supposed, but part of casting equipment. These double furnaces had a lower narrow part to be filled with charcoal while the ore
was filled into the wider upper part. We find similar furnaces in Africa
(50) and this type was found in the mining district of prehistoric Tirol
(Schmaltal, Tarxdorf). There is no doubt that these furnaces permitted
continous smelting as their long use proves, they must have worked
with a forehearth in which slag and black copper were separated. Shaft
furnaces of early date were found near Mitterberg and in the Roman
mines of Populonia and Rio Tinto furnaces of the "bloomery fire"
or "Catalan hearth" type common in the production of wrought iron
seem to have been used for the smelting of copper ores, or may be the
refining of black copper. Better suited for this refining process is the
"camera", a cupola furnace like the pottery kilns described by Pliny
(51) which was also found near Salzburg and in Lorraine and which is
far better suited to reach high temperatures and to melt copper. It
seems from the few remains that have been inspected by experts that
the Romans concentrated their ore by handpicking until it contained
about 5% of copper as a higher percentage would give a high loss of
copper in smelting. Roasting seems to have been carried out on beds
of stones or loam. Several of these covered with copper slags have been
found at Mitterberg and Roman practice does not seem to have differed.

The fluxes used in smelting depended of course for a great deal on
the impurities of the ore to be smelted. In Cyprus the Romans used a
flux with a high manganese content, in Rio Tinto different forms of
quartz, in Thasos lime has been used. The matte recovered in the last
of the two smeltings commonly executed was returned to an earlier
stage and also played the part of a flux. It seems that this was already
understood by the early prehistoric smelters of Mitterberg. After the
double smelting refining of the black copper followed, perhaps not

only in some type of furnace, but also in crucibles. In a passage of his Natural History (52) Pliny says: "At Capua it is melted by a fire but not of coals but of wood, poured into cold water and cleansed by means of a sieve of oak." Bailey in commenting on this passage (53) suggests that *cribo* stands for *ligno* and that Pliny really meant to describe poling, which would make this the earliest passage. The purity of Roman copper would allow this supposition. It is hardly possible that the Romans got 25% of copper out of their ores in Spain as Diodor (54) and Strabo would have us believe. No exact analyses of Spanish-Roman slags are available but the Roman slags from Dacia often contain up to 50% of copper! The Romans were certainly the first to work sulphidic ores generally. Most of the Roman copper in trade or refinery hoards consists of copper which by the peculiar structure and the surface of the bars and cakes together with its sulphur content can be shown to belong to copper prepared from sulphides. This form of black copper seems to have been the regular trade quality, though we do also find smooth, sulphur-free cakes of refined copper.

Dioscorides and Pliny give many passages referring to the medicinal uses of the byproducts of copper smelting and refining. Roman copper was often intentionally alloyed with varying percentages of lead "to make it pliant and giving it a pleasing hue" as Pliny says (55). In the same passage he says: "In Gaul they only roast twice, though the quality of the metal depends to a very great extent on the frequent repetitions of this operation." For small quantities of refined copper for medicinal use roasting with coals and honey is mentioned (56). Pliny also recognizes several qualities of refined copper, which he describes in another passage (57): "We shall now turn our attention particularly to the different kinds of aes and their composition. Cyprian aes comprises crown-aes (aes coronaria) and bar-aes (aes regulare), both of which are malleable. Coronaria is beaten into leaves and dyed with oxgall to make imitation gold for stage crowns. Both bar-aes and aes-caldarium are manufactured in other mines also, differing in this that aes caldarium is brittle and can only be cast, while bar-aes is malleable; some, therefore, give to the latter and indeed to all Cyprian aes the name ductile". Bailey explains this passage thus": Heated copper cooled slowly becomes brittle, if cooled rapidly malleable and ductile". It seems that the aes coronaria is sheet-copper, the aes regulare normal malleable refined copper and aes caldarium either the more impure black copper or perhaps cast copper containing some zinc. For more analyses of Roman copper would be required to make sure that a special quality of copper was made for casting purposes. As already explained most copper was immediately alloyed with lead, tin or zinc.

Before tracing back the earliest refining processes and their development it will be valuable to review some of the primitive processes still to be observed in other parts of the world and to mention some of the results of investigations into the methods used at Mitterberg and other prehistoric smelting sites.

The Chetri in India crush the sulphidic ore they have gathered, mix it with cowdung, dry these balls and roast them. The roasted product is then smelted in a furnace built up of rings of fireclay in which alternate layers of charcoal and roasted ore have been filled. The slag of iron production is used as a flux (58). The gypsies use very similar methods and apparatus, but they refine old discarded pieces of bronze, brass and copper in graphite crucibles, this is clearly a later acquisition and does not belong to the traditions of smithcraft exported from their original home in India.

The natives of Persia (59) roast their sulphidic ores after handdressing in a cone-shaped mud furnace about 7' high with airholes and a door for drawing the roast-product. This roasting requires about 35% of fuel. The smelting of the roasted ore is effected in a small blast furnace about 9" in diameter and 18" deep.

The Japanese used very primitive methods until lately (60). Roasting and smelting their ore in a simple "hole in the ground" clay-lined furnace with the aid of blast air from handbellows (fuigo) or footbellows (tatara). The copper is desilvered by alloying with lead and liquating. A bowl-form refining crucible made of clay and chopped straw is used for refining. The cakes produced from the smelting furnace are 8—10" in diameter and $1\frac{1}{2}$" high, they are broken by fracturing the cake near its solidifying point as is proved by the "columnar" structure of these lumps. To get a brilliant coloured copper 0.1—0.2% of lead are added. Gowland correctly calls them "Bronze Age methods" yet as he says with this simple furnace all the copper, lead and tin required in Japan were produced as late as 1884 when the production of copper was no less than 8816 Tons!

The negroes of Katanga have more complicated methods than the Japanese. The Basanga clan who hold the secret of working the copper ore, extract the malachite from shafts dug into the soft siliceous dolomite. The ore is crushed and washed in streaming water in the way gold is "panned". Two furnaces of 3' diameter and 5' high are used for roasting and smelting. Charcoal from hard wood is used for smelt-

ing. The furnaces built up of termite-cones in half an hour and propped
with branches are filled with 3″ of charcoal and billets of wood. These
are ignited, charcoal is filled on top of them, a layer of ore added, then
charcoal again until the total charge of 80—100 lbs of ore is charged.
After $1\frac{1}{2}$ hour the dehydration and roasting of the ore is finished, the
charcoal is consumed and now fresh charcoal is added and the bellows
are worked to reduce the matte to metal in about $\frac{1}{2}$ hour. First ritual

Fig. 8.
Removing copper from the smelting furnace
(After Gowland, Metals)

water and bits of the bark of six sacred trees are added and many incan-
tations are chanted throughout the work. When the work is finished
the furnace is broken up and the lump of copper is detached from the
hearth by a few strokes of a hammer and cleaned by scraping. About
60—70% of the copper in the ore is recovered and in the whole period
of less than $2\frac{1}{2}$ hours 24—28 lbs of black copper are produced. Refining
is now carried out by breaking up the cakes and mixing them with
charcoal in crucibles made of termite cones. The crucibles are heated
in a furnace and ingots of 4—6 lbs could be made from each charge,
but generally the copper is cast into X-shaped moulds into ingots of
25, 50 or 100 lbs. Characteristic for their work is the lack of a proper
basic flux for the silicious gangue of the malachite, whereby the efficiency of the process is less than possible with more suitable methods.

The prehistoric refineries of Mitterberg, Bischofsofen and others have been studied in detail (61). The pyrites worked in Mitterberg sometimes contain from 20—40% of copper but the average is about 12%. The roasting was conducted in heaps of ore and fuel. Further smelting furnaces were constructed of slabs of slate smeared with clay. The oldest furnaces had already a fore-hearth to avoid stoppage by the settling of copper matte under in the furnace in front of the tap hole. In the earlier furnaces we find one temporary forehearth, later two are built together with the furnace. In the fore-hearth slag and matte were separated. The smelting was conducted in three stages, the first to produce a copper matte of 30—40% copper content, the second to make a blue-metal of 65% copper, then a third produced a black copper of 95—96% copper. The black copper was then refined but seldom on the spot as the ingots and cakes found have only 94—97% copper and the commercial product seems to have been black copper.

It will be noticed that even in its simplest form which does not seek any efficiency of extraction of the metal from the ore, the operations consist of a series of roastings and smeltings followed by refining. Sometimes it is possible to combine these operations in one continous smelting but always at the cost of efficiency, and always the two distinct phases of roasting and smelting remain traceable when sulphide ores are worked. It will also be noticed that even when working such simple ores as malachite fluxes may be necessary to slag the gangue.

However, no matter how complicated the smelting of copper from such complex sulphidic ores may seem, the ancients mastered the art thoroughly. Recent research on ancient copper implements and objects (62) revealed that they understood many of the niceties mentioned above and obtained a good and pure copper or a copper-alloy without too much difficulty, even if their methods may seem wasteful to us as they left far more copper in the slag than the modern metallurgist could afford to do. What we learnt from these investigations can now be applied with profit if we seek to unravel the evolution of copper metallurgy using both the technical and archaeological data at our disposal.

6. *The evolution of copper metallurgy*

In retracing the steps which led primitive man to work native copper and copper ores these primitive methods are of great help and we must also draw on the practical tests made by Gowland,

Coghlan (63), and Witter (64). The latter's work should be especially noted for the careful and scientific way in which he retraces the basis and evolution of copper metallurgy in Central Germany and the correct and inspired application of modern research to the ores and copper objects discussed. Coghlan's papers are of outstanding importance because he has for once repeated and improved upon the experiments of Gowland and he has placed the theories on the origin of copper metallurgy on a firm base.

Witter, who was not yet in possession of Coghlan's data, drew a table of the different stages of copper production, which we have amended (page 30)! It would then seem that we must distinguish five stages of evolution, which were already discussed when we tried to solve the mystery of the origin of metallurgy in general (65).

The earliest stage is the *shaping of native copper*, which we fixed tentatively in the sixth or fifth millennium B.C. When looking for gold in the beds of the mountain streams the prehistoric prospector noticed larger lumps of dark stone which when hammered looked like gold. The native copper looks like purplish-green or greenish black nodules, which once scratched or rubbed show their yellowish-red kernel of pure copper. However, not all forms of native copper would be useful, for though native copper is a soft metal and as found in nature its ductility is poor when not annealed and hammering it would embrittle the very tough lumps and cause cracks, the spongy form of native copper being already naturally brittle would be less suitable for fashioning by the Stone Age artisan. Still the thin plates and arborescent growths of native copper are useful and they are found in relatively large quantities in Cornwall, France, Hungary, Central Germany, Russia, Asia Minor (Ankara, Arghana) and the Semnan district of Iran (near Damghan) and also in the Ural mountains, the Altaï and the Pamir ranges. The discovery of the malleability of native copper was a major discovery which may be tentatively dated somewhere about 5000 B.C. By applying their very limited Stone Age techniques the Neolithic artisans selected small suitable pieces of metal and (cold)-forged and ground them into awls, pins, hooks, etc. like the North American Indians did in the days of Columbus. They had not yet become the first smiths to herald the dawn of the Metal Ages. Objects of this type have been found at Badari in Egypt, in Vinça I in the Danube valley and in other excavations in Asia Minor, Mesopotamia and Palestine but metallographical research has still to define whether these pure native copper objects belong to this earliest phase or to the second one.

Annealing native copper that is alternately heating and hammering native copper was the next step, a discovery that may be dated about 5000 to 4500 B.C. Copper until then had no advantage over gold, it

Table I

Stages of early copper metallurgy

A. *Shaping native copper* (hammering, cutting, bending, grinding, polishing)

B. *Annealing native copper* (heating and hammering)

C. *Smelting oxyde and carbonate ores*

    1. Smelting ore (in wood- or charcoal-fire over clay-lined pit with air)

    regulus ◄————————————————► slag (thrown away)

D. *Melting and casting Copper*

Melting native copper or regulus from C. 1 over furnace or fire in crucible and casting into stone, clay or sand moulds. Fashioning as under B. 1 or by hammering cold, finishing by grinding and polishing.

E. *Smelting sulphide ores*

    1. Roasting the ore (to remove bulk of sulphur)
    2. Smelting roasted ore (with charcoal in low shaft furnace)

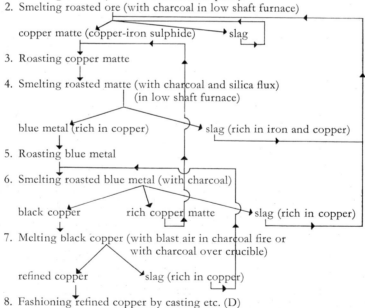

copper matte (copper-iron sulphide)   ► slag

    3. Roasting copper matte

    4. Smelting roasted matte (with charcoal and silica flux)
                    (in low shaft furnace)

blue metal (rich in copper)   ► slag (rich in iron and copper)

    5. Roasting blue metal

    6. Smelting roasted blue metal (with charcoal)

black copper   rich copper matte   ► slag (rich in copper)

    7. Melting black copper (with blast air in charcoal fire or
                 with charcoal over crucible)

refined copper   ► slag (rich in copper)

    8. Fashioning refined copper by casting etc. (D)

Note.   The possibility of returning intermediary products of refining to earlier stages to increase efficiency has been indicated. In earlier periods of smelting such refinements were of course not yet appreciated.

could be used for small ornaments only, but by annealing it was possible to shape it into further forms without making it too brittle and to use the frequent forms of native copper which hitherto had been excluded from use. How this discovery was made we do not know. It may be that primitive awls were heated to assist penetration, that a lump of copper dropped into the fire and its better malleability was then discovered, or that prehistoric man applied the "heat-test" which remained so common with unknown or less useful substances in early technology and science and still forms the readily applied test of the youthful dabbler in chemistry. Anyhow by making the metal soft in the fire and by hammering which sequence of operations could be repeated ad libitum the first smith could avoid to embrittle the copper object and fashion it to his taste far more easily than hitherto. Especially the larger lumps and nuggets, which require annealing in order to avoid the formation of cracks, could now be worked and smaller lumps could be forged together to some extent. It can be truly said that this discovery meant the birth of the smith, who thus preceded the first metallurgist who reduced ores. His improved but still very limited technique made it possible to shape more complicated objects more easily.

A considerable body of archaeological material belongs to this "hammered copper culture" on typological grounds but more metallurgical research will be needed to define more closely the extent of this phase. It is fairly easy to prove that a certain object was made of native copper and how it was worked. Not only is native copper very pure but also only few impurities are known to occur in it, viz. gold, silver, iron and sometimes antimony. Hammered native copper has a peculiar "twinned" microstructure, cast pieces show the typical "cored" microstructure. Thus it was possible to prove that an Hungarian axe-hammer of about 1700 B.C. which was thought to consist of hammered native copper, really was native cast copper (66).

The second major discovery was that of the *fusibility* of copper which made the melting and casting of this metal possible. This phase is marked by the appearance of castings of simple form, such as would be produced from open moulds, or at most by simple univalved moulds furnished with a cap or backing. The Danubian axe-hammer on which the Ancient Mining and Metallurgy Committee reported (67) in 1951 seems to belong to this phase. It was made of very pure (probably native) copper cast in an open-hearth mould, after cooling the seam was very carefully removed by hammering.

On technological grounds we have good reason to believe that this simple melting technique preceded the application of the third major discovery, the smelting of ores, but probably it did not last long.

Reduction of oxyde and carbonate ores together with the melting and casting of copper form the beginning of the true Metal Age and the start of industrial copper metallurgy. It was formerly generally thought that the casting of copper preceded the reduction of ores but Cogh-lan's experiments have proved the contrary. Once it was discovered that the application of heat made the red stone more useful than the yellow gold the value of this red stone must have been greatly enhanced, it may have been considered even more valuable than gold, as it still was in early historic times in some regions. Now the search for further supply must have led to the finding of other green and blue stones, which did not become red by rubbing only, they had already been used as an eyepaint or for glazes and their reduction achieved in the pottery-kilns must have been a logical extention of the "heat test" so often applied. Coghlan proved that the favourite camp fire theory was un-tenable as the heat in camp fires does not exceed the reduction tem-peratures of the oxydes and carbonates of copper which are fairly high (700—800° C), though the campfire was hot enough (600—700° C) to achieve a maximum annealing effect of native copper. In the pottery kilns then well known as is proved by the wellbaked prehistoric pottery of Egypt, Mesopotamia and Iran the high temperatures required for the reduction of the ores as well as for the melting of copper (1085° C) could be easily reached. Ground ores mixed with charcoal heated in such kilns give a perfect regulus of copper. The later way of reducing ores was to heat the ores mixed with charcoal in a claylined hearth of furnace with the aid of blast air. The primitive "hole in the ground" furnace so often mentioned by Gowland would not do the work with-out this blast air, and therefore the construction of furnaces for the reduction of ores presupposes the knowledge of forced draught, which is one of the outstanding principle of a good pottery kiln. The furnaces with natural draught used in Derbyshire until the XVIIIth century and the primitive furnaces with air-pipes built in to encourage this draught all show that the users were quite conversant with the idea that blast air was necessary to reach the high temperatures re-quired which could not be attained in an open fire alone.

The development even of this simple furnace must have required many years during which some form of crucible melting in a pottery kiln must have been used. The early furnaces were small and the amounts of copper produced can be measured by weighing early copper ingots or cakes which are something in the way of 140—160 grammes, that is sufficient copper for one tool only. It was only by gradual experimenting that the early metallurgists hit on the idea of filling up the furnace with alternate layers of charcoal and ore thus increasing their production. Later crucibles may hold some 20 lbs, but in the classical period the metallurgical furnaces could produce up to 100 lbs. of metal. The earliest reduction experiments were not as easy as they looked, for the first product of primitive smelting does not look very encouraging, it is a spongy mass of incompletely fused metal still containing cinders and extraneous matter and not like the beautiful red regulus which crucible smelting in a pottery kiln would yield. Reheating and hammering liberates the cinders and bits of unreduced ore and a lump of unrefined black copper is obtained which can be refined by returning it to the fire and remelting it. The size of prehistoric ingots of somewhat later date than those mentioned above point to a hearth of about 1' diameter which would give the ingot a diameter of about 8—10" and a height of $1\frac{1}{2}$". Lining the furnace was another refinement for such a clay lining would tend to keep the copper pure. It would also seem that very early a distinction was made between the smelting of the ore in a furnace and the refining of the black copper obtained for which reduction in crucibles still remained common.

The pecularity of early metallurgical crucibles is the effect of heat on side and rim only. This points to the heaping of charcoal and black copper over the crucible and either heating it in a kiln or heaping a fire around it and increasing the temperature with the aid of blast air from a blowpipe (as is still common among negroes and as we find depicted in Egyptian tombs) or from bellows. We know that the blowpipe was used by early prehistoric metallurgists because we have found the clay nozzles or balls with which the end of the blowpipe was protected against the effects of the fire, but we do not exactly know the date of the earliest bellows. The earliest picture of bellows occurs in a Theban tomb of the New Kingdom and it has often been said that bellows were invented around 1580 B.C. but from the look of these first bellows they must have quite a period of evolution behind them, thought it is still impossible to fix a further date for their inception. Clay nozzles for bellows have been found in many Late Bronze Age sites in the Near East and in Europe.

Melting and casting copper, that mysterious cycle of melting, casting and solidifying, must have followed the earlier discovery of the transmutation of the blue and green stones into the red tough metal very closely. It is probable that both inventions took place and spread rapidly about 4000—3500 B.C. The possibility of thus remoulding old tools which had become unsuitable must have led to the recasting of many of them, as the copper was still an expensive and valued material. This may account for the disappearance of many implements originally made of hammered native copper and the comparatively rare finds of stage II. This is quite plausible in view of the many battered and broken implements found in founders' hoards. Crucible melting was probably known from this time as we argued from the earliest method of melting shown by the crucibles found. Cline thought that the negroes adapted it to copper metallurgy from their imported knowledge of steel manufacture, but this can not hold true for the Ancient Near East. At Mitterberg it was found that the crucibles would hold about 5 to 6 Kgrs of copper. With crucible smelting go not only blow pipe or bellows but also such instruments as tongs, etc. without which no handling is possible.

Casting also introduced new methods of forming the metal or rather pre-forming it in open moulds, then in closed moulds or valve moulds, and gradually more complicated forms of casting such as core-casting and the cire-perdue method were evolved. The lack of a proper statistical-chronological series of analyses does not permit us to fix the exact date of the transition of this early metallurgical state to the last phase of copper metallurgy, the *smelting of sulphidic ores*. It comes no doubt later than the smelting of oxydic ores though Wibel and Much had a different theory and the slight possibility remains that early metallurgists chanced to smelt sulphides now and then under especially fortunate circumstances. Siret found proofs that carbonates were smelted in early Southern Spain, and in the pile dwellings remains of carbonates and silicates of copper were found near smelting sites, etc. Always in the case of sulphides we find preliminary roasting followed by smelting and refining, though the latter is often absent as the impure black copper was the common commercial product. The earlier stages when outcropping veins and lodes were worked were over when these soon gave out due to the increasing demand for copper, especially as its properties were improved by the discovery of bronze. It is difficult to fix a date for the introduction of sulphide smelting, but it is certain that this had practically completely supplanted carbonate smelting by the Roman period. The principles of roasting are connected with the production of lead and silver from galena and from the few analyses of copper known at present one would venture to place the earliest smelting of copper sulphides in 2000 B.C. or thereabout. We have already pointed out the evidence of Mitterberg and other sites as to the early understanding of the different phases of working sulphides and the early evolution of the appropriate apparatus. The copper from these sulphide ores is easily recognisable in the puckered surface of the cakes or ingots, the analysis is quite like that of modern blister copper, but if only a trace of sulphur is found it is not prepared from sulphides and may belong to an earlier period.

The black copper produced was not generally cast into ingots in the earlier periods but broken while still brittle (just under the solidification point), as shown by the columnar structure of these pieces. Later we find ingots mainly in the form of hides in the Eastern Mediterranean and in the shape of round cakes in Western and Central Europe, where neck-rings or torques seem to have been a common form of barter too. Copper wire was mostly fashioned by hammering often in V-shaped grooves, it seems that the drawing of wire was in use in Egypt since the Middle Kingdom. Joining was often effected by riveting, but brazing was known to the Sumerians and soldering in different forms was very common in the East until Hellenistic times, casting-on being a Central European speciality. Much can still be learnt from a better chronological studies of copper and bronze hoards and their distribution in time and space (67). Four types can be distinguished, viz. *domestic hoards* consisting of a few pieces of many types, *votive hoards* of objects to propitiate the deity, *founders' hoards* made up of old implements, cakes and ingots and *commercial hoards* of raw and half finished tools and weapons and ingots.

Before turning to the history of copper in the individual regions of the Ancient Near East we have to mention a few details on the general characteristics of this metal.

7. *Copper, its characteristics and impurities*

Copper whether native or smelted has always a slight percentage of impurities; even refined copper contains arsenic, antimony, lead, iron, zinc, tin, nickel, silver, gold, and sulphur of which gold, silver, iron and antimony belong to native copper proper, the others to smelted copper. As these impurities may amount to something like 3% in ancient copper, they have some influence of the casting properties and the hardness, especially the silver, arsenic, antimony and nickel content. These rather impure copper types might be called "pre-bronzes", though the earliest true alloys are intentional mixes of copper with lead and antimony. These impurities of ancient copper are not always a fault of the refiner as even modern electrolytic copper still contains 0.1% of impurities.

In the tables III A & B we have again given the different copper ores and their formula, but this time together with the impurities which may be expected when such ores are used. From these tables it will be clear that nearly every copper ore, containing sulphur, antimony, arsenic or lead, has up to a few percents of zinc. Nickel is very rare in these ores and hardly ever present in more than traces, as nickel ores are not genetically connected with copper ores, but the nickel is introduced into copper as a contamination of the accompanying iron ores. As the iron is slagged away during the smelting the nickel enters the copper. In table II we give a few very rare nickelbearing copper ores which up to the present have been found in America only.

There is a genetical connection between nickel, cobalt and iron compounds, but none between copper and nickel ores. Hence the former Sumerian Copper Committee had great difficulty in tracing nickel-bearing copper ores which it believed to be the source of the Sumerian copper objects. These traces of nickel may enter the copper during the smelting process with the flux or from the lining of the furnace. Hence it may be that the relation between copper and the ratio nickel/iron is more characteristic of the original ore used than the nickel/copper ratio which the Committee followed up. The difficulty of identifying the original ore lies in the mist still enveloping the operations carried out with the material between the extraction of the ore and the finishing of the tool or weapon. We should work our way backwards unless we want to introduce many question marks by not investigating these intermediary operations. Hence more emphasis should be given to extensive metallographical analysis of metal objects in our collections. Then we should retrace our steps by investigating what materials were used in building the various types of furnaces and if possible how these furnaces were worked. We should also know the tools of the smith and the way he used them. A most important question is the temperature at which the smelting and melting furnaces worked, here Coghlan set a proper example in the footsteps of Gowland, for without this crucial knowledge many problems cannot be solved. More attention should also be devoted to the compo-

Table II

Some rare Nickel bearing Copper ores (found in America only until present time)

Ore	Formula	Copper %age	Colour	Iron	Zinc	Cobalt	Nickel	Silver	Arsenic
7. Algodonite	Cu$_6$ As						—0.08%		
8. Whitneyite	Cu$_9$ As					0.44—0.61%			
9. Mohawkite	Cu$_3$ As	61—68		traces		3.3 —9.2%			28%
10. Keewenawite	(Cu. Ni. Co)$_2$ As					18—31%			

7. Michigan.
8. Michigan.
9. Mohawk mine, Michigan   } Very rarely found in normal copper deposits.
10. Michigan.

Table IIIA

Common, easily reducible Copper ores

Ore	Formula	Chemical compound	Percentage of Copper	Colour	Iron	Zinc	Silver	Nickel
1. Cuprite	Cu_2O	oxyde	89%	red	traces	traces	—	—
2. Melaconite	Cu_2O	oxyde	89%	black	traces	traces	—	—
3. Malachite	$CuCO_3.Cu(OH)_2$	basic carbonate	abt 56%	emerald green	{0.09—6.20 FeO	{4.58—27% ZnO	—	—
4. Azurite (Chessylite)	$2CuCO_3.Cu(OH)_2$	basic carbonate	abt 55%	vivid blue	traces	0.1—5.3% ZnO	—	—

1. So-called "red copper ore", formed by erosion of copper-ores, sometimes mixed with limonite (Fe-bearing ore).
2. "black copper ore", occurs in Urals and Caucasian range.
3. Sometimes large ZnO content by admixture of aurichalcite ($CuCO_3.$ $Zn(OH)_6$).
4. Somewhat rarer. The "uknu" of the Babylonians according to Meissner from Badakshan or Media (?).

Table IIIB

Somewhat rarer but easily reducible Copper ores

5. Atacamite	$CuCl_2 . 3Cu(OH)_2$	basic chloride	abt 59%	green	—	—	—
6. Chrysocalla		hydrous silicate	abt 30%	green bluish green	—	—	—

5. Occurring in Chile, Australia, Arizona, Africa, rare.
6. Mentioned by Theophrastus as found in Cyprus(?), rare.

N.B. These data and the other geological data were compiled with the help of Prof. Caron of the University of Delft and Dr. Zermatten of the University of Amsterdam.

sition of the ancient slags, which will also reveal data on the fluxes used during smelting. Also ancient documents may also guide us to the important point whether black copper or matte may have been the trade object of foreign countries to be refined by the local smith or whether the ore was completely refined in situ.

Returning to our point what difficulties the ancient smiths may have had with the smelting and working of copper, we are sure that the simple oxide and carbonate ores mentioned in table III would be directly reducible by heating with charcoal at a dull red heat, as would lead from its ores, whereas iron and tin would demand a higher temperature. However as the copper would form a spongy mass difficult to deal with, the temperature should be raised to melt the metal, e.g. some form of blast should be applied.

We saw that sulphide ores had to be roasted first, this operation, driving off the sulphur, once started, is self-continuing but its success depends on skilful and proper control in order to convert the ore to the oxide. These complex sulphide ores (Table IV) usually contain much iron as well as arsenic, antimony, zinc, nickel and silica, which will enter the copper metal in proportions depending on smelting conditions. The copper matte usually contains about 30—50% of copper contaminated with suphur, iron, lead, zinc, silver, antimony and arsenic. Roasting does volitalize part of the arsenic and antimony but their stable oxides are also formed and then later reduced together with the copper oxide! These reactions complicate the correlation we are seeking between the contents in an ore and the metal obtained from it and we must not attach too much importance to variations in composition which may have been just what might be expected from normal practice in early times where such important points as temperature control were hardly extant.

During the subsequent smeltings with charcoal and siliceous fluxes the iron oxide can be slagged off by adding sand to the molten mass and thus the final product, the "black (blister, coarse) copper" contains some 95—97% of copper together with some copper oxides and traces of sulphur, iron, lead, zinc, etc. During the final smelting ("flapping") with charcoal and blast air the final product, "tough-pitch copper" of over 99.5% purity was obtained. However, part of the air used in smelting will form cuprous oxide, a decided troublemaker for the coppersmith, as it makes his copper brittle. This could be avoided by deoxidizing the copper to the correct percentage of cuprous-oxide by "poling". Having skimmed off the slag a log of green hardwood is

Table IV

Copper ores, involving "Roasting" and "Smelting"

Ore	Formula	Copper % age	Colour	Iron	Zinc	Cobalt	Nickel	Silver	Arsenic
1. Chalcocite	Cu_2S	80	black, brittle, dull	—9.9%	—11.54%		—2.40%	—16%	—
2. Covellite	CuS	66.5	dark indigo blue		—6.0%				—
3. Eurobescite (Bornite)	$3Cu_2S.Fe_2S_3$	56 (50—70)	coppery blue red	—17%				—	
4. Chalcopyrite	$Cu_2S.Fe_2S_3$	35	brass yellow metallic lustre	—30%	—4%			traces	—
5. Enargite	$4Cu_2S.(SbAs)_2 S_3$	45	steelgray to iron black		—6%			traces	13.3%
6. Tetrahydrite	$Cu SbS$	30—48		—4%	traces			traces	

1. Nickel bearing ores in Bohemia and Serbia only.
2. So-called "indigo-copper", somewhat rarer than above mentioned ore.
3. Rarely containing lead (—10%) and zinc (—12%) (Montana, U.S.A.), so-called "purple copper ore".
4. Often traces of gold, selenium, thallium.
5. Both cobalt and nickel occur rarely.
6. Contains traces of silver very often, rather rare.

thrust into the molten metal. It catches fire quickly and will evolve
hydrocarbon gases which reduce the oxygen content of the copper.
The ancient smith could test this by sight, for a sample of copper containing a cuprous-oxide content of about the normal 0.4% would be
good malleable "tough-pitch" copper. It would need more poling if
it had a ruffled surface when cooling and an orange or yellowish fracture. Hence such tests would be well within the means of the ancient
metallurgist and from our finds it is obvious that all these operations
were properly controlled before 2000 B.C.

The analyses of ancient copper objects show that the craftsmen normally used a copper with a reasonably correct percentage of impurities
(or sometimes alloys), depending on the particular purpose for which
the metal object was to be used. Ancient hand-working allowed a wider
range of impurities than machine-tooling and hence the higher percentage of impurities in ancient coppers did not matter too much in
most cases. Only in case he was producing the best possible material
or if he was catering for a cheap market he made metal objects which
were an exception to this rule. In some puzzling cases the tools may
for instance never have been intended to be used as such but they were
simply to serve as votive offerings. The Egyptian bronzesmiths are
known to make lead-bronzes for such occasions, which would never
have stood up to real handling at all.

Some of the early very pure copper objects have been shown to
have been smelted from pure ores like malachite or the like but as
the situation deteriorated and deeper sulphidic ores were worked the
metallurgists had to learn and live with the unavoidable impurities in
his copper on many occasions. Such impurities may run up to some
3% and often gave products which were easier to cast or harder and
tougher. A series of analyses on Irish copper objects (68) showed the
early use of sulphide ores of copper (Early Bronze Age!), the use of
arsenic-antimony alloys for implemental work and the controlled
production and purity of the metal obtained, the working qualities
of which did not fall far behind those of the average prehistoric tin-
bronzes.

Probably experience and skilful control of the processes discussed
gradually led to deliberate alloying attempts and the first "bronzes".
Hence these early bronzes also contain all kind of contaminations
which later bronzes avoid, being made by smelting pure "poled"
copper with tin ores rather than by smelting matte or black copper
with tin ore. The early copper more or less alloyed with arsenic, anti-

mony, silver and other impurities was easier to melt, hot-forge or cast. Casting was another operation which led to the quick introduction of bronzes once it was known how to compound them. Pure copper has a tendency to "gas" when cast producing a porous casting, 1% of tin or arsenic lessen this tendency considerably though with such a metal one would still prefer open moulds. Good tin-bronze does not "gas" and permits the use of closed moulds. The early smiths carrying around their clay or stone moulds were dependent on the development of their furnaces, much more so than the settled town-smiths. In order to obtain sufficient metal for casting they probably worked with lined holes as "sunk furnaces". For cire-perdue casting they could only use bronze for here "gasing" was completely detrimental nor could very large runners and risers be used. Closed metal moulds were thus a direct consequence of the development of bronze metallurgy. Such moulds also led to the so-called "slushcast" technique of producing hollow castings. The mould was filled completely with molten metal and after the metal in contact with the mould-surface had set, it was quickly inverted to pour out the unsolidified metal and thus form a hollow casting. When discussing bronze we will revert to the point that the impure metals of early days led to bronze, which new branch of metallurgy led again to techniques particularly suitable for such bronzes and to the manufacture of deliberately compounded alloys. Such alloys may cause difficulties in practice, e.g. segregation, etc., but their advantages are so obvious that the ancient smiths were not deterred by the few disadvantages which they quickly conquered (69).

Many stories are circulated of lost secrets by which the ancients could harden their copper tools, but the Bureau of Mines (U.S.A.) has definitely proved that the only possibility of hardening copper is cold hammering, that is hammering at not too high temperatures (70). It is impossible to harden copper by heating and quenching like steel!

Still the ancients did indeed believe in the effect of annealing and quenching bronze in the waters of certain wells and we shall have to deal with this when discussing bronze.

In scientific terms: hammering copper brings Brinell hardness from 87 to 135, that is more than is achieved by the alloying with the normal 10% of tin to make bronze and it approaches the hardness of mild steel. The ancients seem to have been very concious of this fact as the normal way of getting a good cutting edge on a tool after fashioning the object by casting and annealing is hammering along this edge. The difficulty lies in the fact that this hardness is only temporary and that the operation needs to be repeated regularly to ensure a good tool for cutting hard stones. In that case they refashioned their tool by annealing and hammered the cutting edge afterwards. This frequent reworking of tools had its disadvantages, for photomicrographs of ancient copper show that the ancients not only adopted cold-working, but also often heated their product in open fires, causing the formation of copper-oxyde, which alloyed with the copper and though initially hardening it, somewhat larger percentages will soon embrittle it. Then the entire tool has to be remelted, refined and recast (71).

The gradual evolution of copper metallurgy has been doubted by some authors who point to the widely varying composition of ancient copper and bronzes but modern analysis made it clear that these structural peculiarities may be readily attributed to the crude methods of smelting and refining and that the products grow more uniform as the skill of the ancient metallurgist grows (72). Modern research has also made it clear that there was no change or disintegration in the structure of metals even in 6000 years under normal condition except the formation of a patina and may be corrosion of the surface layers. The features of initial corrosion and of patina form our most reliable proof of the ancient origin of metal objects. That the characteristics of these objects vary much is also partly due to the different origin and composition of the ores smelted and may in some cases give a lead as to the origin of these ores.

It is impossible to give a reliable estimate of most ancient copper mines but in two cases a tentative figure can be given. Lucas calculated the total copper output of Egypt (including Sinai) during 1400 years at about 10.000 Tons, that is 7.7 Tons a year and the production of Mitterberg during 1200 years was 20.000 Tons that is about 17 Tons a year.

8. *The story of early copper*

Copper is not found in *Egypt* in the Merimde culture, but it is the earliest metal as several copper objects were found belonging to the Badari culture (4000 B.C.), while gold and silver come in S.D. 42 only. Here again copper is employed before gold. Brunton found in Badari graves some beads of narrow ribbon copper and a stout pin or borer, needles and a fishhook. The pins may have served to fasten the mats in the burial pit. The copper is fashioned by cold working and in imitation of the shaping of flint and bone and therefore belongs to our stage I. Malachite is already known. These early Egyptians had not long abandoned the hunting stage though they have their copper and ground celts. A lump of copper found at Qau would point to local working though there is no proof according to Lucas that native copper was ever found or used in Egypt. Still he admits that some of the Badarian beads may have been made of native copper and probably as the technique is very much like that of stage I we must wait for the proof until some of these finds have been properly analysed. In the Early Predynastic, or Amratian period (3800 B.C.) the forms multiply and grow somewhat more complicated though still native copper seems to have been worked. We find an adze, bracelets, rings, chisels, harpoon-heads, needles and tweezers in the Middle Predynastic, or Gerzean culture (3600 B.C.) taking the place of the earlier flimsy tools. There is a gradual change to the metal types though only a dagger of S.D. 60 can be said to have a specific metal shape. Still the Gerzean period means contact with Mesopotamia and Susa according to Scharff and in the next Late Predynastic period (3400 B.C.) we definitely reach the Metal Age of practical copper weapons and tools, flat axes, double-edged knives, harpoons, rhomboid daggers, flat tanged spearheads and a copper ferrule. The Badari copper was already supposed to come from the North (may be from Sinai) and when after the flaking of flint deteriorates and metal types begin to appear many have thought of Asiatic influence. De Morgan speaks of a Sumerianised Dynastic race which came to Egypt by the way of Magan!

A predynastic axe was analysed and found to have been cast of impure copper, then hammered and annealed by heat treatment under 800° C. Afterwards its cutting edge was hammered to increase its hardness (73). The copper was 97.35% pure, the rest consisting of 1.28% of nickel and 0.05% of arsenic with minor impurities. This proves that by Late Predynastic times the principles of our stages III and IV were understood. By Early Dynastic times heavy axe heads, adzes, chisels, knives, daggers, spears, ornaments and household utensils show that metallurgy was then fully appreciated in Egypt. Some early Dynastic chisels consist of pure copper with 2.5% of silver and 4.1% of gold and this led Desch to consider them to be manufactured from native copper, but Lucas doubts this and points to ores from the eastern desert, which contain precious metals in the same relative quantities.

Many and wild are the theories as to how copper metallurgy was introduced into Egypt, and by whom. Wiedemann suggests Asiatic invaders, Naville South Arabian Hamites and so does Budge; O'Leary and Spielmann claim Caucasian origin, but Petrie more cautiously suggests "North Syria". Hall suggested an Asiatic origin and would look for the earliest imports of copper to Cyprus, because he held that the earliest Egyptian weapons showed Cypriot style but he was fervently attacked by Elliot Smith (74) who claims that copper metallurgy was invented in Wadi Alaqi during the mining of malachite there and he adopts the "camp-fire" theory which we have already discussed and dismissed. It was shared by Reisner, Breasted, Moret and Lucas though the latter showed that Wadi Alaqi was an unlikely spot for the discovery as the exploitation of the ores there started much later. Quiring was quite right in connecting the invention with copper glazes, though he thinks it was made in Egypt during the Gerzean period. Lucas (75) also favours an Egyptian origin as he reasons: "Unless it can be clearly proved that copper was known outside Egypt at a period anterior to its use in Egypt (which has not been done and here we find the complete evolution from the simplest object to the most complex one) it is only reasonable to credit the Egyptians with the discovery!" We have already pointed out that it was mainly a question of Near Eastern chronology, but the archaeological work of the last thirty years has changed the aspect of the problem as Lucas put in 1934 and we may now safely assume an Asiatic origin and claim that true copper metallurgy (our stages III and IV) was brought to Egypt by the Asiatic invaders of Gerzean culture. Thus in the long run De Morgan may have been right and Dykmans (76) had no right to say that he sacrificed everything to his false god "le mirage asiatique".

Indeed modern archaeology tends to regards Badarian copper as almost certainly imported, but believe that in Amratian times native copper was shaped as was native gold. The Amratians also knew malachite, turquoise and galena. The Gerzeans obtained stones and copper ores from Sinai, they smelted and worked copper and by late Gerzean times Egypt definitely has a metal culture, copper having become an utilitarian base material. It is almost certain that the basic principles of this metallurgy were derived from the earlier metallurgists of Northern Syria and Mesopotamia, the materials were plentiful in Egypt itself and need not be imported.

The claims for an original African centre are very poor. Frobenius looked for a centre of metallurgy in Nubia, but even very late in historic times bronze had to be imported there! Still Partington says: "Quite likely that archaeological investigation will establish Africa as an early source of copper, but the evidence so far available is not convincing". Indeed there are even few signs that Egyptian metallurgy had any influence on negro metallurgy as we know it now and which seems a fairly recent growth. Cline in his detailed study of Negro metallurgy states that copper came to Africa long after iron and until recently was used almost entirely for ornamental purposes as iron was far more suitable for tools and weapons. It also serves as a medium of exchange. It may be true that Diodor states that gold was dug in the Nubian mines by means of copper or bronze chisels and that Herodotus states that Lybian women wear bronze ankle rings (77) like the Nubian women (78), but on the other hand Abulfeda state that the natives of Sofala held copper more valuable than gold and that Darfur still imported copper from the Mediterranean until late. The negroes of Katanga learnt copper metallurgy from traders (79) and Ibn Batuta mentions large imports of copper from Takadda (Agades) to the South. Leo Africanus mentions copper trade by the way of Numidia and West Africa got its earliest copper from traders. It is now smelted by negroes in Transvaal, Katanga, Angola and parts of the Congo territory but copper metallurgy fades out north of Lake Nyassa. The Muslim works at Hofrat en Nahas date of the XIXth century. The claims for early contacts between the prehistoric refineries of Rooiberg, Transvaal and Egypt depend upon the correct solution of the Zimbabwe problem and there is no evidence that these contacts were so early, that one could suppose with Dart that Egypt, Elam and Mesopotamia got their ore from South Africa (80).

The possession of good knowledge of copper metallurgy at the beginning of the Dynastic Period in Egypt does not al all mean that copper now had superseded stone as a material for weapons and instruments. This can easily be illustrated by studying the Egyptian weapons. Though since predynastic times daggers were made of copper, and flint was dropped as a material for these arms, arrow heads for instance were still made of flint when the earliest copper arrowheads appear in the XIth dynasty and the latter do not become common before the XVIIIth dynasty but are quickly superseded by bronze arrowtips. Still in the Persian period flint arrowheads are far from rare. Of course this may have something to do with the properties of copper and bronze which are not always more suitable that flint or other stone for every application and in the case of arrows flint has proved to have more penetrating power than copper (81). In the Old Kingdom the king's weapons were very often still made of stone and so we find the the usual stone mace-head side by side with the copper battle-axe, but often for obvious traditional reasons.

Many authors thought that iron must have been known at an early period because it seemed impossible that the Egyptians could have worked hard stones like granite with copper instruments only. It is probable that this idea was initiated by Wilkinson (82) who writes: "No one who has tried to perforate or cut a block of Egyptian granite will scruple to acknowledge that our best steel tools are turned in a very short time and require to be retempered". But then steel a hundred years ago was not what it is now! Still his opinion is endorsed by such metallurgists as Garland. Others believe in secret hardening processes. This started already with Homer, who said that chalkos could be hardened by quenching, but in reality it would become soft. Neither does quenching in special waters such as Pausanias (83) advocates improve copper. We could cite an analogous case from the New World and stress Prescott's statement that the Aztecs worked granite with copper implements and siliceous sand, if archaeology did not bring us the proofs in Egypt itself. We need only mention the actual tools used for stonecutting as found at Saqqarah by Lauer. The time-element so worthless in the East, is often forgotten and almost infinite patience together with hammered copper, emery or obsidian cutters and grinders and abrasive powders were probably the agents employed in achieving the stupendous results which we admire after so many centuries. Therefore the "iron or steel theory" even if supported by an expert like Hadfield should be discarded (84).

The Egyptian copper ores are mainly easily reducible ores, ferrugineous and siliceous sands for fluxes abound. The main ore of the Sinai was a friable sandstone with nodules of malachite and chrysocolla (and native copper as De Morgan reports?), which by crushing and sieving could easily be concentrated. Azurite was mined in Egypt for copper and pigment of the artificial blue frit, malachite for eyepaint, mural painting, glazes but principally for copper-smelting; chrysocolla was mined both for copper and eye-paint. According to Lucas the Sinai ore contains 5—15% of copper (sometimes up to 18%), the south-eastern mines an average of 3%, Abu Seyal 36—49%, Abu Mammamid 13%. On the evidence of the slag heaps at Wadi Nasb, etc. Lucas estimates the output of the Sinai mines upto the XIIth dynasty at 5500 Tons of copper. The slagheap at Seh Bab points to

13—25 Tons of copper, at Kubban 12 Tons. Taking into account that the imports from Asia began to pour in and mining at Sinai stopped the total for Sinai may have been 8000 Tons, that of all the Egyptian mines 10.000 Tons by that time. Though this figure seems small we must not forget that this was the entire world's production in 1800 A.D!

Kubban fort was not occupied before the XIIth dynasty and therefore mining there is unlikely for earlier periods. On the other hand no tribute of copper from the South is mentioned in Egyptian texts. The eastern desert mines were always in the hands of the Egyptians, but at Abu Seyâl it is doubtful whether any serious mining took place before the days of Seti I and Ramses II (XIXth dynasty). The copper mines there are mainly open cut workings or tunneling for strata near the surface.

There is no proof that the mines of the eastern desert or Sinai were worked in Roman times, though it remains possible that they supplied local needs. Mention is made of copper mines in the Fayum at Dionysias and Pelusium discovered under the Ptolemies on the south bank of the Birket Karûn in several papyri (85). It appears that they were abandoned in the Early Imperial Period to be reopened later on, for in A.D. 104 an impost is taken of 3 denaries for 72 Minae of copper. When they were abandoned again we do not know, nor do we know anything about the mines of the Thebaïs which Diodor mentions (86).

Copper was smelted as early as the Middle Predynastic period as is proved by the manganese content of a copper axe-head of that date and of metal bands of the Ist and IInd dynasty mentioned by Lucas. This smelting at least in a charcoal fire with the blow-pipe (or perhaps only the melting of copper) is pictured in the tomb of Ti (Vth dynasty). Early Egyptian copper is of course still impure, it contains arsenic, bismuth, iron, nickel and copper-oxide as impurities. The small amount of arsenic is usually attributed to the working of Sinai ores in which this element does occur. Sebelien analysed an ore from Wadi Nasb which contained 21.65% of copper and 0.45% of arsenic (87). Still notwithstanding the often repeated statement to the contrary these small amounts of arsenic have no effect on the properties of copper, the occasional high percentages of 3—4% do have the effect of hardening copper, but they embrittle it at the same time and render the copper practically useless for cutting hard stones (88). It is true that 1% of arsenic or bismuth has the effect of decreasing the viscosity of molten copper and therefore it facilitates the casting of pure copper, which is always a difficult job. In later periods the arsenic content is far lower, usually not more than traces which is ascribed to the working of Egyptian or Asiatic ores. The bismuth (which Sebelien wrongly wanted to use as an indication of Cyprian origin of the copper!) has a good effect on the results of cold hammering, but the iron taken up from the flux or from the ore itself has more hardening effect than the other impurities. In general early Egyptian copper has all the characteristics of "underpoled" copper. Casting and cold hammering of the cutting edge seems to have been the standard method of manufacturing tools

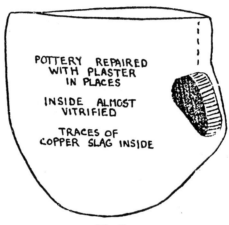

Fig. 9.
The earliest copper crucible, found at Qau
(After Brunton, Qau and Badari)

and weapons. The cold hammering was, so Lucas thought, necessary because of the lack of proper tongs to handle heated lumps of copper! As a matter of fact a Ist dynasty dagger, a XVIIIth dynasty copper knife and a small chisel of Hellenistic date were all found to be hammered into shape cold from a cast rod of copper. Sometimes, especially at later date we find that the "cored" structure specific of cast objects has disappeared because it was annealed. For annealing was not too easy in these days. The anvil was usually but a flat piece of diorite, basalte or granite on a short foot and the hammer was usually a piece of stone without a shaft. Only in the Iron Age the shafted hammer came into use in metallurgy for now the craft of the smith was mainly the use of the hammer. It is strange that though the stone-cutter and miner knew shafted hammers as early as the Old Kingdom, this implement was not yet used in metallurgy at least we never found an example of a picture of such a hammer. Still as hammered and annealed objects are fairly frequent at this early date some sort of tongs must already have existed. Cold hammered copper sheet if often employed. The 400 M. long waterpipe in Sahure's pyramid temple is made of beaten copper without a trace of solder; ewers and basins, for instance the ewer of Hetepheres are mostly beaten copper as are parts of the large statue of Pepi I and his son. Possibly these objects were made by hammering copper on a wooden core (89). Spouts and other parts are often cast and inserted; joining by rivetting or nails are practised.

Fig. 10.
Two feats of the ancient Egyptian copper workers
commemorated on the Palermo Stone (After Sethe)

Casting is of course known and practised. Open mould casting was soon practised in stone (steatite or serpentine) moulds if the objects were meant as mass products. Core-casting using a core of clay and charcoal is practised from the IInd dynasty onwards, but it came to the fore only when bronze came into general use, as casting copper in a closed mould is very difficult. Still parts of the Pepi statue were cast by the cire-perdue process (90). Examples of moulds were found at Illahun and Kahun.

After casting the hard skin was removed by grinding. We posses pictures of casting but they date from the Middle Kingdom only or later (Tomb of Rechmire, Tomb of Menkheperrasonb) and in that case the closed mould would point to the casting of bronze. The colour of the cast metal is given as yellow brown and may indicate bronze as copper is usually coloured blue or red. Though the colour blue was formerly thought to indicate iron only (Lepsius) and red copper, it is now thought that these colours on Egyptian wall-paintings indicate objects with a patina, mostly tools by the blue colour and new copper by red. Of course one should not use these colours as strict arguments but one should be led by colour and inscription.

Pictures of metallurgists smelting copper with the aid of a blowpipe have interesting inscriptions which have been discussed both by Erman (91), and Montet (92). One important one reads: "It is molten, knock hard at its bottom, here is a new pot", which probably means that copper has been melted and the foreman is summoned to thrust open the clay stopper at the bottom of the melting pot to let the copper flow into a new pot. Another one reads: "Come quick to the good sight, and stirr well in the crucible", which probably refers to the re-fining by "poling" or some other refining manipulation in which the contents of the crucible are stirred. From Table V it will be clear that the Egyptians had an extensive nomenclature covering many aspects of copper metallurgy.

Apart from the archaeological evidence there are some interesting references to two lost works of art executed in copper, which show the high skill of the Egyptians at an early date. Sethe (93) found these inscriptions on the Palermo stone (Fig. 10):

(Recto, year 4, row 5) "making copper the king's statue "High is Kha'sekhem-wy"
(Verso, year 2, row 5) Re in the sun temple "Heart's desire of Re" copper, 8 ells the evening boat and the morning sunboat.

of which the first refers to a statue of the king in copper and the second to two copper boats, 8 ells long, for the sun temple of Re: pieces which indicate that these metallurgists did not fear to make larger works of art in copper such as we have found in the case of the Pepi statue.

We have now to consider the Sinai mines where as Breasted claims "autocrats set their feet on the way to aggresion 5000 years ago" by becoming masters of the supplies of copper, the material for their weapons of war. No prehistoric remains were found in the peninsula by the Woolley and Lawrence expedition of 1913/14. Still it is possible that the mines were visited in predynastic times, though it is probable that the malachite and turquoise were obtained from the local in-

Table V

Egyptian copper metallurgy nomenclature

	HWB	
ipwt	I. 303. 11	State-planned expedition for the extraction and smelting in Sinai
bj3w	I. 438. 6	yield of copper ore
bj3	I. 436. 1	copper (later bronze or metal in general)
h3w n bj3		granulated copper
bj3 km	V. 124	black copper
ḥsmn	III. 163. 4	bronze
ḥmt n 'dn. t	I. 242. 3	"medical" copper (against the 'dn-demon)
ḥmt	III. 99. 12	(copper) ore
śtf. w	IV. 342. 9	to smelt (cast ingots)
wdḥ	I. 393. 12	melting or casting copper (alloys)
nbj	II. 236. 6	melting, smelting, casting
ḥrj. t	III. 148. 15	metallurgical furnace (late term)
mn. t	II. 68. 16	melting (charcoal) fire
mnḏ. t	II. 93. 9	part of furnace ("eye")
wdj r ṯbt. f	V. 363. 2	remove plug from tap-hole
ḥś	III. 164. 10	scoria ("excrements")
wrmw	I. 333. 6	scum of copper, dross ("brain-mass")
'ḥw	I. 223. 20	furnace man, stoker
sm3. w	III. 450. 16	(join) alloy (metals)
ḥmt. n. šm3 pr	IV. 468. 1	smelters of the smelting house
ḥmtj	I. 438. 3	metallurgist, coppersmith
ḥmm	III. 95. 12	copperworker
ḳm3(w)	V. 36. 16	metal-worker
ḳḥḳḥ	V. 76. 6	to emboss
ḳm3	V. 36. 16	to hammer
dbn	V. 438. 9	ingots (bars of 91 grammes)
nmś. t	II. 269. 9	bars of metal
ḏb. t	V. 554. 9	bars of metal

habitants, the ancestors of the Mntw of the Egyptian texts, by barter as long as these stones were appreciated as semi-precious stones. At least as early as the First Dynasty the mines became important as a source of copper ores. Jarvis' statement that the mining rights were acquired from the Mntw in the XIIth Dynasty lacks proof, but it is certain that mining in the Sinai met with opposition from the local Bedawi and every expedition was acompanied by troops. Apart from the mining centres and the temples belonging to them there are no signs of Egyptian civilisation. The greatest problems were the Bedawi and the lack of water and proper fuel, though de Morgan states that there was more water in ancient times. The Egyptian word for malachite, *mfk3t*, first became the name of the earliest mining district, Wadi Maghara, then it became a synonym for the whole peninsula, where Hathor was worshipped as the Mistress of Malachite in the great Serabit el-Khadîm temple. Indeed its more official name was "ḥtjw mfk3t" (the turquoise terraces) (94). The exploitation was already intense in the reign of Smerkhet of the First Dynasty and continued throughout the Old Kingdom, though Snefru was later regarded as the great founder of the Egyptian mining there and he became a patron god of the region and gave his name to several roads and stations of the

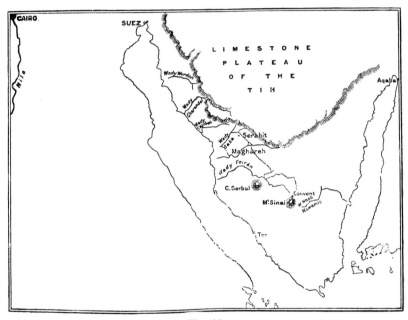

Fig. 11.
Map of the Sinai district (After Petrie)

Eastern Delta. There seems to have been a break of the production between the VIth and the XIth Dynasties, the old centre Wadi Magarah has 45 inscriptions of which 22 are Old Kingdom inscriptions mainly of the Vth Dynasty and 21 date of the Middle mainly of the XIIth Dynasty. Then the most important centre seems to have been the region of Serabit el-Khadîm, where the great temple has no less than 189 Middle Kingdom inscriptions, mainly of the XIIth and XIIIth Dynasties and 83 dating mainly from the XVIIIth to the XXth dynasties. There are no inscriptions later than the reign of Ramses III (about 1175 B.C.), when the copper ores seem to have given out except in one shaft of Wadi Nasb. Fuller inscriptions giving us some details on the exploitation date from the Middle Kingdom onwards, the earlier mention the names of the kings and leaders and officers of expeditions only. It is strange to note that the expeditions to Sinai started from Upper Egypt by Wadi Hammamat and thence by sea to Sinai. The eastern desert route seems to have been difficult because of the unruly Mntw and the sea route through the Gulf of Suez was full of shoals and unfavourable trade winds.

It seems that the Egyptians have also struck north (95) and even penetrated the Wadi Arabah in their search for copper ores, for there

Fig. 12.
Copper mines of Magarah of the XIIth dynasty,
with huts of the miners in front (After Petrie)

a rectangular building and a group of huts was found near Bir Thineil, which seems to date from the reign of Ramses II (1220 B.C.).

The ores of the Sinai mines consisted of turquoise nodules in sandstone, chrysocolla, sandstone impregnated with malachite and chrysocolla (which would give a poor yield if exploited), but principally veins of malachite, containing some azurite and a little chrysocolla. The Sinai ores were not as rich as those of the eastern desert of Egypt, but the latter consist mainly of chalcopyrite, which could not yet be worked in these early days. But in Sinai the oxidation zone of the copper ores extends to a depth of 250′ and thus allows the mining to a far lower level. The veins of ore vary from 2′ to 5′ in thickness, assaying from 5—15% of copper, they were exploited upon a depth of 135′. In the different districts we find galleries driven into the rocks

and great caves excavated leaving pillars of natural rock to support
the roof. Most of these shafts are horizontal and ventilated by vertical
air-shafts. Shelters and walls across the wadis were erected to protect
the miners from sudden floods. The settlements consisted of groups
of stone huts generally built on a mound and encircled by walls like
a kind of fort against sudden attacks by the Mntw. The mines of Wadi
Maghara were the earliest, then in the XIIth Dynasty the Serabit el-
Khadîm region was the centre and in the New Kingdom the mines
of Wadi Nasb were exploited too. Upright memorial stones and heaps
of stone (gangue?) show the entrances of the ancient mines.

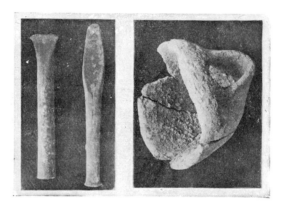

Fig. 13.
Copper chisels and crucible found in the Sinai mines
(After Petrie)

The amount of copper ore in Sinai has been exaggerated by some
authors and Lepsius made the mistake of holding banks of manganese ore to be slags of copper refining, but de Morgan belittled the
production of Sinai. Lucas' conservative estimate of the total output
of Sinai in the 1400 years of mining amounts to 8000 Tons and it
seems that Glanville's attack on these figure (96) on behalf of Rickard's
lower estimate is unwarranted. The production in later centuries may
have amounted to about 5 Tons per year. From the remains found in
miner's huts it would seem that the exploitation for turquoise and
malachite as precious stones continued after the value of these ores for
copper production had been appreciated. The houses do not only
contain pieces of turquoise, malachite and copper, but also great
amounts of copper slag and waste scrap of smelting. Chips of copper

ores, many broken crucibles and part of an ingot mould were found. The debris of the furnaces consist of double rows of stones filled in with gravel or blocks of sandstone. The ancient slag contains upto 2.75% of copper of which half is often in metallic grains indicating that only the oxidized mineral was smelted, the "bi3 ḥr ḫ3śt.f" (ore of the desert). Picks and pounding instruments, mostly of stone or flint served the miners. A few picks and chisels of copper were found and must have been used though they are too soft for mining in heavier gangue.

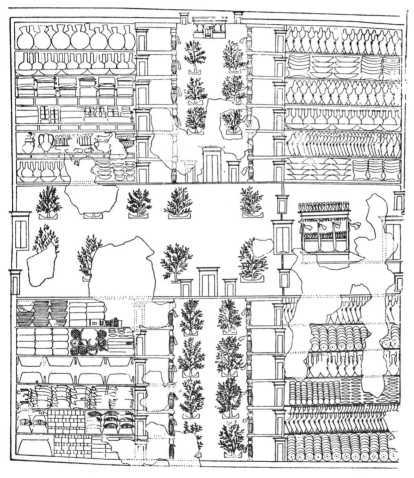

Fig. 14.
Ingots of copper and bronze in the king's storehouse at Tel Amarna
(See right hand top corner)

It must have been difficult to get good fuel for smelting purposes. The charcoal used for reduction of the ore was made of acacia wood (as Bauerman proved as far back as 1868) and the fuel for the furnaces must have consisted of desert plants and shrubs unless the roots of the high sari-grass and of the papyrus plant were used as they were in Egypt itself (97). Nozzles and end-pieces of blow-pipes made of clay were found and indicate that the smelting was conducted with the aid of blast air. The crucibles were made of clay mixed with quartz sand, but were too weak to be transported and must have been emptied by tilting. Their form is hemispherical like the sign for copper in hieroglyphs. It is possible that black copper was produced on the spot and sent to Egypt to be refined, but the presence of moulds for ingots of copper would point to refining. (98). The copper was cast in brick form, of which the sign dbn, the common weight of 91 grams reminds us. The later blocks of imported copper have either the hide-form common to the Eastern Mediterranean or the shape of round cakes. It is not known whether the ingots had standard weights, but this would appear from their pictures in treasure-houses (Fig. 14).

The mining season lasted from January 15th to May 15th, thus avoiding the hot season. It seems that certain daily impost (bkw) was exacted from the miners, who according to the inscription of an official Amenemhet worked in small groups of 5 (or 15?) (99). An official called Harrure left an interesting stela which mentions that this expedition arrived in the third month of the second season (*prt*), although "it was not the season of coming to these mines" for "the highlands are in the summer's heat and the mountains burn". He asks the workmen who either are already present and stay in the settlements of perhaps are old-timers and have visited Sinai more than once, whether the season would still be favourable for mining and they reply: "There is always malchite in the mountain, but the *inm* does not come in this season. We have heard the like before, the ore (copper?) did come in this season, (but) the *inm* lacked." But Harrure persevers as his expedition had gone well up to that moment and his energy is rewarded. He succeeded better "than anyone who was here in times of old" and the copper "left nothing to be desired, the inm was good, a treat to the eyes and the product was better than in the accustomed season".

Now the word *inm* ( ) used in this text means "skin" and is also used in the meaning "outward appearance". There are two possible explanations of this otherwise unintelligible text. For the first explanation we should remember that many primitive tribes still add certain substances to the smelting furnace without which the proper metal was not thought to form itself from the ore. The negroes of the Katanga region for instance sprinkle the empty furnace with ritual water and add to the ore and charcoal six bits of bark of certain sacred trees. The *inm* in our text might therefore refer to the bark of certain plants or trees which was added to the smelting furnace but which was not in the proper "magical" condition in summer. There are also several traditions which allow a second interpretation. Some African tribes such as the Baluba and others believe that the smelting furnace should never be placed in the sun, especially not in the full heat of the summer sun, and the copper should always be run into the mould in the shade as otherwise the copper would blister. It is possible that there was a similar Egyptian tradition which said that copper, reduced in the heat of the summer sun, would have a bad skin and not the usual hard skin (a thin oxyde layer on the surface of the cast copper) which after removing by grinding would reveal a beautiful bright copper. It is even more probable that this "skin" refers to the fact, noticed by Davey (100), that the Sinai turquoise is rather instable and easily turns from a sky-blue to green or from green to a flat grey and the ancient Egyptians probably looked upon certain of these colours as an indication that the ore was worthwhile or ready for smelting.

In charge of these expeditions we usually find a high court official very often connected with the treasury for instance the *iry 't n pr. ḥd* (official of the White House) of *wr pr. ḥd* (chief of the White House) or often *sḏȝwty* (sealbearer). Such are the leaders of expeditions of the XIIth dynasty, Khnemsu, Harnakht, Sebekdidi, Ameni, Sebekhirhab, Ptahwer, Amenemhet and Harrure who erected stelae in the Sinai region. They command chiefs of transport and their sailors, generals with their troops, scribes, guards of the storehouse, etc. The mining staff consists of prospectors, collectors, controllers, coppersmelters (ḥmty), foremen of 45, and the common labourers. It would seem that all these expeditions were state affairs and that the copper smelting of Sinai was a state monopoly, an ancestor of the later Ptolemaic monopolies.

There are still several difficulties in the reading and interpretation of the sign and determinatives for the Egyptian word copper. The word for copper is now generally read as biȝ (formerly ṯsd) (though Lepsius still read it ḥmt) by Erman, Weill and others, though Gardiner still wavers and gives bi3 as the early reading and ḥmt as a later one (though solely based on the Coptic chomnet). The old sign with which bi3 is written is a hemispherical pot, later in the Middle Kingdom often the "tooth" is added and still later the hemispherical pot is substitued by the "basket" sign (Gardiner W. 10) or even the "incense pot" sign (Gardiner R. 7) (XVIIIth and XIXth dynasties). On the other hand the old hemispherical pot is often exchanged for the "red earthenware pot" sign (Gardiner, W., 13). In some Wadi Maghara inscriptions it is clear that the original pot was a picture of the melting crucible, as sometimes the small spout is still visible. The "hemispherical pot" sign is exactly like the crucibles found at Badari and in Sinai, which have the shape of a tobacco pipe without its stem. It is possible that the word *bi3* means "molten metal" and was depicted by the crucible in which it was obtained. This also means a terminum post quem for the origin of this word, as a crucible means knowledge of the reduction of ores and the melting of metals. Weill suggested that the word *bd* (later *bt*) for crucible is related to *bi3* and was originally its nisbe-form *bi3 . j* (101).

Sethe derives his reading *bi3* from the Coptic *barot*, "grown metal", "pure copper" against the Coptic *benipe*, iron, the sky-metal. From the Coptic *chomnet* he also derived the reading *ḥmtj* for the sign for smith or artisan. In the earliest texts the word *bi3* is determined by the small sign in the form of a drop, usually interpreted as a picture of a "loaf of bread" (Gardiner, X, 3) but in this case probably a lump of metal or a copper axe-head! It is always followed by the small circle, the determinative of metals in general, or materials in the form of grains or small rounds particles. From the Middle Kingdom onwards it is usually exchanged for the "ingot" sign (Gardiner, N, 34) to which often a luniform determinative is added in Ptolemaic times. The "harpoon" determinative occurs when the harpoon of Horus is written with the *bi3* sign.

Von Lippmann is wrong in connecting the Coptic *chomnet* with the Greek *chyma* ("casting") because the latter is derived from *choanein*, "to melt" and "to cast". Rickard's supposition that the word *bi3* first meant "stone", then "copper" and then "metal in general" is unwarranted.

Two other words connected with copper were formerly translated "iron" by Lepsius (102). The first, *ḥsmn*, is the word for bronze that occurs since the Old Kingdom. Another word for a copper-alloy, possibly bronze or brass is the Late Egyptian *tḥś . t* (HWB IV, 396).

The following kinds of copper are mentioned, in later texts after the XVIIIth dynasty): *bi3 stt* or Asiatic copper (brought to Egypt as tribute of booty) and *bi3 km* or black copper which is probably exactly the same as our Schwarzkupfer, black copper, which was imported in Egypt and refined there. The copper ores known to the Egyptians, that is those ores mentioned in connection with copper, are *ḫbsḏ*, lapis lazuli (which is a semi-precious stone) or azurite (a copper-ore) and *mfk3t*

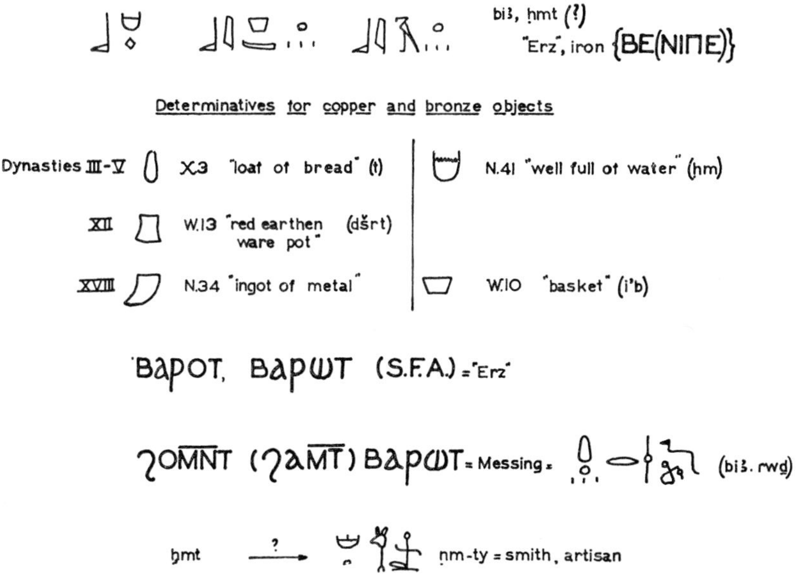

Fig. 15.
Egyptian terms for copper

(later *mfk*), malachite or turquoise, which the Egyptians do not seem to have distinguished properly.

It would seem from the texts that the home-production of Egypt began to decline or could no longer supply the growing demands of the copper industry of the New Kingdom. Hence since the XVIIIth Dynasty more and more mention is made of imports of copper from different parts in Asia sometimes as booty, sometimes as real (or may be fictitious!) tribute, but also as an object of trade. All paintings show us the Keftiu bearing hide-form slabs of copper as a tribute (or probably a well paid article!) to Egypt and the storehouses of El-Amarna show rooms full of these bars and also of bricks and cakes of copper. The Amarna letters bear witness of a lively trade in copper between

Alašia (Isy) or Cyprus and Egypt to which we shall revert later on. The annals of Thothmes III mention "vessels of copper and bronze" brought from Zahi (103), the western coast of Phoenicia where from times immemorial a copper- and bronze-industry seems to have thrived. In a text on the tribute of Isy (Cyprus) Thothmes mentions that he received "108 blocks of pure copper weighing 2040 deben" which if taking the deben at 93 grammes gives a mean weight of about 1.75 Kgrs per block (104). Taking this average weight as a standard the tribute from Retenu (Syria) (105) in general amounts to 70, 140, 6257 Kgrs. and Amenhotep II says that he took no less than 500.000 deben or 46.500 Kgrs.! Part of this booty were vessels of copper and bronze, part blocks of copper. They were used for weapons and tools, but also for architectural purposes. No less than 200 doors are mentioned in these texts and are said to be "mounted with real black copper" or to be erected of copper made in one sheet (106). Asiatic copper is also often mentioned (107). Much of this copper must have originated in Asia Minor or Armenia to be worked in Syria but there is no proof that copper came from Mycene and Crete to Egypt as Erman claims unless in the form of objects of trade not as a mineral product of the country. In this same period bronze comes into general use and part of the copper will have gone to its manufacture. The Tomb of Rech-mire shows us the "bringing of the Asiatic copper which his Majesty captured in the victories of Retenu, in order to cast the two doors of the temple of Amon in Karnak" (108). The great Abydos inscription of Ramses II mentions "impost of God's Land in copper" (109), wherever that may be. And the god Ptah blesses Ramses II on the Abu Simbel temple saying: "I have wrought thy limbs of electrum, thy bones of copper, thy organs of iron". (110)

Enormous quantities of copper are mentioned in the Papyrus Harris amongst Ramses III's benefactions to the gods. In a period of 31 years Amon received no less than 2437 Kgrs. of copper, Re 291 and all the gods 15.645 or a total of 18.373 Kgrs. as "black copper, copper in vessels and scraps, black copper for balances, copper in beaten work, copper in vessels or simply copper" apart from statues in copper, doors of cedar mounted with copper and other gifts.

The story of Ramses III's expedition to the land of '3 . ti . k3 is the last reference to Sinai as a copper producing country if we may identify this land with Sinai (111): "I sent forth my messengers to the country of Atika to the great copper mines which are in the place, their galleys carried them, other on the land journey were upon their asses... Their mines were found abounding in copper, it was loaded by ten-thousands (of blocks?) into their galleys. They were sent forward to Egypt and arrived safely. It was carried and made into a heap under the balcony (of the palace), in many bricks of copper like hundred-thousands, being of the colour of gold of three times (thrice refined gold)".

The Piankhi stèle mentions stores of copper at Memphis.

Real tin-copper bronze became common in Egypt about 1500 B.C. but in order to save the precious tin lead bronzes were used when the use of the bronze permitted it. In later periods the lead content of ordinary bronzes seems to have been definitively higher (112). Dunham (113) found magnesium in some Egyptian bronzes, but this is certainly not intentionally added to the alloy to increase its hardness but is must have been a fortituous impurity since the metal magnesium is only a very recent conquest of the metallurgist. The Egyptian bronze-workers were not only skilled workmen who could make very intricate bronze objects (114) but they also understood the art of plating copper objects (115).

The smith was not a highly honoured person in Egypt if we may judge from the Papyrus Sallier and in the records of the Royal Tomb robberies under Ramses IX several copper-smiths are mentioned among the robbers. Still the Egyptian copper-smiths were the equal of their fellow craftsmen in other countries and even in Roman times produced good work. In Ptolemaic times Egypt had a copper standard and the value of copper as compared with that of silver was 1 to 400 or 500 or better in view of the high price of silver in Egypt if compared with gold the value was about 1 to 1000. If Egypt ceased to be an important copper producing country in these late times, this was due to its gold production which enabled it to buy Asiatic copper as it procured its silver from the north. Therefore the statement of Ibn Alfaqih (about 902 AD) that copper came from Egypt must be wrong unless he meant to say that Egypt had a copper-working industry.

If we now turn to *Palestine and Syria* we find that though copper was mined in the Lebanons and the Wadi Arabah, neither of these two regions was an important copper producer in Antiquity even if "Hiram of Tyre was cunning to work all works in brass".

Modern excavations have shown that copper was used more widely and longer than even Barrois thinks in his excellent manual of Biblical archaeology (116). Not only did the cavedwellers of Southern Palestine between Hebron and Ashdod use a little copper, but by 4000 B.C. a pure copper Ghassulian metallurgy casts and fashions copper axes, chisels, hammers, points and hollow maceheads, which implies a high degree of metallurgical skill (117). The metallurgical activities were concentrated in one of the small settlement of the Beersheba group (Abu Matar), the malachite being brought from Transjordan some sixty miles to the east. By 3000 B.C. copper and soon after bronze begin to dominate over stone tools, flint begins to disappear and copper implements of mostly Mesopotamian (sometimes Cyprian) types are used. Such early copper and bronze objects hail from Teleilât Ghassul (118) but also from Tell Jemma (formerly known as "Gerar") and Tell el-Hesy (Lakiś?) (119). Several objects from Tell Beit Mirsim, which site Dossin believed to be "Debir, City of copper" (120), were examined carefully (121). An axe-head was found to be 99.25% copper with an unusually low iron content, which had been cast in an open mould and received its final form by cold and hot forging, the cutting-edge having been produced by cold-hammering. A mace-head also proved to consist of practically pure copper and it looks as if tin was still sufficiently rare in the sixteenth century B.C. These two objects were made from different types of copper ore! Two large copper forges of Early Iron Age date were found at Rumeileh and at Deir 'Allâ in Jordan seasonal smelting carried out by farmers from the region led to the erection of several furnaces (122).

There is little to guide us in the *Bible*. From the first the evidence therein is complicated by the fact the term *nèchoŝeth* (possibly connected with *nahâŝ*, to glisten) is used for copper, bronze, and brass, and thus is as ambiguous a term as *aes* and *chalkos*! Copper is said to be "dug in the mountains" (Deut. 8:9) or "molten out of the stone" (Job 28:2), but there is no further information about the art of metallurgy, which the inhabitants may have learnt from Egypt though influences from Mesopotamia have always been very strong. Furnaces were known, probably several types for some texts have the word *kur* (Deut. 4:20; Jsa. 48:10; Prov. 27:21), but Gen. 10:28 has *kibŝan* and they differ from the furnace used for lime-burning mentioned in Dan. 3:6, the *attûn*. The bellows (*mappûah*) were known, as was the crucible (*maṣrep*) and the art of casting in open and closed moulds was known in later times, core casting being mentioned in Bel and the Dragon 7, where Bel is called "clay within and brass without". Though "copper" is a natural metaphor for indestructible or strong (Ps. 107:16; Isa. 15:2; Job 6:12) it is doubtful whether the early Hebrews worked copper mines themselves as Deut. 8:9. and Isa. 51:1 would imply. It is of course known that Israelites worked in the Sinai mines and they may have brought their knowledge to Palestine. But then, though the smith is said to work both copper and iron (Gen. 4:22), the Israelites were not capable of making large pieces (1 Ki. 7:15, 46) and at the time of the conquest we read that "there was no smith found throughout all the land of Israel" (1 Sam. 13:19—20). It has been stated that "the repeated references to the purification of metals and refining from dross in the Bible are probably of Persian origin (Reitzenstein)" and though Mesopotamian and Syrian tradition may have played a large part too, we should not concede too much metallurgical knowledge to the Israelites. On the other hand it goes too far to suppose with Benzinger that the Israelites never smelted themselves. Copper was abundant in Solomon's time and tradition has it that this king opened mines in Lebanon.

However we know for certain that king Solomon started mines in the Wadi Arabah, where at present the Israeli Timnah works mine and smelt the chrysocolla of the southern Wadi Timnah containing some 1.5-2.0% of copper. Here the ancient miners dug into a white sandstone layer to extract nodules of copper sulphide containing some 40—50% of copper, washed and smelted them. The discovery of most of these mines in Wadi Arabah is due to Nelson Glueck and others (which work is now being corrected and augmented by Rothenberg) (123). During his explorations which lasted from 1934 to 1940 he also discovered mines and smelting sites on the northern shore of the Gulf of Arabah and he was able to demonstrate that Tell Kheleifeh contained the remains of the ancient Ezion Geber, the smelting and shipping centre of King Solomon. It was still in the hands of the kings of Judah in the eighth century, for a seal of King Jotham was found on the spot (124).

Most of the ancient mines are situated in the Wadi Arabah, which forms part of that large geological fault in which the Dead Sea lies. Among the most important we cite Khirbet Nahas ("copper ruin"), some 35 km south of the Dead Sea, the whole area of which is covered with ruins of walls, large buildings, miner's huts and remains of furnaces. Notable is a large square walled enclosure with side of some 76 m, full of ruins of huts and smelting furnaces. Close to Khirbet Nahas is the mining camp and the spring of Ain Gheweibeh and 3 km to the north-east a much larger one at Khirbet Jariyeh. To the south of Khirbet Nahas, at a distance of some 8 km, lies Feinan, the Biblical Punon (Num. 33.42). This area was well-watered and cultivated and in the neighbourhood copper mines have been discovered, for instance at Umm el-Amad ("Mother of Pillars"). Some 24 km to the south of

Feinan we find a Nabataean mining site at Bir Makhdur and another one some 7 km south of Petra. The largest and richest smelting centre was at Jebel Meneyeh about 38 km north-west of the Gulf of Arabah, which has two very large (336 × 125 m) walled settlements, and nearby we find another large mining site at Khirbet Mrashrash near the Gulf of Aqabah, with masses of copper slag, forming the end of a long line of mining camps along the Wadi Arabah.

These mines were not all worked simultaneously. Bir Makhdur and es-Sabrah were definitely Nabataean and Roman, others of Arab date only. However, Khirbet Nahas and Khirbet Jariyeh were worked in Solomonic days and at Feinan sufficient evidence was uncovered to show, that it was a smelting site from 2200—1900 B.C., then from the 13th to the 6th century B.C. and finally from the 3rd century B.C. onwards exploited by the Nabataeans, the Romans, Byzantines and the Arabs. The southern sites of Jebel Mene'yeh and Khirbet Mrashrash were definitely worked in the days of King Solomon.

The ores of Edom had been known to the Kenites and Edomites for centuries before the advent of the Israelites. The Kenites and the Kenizzites (Chron. I. 4. 12—14) were native to the country and these smiths taught both the Edomites and the Israelites the art of metallurgy. Later we find individual Kenites working as wandering smiths in Israel and Judah, throughout their history the Kenites led a bedouin form of life, like the related Rechabites and Jerahmelites. Balaam prophesied of the Kenites. "Everlasting is thy habitation and set in the Rock (Sela: Umm el-Biyarah near Petra) is thy Nest (Qen)" (Num. 24. 21). We are also reminded of Tubal-Qain, the smith of Gen. 4. 22 and no doubt the Kenites profited from the fall of the Hittite Empire and the subsequent immigration of smith tribes from the Armenian mountains and the spread of the art of working iron ores and producing steel tools and weapons. Edom and Midian abounded in workable copper and iron ores, the Arabah may have been the valley "whose stones are iron and out of whose hills thou canst dig copper" (Deut. 8. 7—9).

The kings of Israel had an open eye for the mineral wealth of Edom. When David subjugated and enslaved the Edomites (II. Sam. 8. 13—15; I. Ki. 11. 15—16) he probably started the mining of the copper ores. Their exploitation was undoubtedly intensified during the reign of Solomon, though he had to contend with guerilla warfare waged against him by Hada the Edomite (I. Ki. 17—19, 25). After King Solomon's death the exploitation of the mines by Judah seems to have languished notwithstanding the efforts of Jehoshaphat to revive them (I. Ki. 22. 49) turning down the help proferred by Ahaziah (I. Ki. 22. 48—50). Then Edom revolted during the reign of Joram and gained its liberty (II. Ki. 8. 20—22).

Then Amaziah recaptured this region (II. Ki. 14. 7; II. Chron. 25. 11—12) and Uziah even took Elath (II. Chron. 26. 1—2; II. Ki. 14. 22). However during the reign of Ahaz the Edomites again took possession of Elath (II. Ki. 16.6) and occupied it until the fall of the kingdom in the sixth century.

This starts a new gap in the archaeological remains which lasts until the third century B.C. when the Nabateans after occupying the country start the old mining of copper which flourishes until after the reign of Trajan, when the Arabah was no longer an important trade highway with Ezion-Geber as its port at the head of the Gulf of Akabah but the trade was shifted from Petra to Boṣrâ. Still the mines were also exploited by the Byzantines and the Arabs for St. Jerome mentions the copper mines between Zoar and Petra, the mines of Phaeno in Idumea, which were worked by Christian slaves in the time of Diocletian, when the Christians were condemned to work in the "metallae". Still these slaves had certain liberties in the seventh century (125). At Khirbet es-Sabrah a 90% pure haematite with some silica was found together with a slag with 2.73% iron, a slightly pure reniform haematite (84%) sample came from Ras es-Sabrah, a similar 84% pure haematite with silica turned up near Qa'ir together with a sample of quartzite stained with iron. A sample from Mene'iyeh proved to be a slag with a high percentage of iron, found together with a sample of quartzite, and samples of quartz, stained with malachite or chrysocolla, and attached to quartz mixed with haematite. This latter sample seems to represent the ore mined in Wadi Arabah, which, as other analyses show, was a quartz containing some 13.5% of iron and 10.3% of copper or a sandstone stained with chalcocite, containing some 7.36% of copper (as found at Khirbet Nahas). The ore at Umm el-Amad consisted of a quartz stained with malachite with particles of pyrolusite (a manganese ore).

A slag found at Mrashrash contained mostly silica with much iron, a moderate amount of copper and small amounts of aluminium and calcium. The report mentions that "the structure of the slags indicate that they were not smelted sufficiently to flow easily, and it is therefore probable that the ore produced reached only a pasty state and was then worked by hand to squeeze out part of the slag contained in it, and yielded an impure wrought iron or an impure copper, as the case may be".

If we turn to the description of the furnaces at Khirbet Nahas we read: "The first furnace built of roughly hewn blocks was 3 m square and has two compartments, one above the other. The ruins are now 1.50 m high. The inside of the lower compartment measures 2.5 by 0.8 metres". A second, circular furnace stands close by, but the author gives no further description of it. At Khirbet Yariyeh a "circular furnace measured 2.6 by 2.9 metres, the square one 2.7 metres. Only a few of the furnaces have still two compartments". Dr. Glueck concludes that in these furnaces the mixed cuprite and malachite of the cupriferous sandstone were smelted or rather worked up to be further refined at Ezion Geber. Shrubs and bushes gathered in the neighbourhood and also charcoal burned on the heavily wooded slopes of the hills of Edom served as fuel. He also believes that these sites were only worked during the rainy season, that is in winter and spring, except at Feinan, where water was available all through the year.

It would seem that these "furnaces", which as far as can be made out from the rather indistinct photographs look very much like the roasting tables depicted by Agricola, served to disintegrate the ore by the action of heat. This agrees with Glueck's suggestion that the natural winds of the Arabah provided the necessary air, which could hardly hold for real smelting. By crushing (and washing if water was available) and hand picking an enriched haematite and the copper ore could be selected and transported to the actual smelters at Ezion Geber. As we have no final evidence that iron was smelted there in the days of Solomon, the iron ores may have been traded or they may belong to later centuries. The typical slag found on these sites certainly points to the mining and roasting of the ore only not to a thorough smelting and the production of black copper and ingots.

Many of the sites in the Wadi Arabah were walled "looking like huge prison camps". We know from patristic literature that the copper mines of Feinan were worked by slave labour, either of Christians or of criminals condemned for their convictions or their crimes. This may have been the case in earlier times, though we must remember that the walls may have been built to protect the miners from marauding bands. The Egyptian expeditions to the copper mines of Sinai consisted mainly of unskilled labour for the mining, crushing and picking of the ores, but the specialist operations of smelting and refining the metals were carried out by free smiths and smelters who joined the expedition. We can hardly believe that in the Wadi Arabah the smelting was carried out by slaves, when even in classical Antiquity such highly skilled jobs were left to free metallurgists and smiths only.

The mound of Tell Kheleifeh contained the ruins of Ezion Geber. Here Dr. Glueck found "in the north-west end of the mound a large building with ten rooms. The walls of the rooms were pierced with two rows of flues, and the main walls were interconnected by a system of air-channels inside the walls, into which the upper row of flues opened. The lower rows completely pierced the thickness of the walls between the rooms. Masses of hard baked clay debris, on which pottery crucibles were placed completed the picture. It was an elaborate smelter or refinery, where previously roasted ores were worked up into ingots of purer metals".

Our suggestion that the Arabah mines produced a handpicked enriched ore and sent this to the smelters to be refined receives some support from a sample from Ezion Geber with a copper content of 56.6%, possibly copper oxide and carbonate, and therefore a copper ore of a purity far exceeding the average copper ore found in the mines of the Arabah. How this copper ore was smelted is not clear from the description of the Ezion Geber smelters, but the many remains of crucibles found in the rooms would tend to point to a crucible smelting of the ore with charcoal, which would suit such an easily reducible ore. In the palace of Mari a series of three rooms was found, each of which had benches along the walls on which crucibles could be heated in charcoal fires (126). Such crucible smelting of copper oxide and carbonate ores was quite common in the Near East in those days. In the Metropolitan Museum we can still see an original crucible containing both copper ore and charcoal found in the room of an Egyptian smith (127) dating from the XVIIIth dynasty that is about 1500 B.C.

On the other hand three more samples, submitted as "ores" proved on analysis to be slags, with their typical appearance, conchoidal structure, porosity, viscous flow lines on their surface and green colorations as the result of oxidation of copper near their surface. However, all these slag samples contain both copper and tin in a ratio averaging from 1 to 13.8 close to the ratio of copper and tin in ordinary bronze as used for tools and weapons in this period. None of these slags shows any signs of metal prills. This may indicate that these slags were rather the product of a metal remelt, such as the smelting of copper and tins bars for the production of bronze would be, than the result of metal production directly from ore. In the latter case it would be almost im-

possible to produce a slag completely free from metal prills. We venture
to propose that at Ezion Geber not only the copper ores of the Arabah
were smelted but old bronze was remelted too and possible new bronze
made from copper and tin ore smeltings.

Apart from this copper was imported into Palestine from Kurdistan
and from Chirbet es Sawra in Northern Arabia as Eusebius informs
us. In Syria and Phoenicia copper was used from the earliest period
onwards. The excavations at Amouq in the plain of Antioch (128)
have revealed early copper tools of the F-phase (3500—3100 B.C.),
and metallurgy was well established by the subsequent G-phase. The
copper-nickel-arsenic alloys were probably natural alloys, the arsenic
would act as a de-oxidizer and facilitate casting. During Amouq G
tin is added in small quantities and this goes to show that this metal
or tin-ore were still scare. In the G-phase smelting was certainly practised as crucibles and charcoal were found on the site. No doubt this
region profited from being on the crossroads between Mesopotamia
and Egypt, and so did several of the coastal towns. In Byblos copper,
gold and silver were in use long before 3000 B.C. and Schaeffer (129)
drew the attention to the statement made by Wainright that tin and
copper ores are found nearby, some 6 Km south of Byblos in the mountains of Esrouan (Kesrwan). May be this local copper was the "bj3 śtt",
the copper of Asia, mentioned in Egyptian texts of 2400 B.C. The
biblical term for copper and bronze, neḥošet, may have some connection with the "Nuhašše" of the Amarna letters, which seems to
refer to Nii near Aleppo or Riḥa near Damascus, where local copper
deposits were found. Damascus was reputed to have an important
copper industry (2 Ki. 16.10) then as it has now.

We will have occasion to refer to the archives of Syrian towns such
as Alalakh and Mari when discussing the bronze and copper metallurgy
of ancient Mesopotamia, but nearly all Syrian towns have yielded
evidence of a flourishing copper metallurgy. The ancient Ugarit (Ras
Shamra) was an important centre of copper and bronze working,
importing its copper from Asia and Cyprus and selling its products to
the South and West, perhaps also to the East. There is no site in Syria
or Palestine where so many tools and weapons have been found (130),
a hoard found in 1929 contained no less than 74 pieces. From the fourteenth century onwards the influence of Mycenean metallurgy is sensed
in this international trade-centre. Though the importance of Phoenician
trade has been greatly exaggerated by earlier generations it remains (131)
true that the North Syrian ports played an important part in bringing

together the Mediterranean world and the countries around Mesopotamia, though the high-days of the true Phoenician civilisation of Sidon and Tyrus are now estimated not to have lasted longer than about 1100 upto 800 B.C.

The importance of *Cyprus* as an copper producing centre is obvious to any student of ancient history. The isle of Aphrodite is even said to have lent its name to our term for copper. It is the *Isy*, *Asy*, or *Alašia* of the Amarna letters, the *i3-r3-š3* of the Egyptian texts the *Iatnana* of Assyrian documents. Though Wainwright contented that *Asy*, *Isy*, was the Orontes and *Alašia* the coast between Arvad and the Orontes (132), the grounds for the identification of *Alašia* with Cyprus are

Fig. 16.
Smelting furnaces at Kherabit en Nahas (After Glueck)

numerous (133) and it has been proved beyond doubt by the bilinguis found at Tamassos mentioning the *Apollo alasioteas* (134) as Schachrmayr showed. There is no doubt that Cyprus was already called Alašia in eighteenth-century cuneiform documents and Dossin (135) argued, that the name might mean "Copper Islands".

This would already constitute sufficient proof against the contention of Davies that the Cyprian mines were hardly worked in the prehistoric period (136). He mentions that Early and Middle Cypriot copper is sharply separated from Late Cypriot copper by the presence in several cases of considerable amounts of arsenic which might point to contacts with Egypt. There are plenty of signs of exploitation from the classical period onwards. But archaeology has provided the counterproof. Casson has already pointed out that Temesa mentioned in the Odyssey (137) is the Tamassos in Cyprus as was stated by Diodor and Strabo

(138). Furthermore the ingot of Enkomi with its Cypriot sign is certainly preclassical and then the large Skouriotissa mines were worked in the Bronze Age as is proved by the Mycenean settlement of Katydhata partly over these older remains.

In recent years proofs have been found that copper metallurgy started in Cyprus at least around 2600 B.C. in copper mines like those of Ambelikon (139). Further copper-workshops of the second millennium have been found at Enkomi and Karamalla (140) and there is now such a wealth of archaeological evidence (141) that the island conducted a brisk trade in copper ingots at a very early date (142).

The early Cypriot metal forms are very primitive up to the Mycenean period and it is though that the island was peopled by chalcolithic tribes from the mainland of Anatolia. Metallurgy did not come to Cyprus prior to Egypt and though there were probably contacts between the island and Egypt in the third millennium B.C., there is no question that Cypriot metallurgy did influence Egyptian metallurgy as Hall formerly supposed. It is doubtful whether any true Neolithic civilisation existed in Cyprus. Gowland stated that the earliest copper worked there was native copper, but he brings forward no substantial proof for this statement except that the copper is very pure, which is quite in line with early smelting wasteful though it was.

Though classical tradition credited the Cyprian king Kinyras with the discovery of copper (143) we may now conclude from the variety of copper objects found that copper mining began at least in the second half of the third millennium B.C. There were mines near Lithrodónta (Larnaka district), at Marion (Arsinoë) which may be the Aimar mentioned in the Medinet Habu inscriptions, and at the now largely exhausted mines in the hinterland at Tylliria. The richest mines are said to have been near Soli (144), Tamassos (of which Strabo says (145) "there are abundant mines of copper in which are found chalcanthite and also the rust of copper which latter is useful for its medicinal properties... The mines helped against the thick forestation since the people would cut down the trees to smelt the copper"), Amathus (146), Kurion (147) and Krommyon. In the opinion of Myres Marion was the headquarters of copper trade to the West from Geometric to classical times.

Most probably mining started by extracting native copper, which was very pure and which is still found in certain Cyprian mines. The earliest copper daggers found in Cyprus are of 97.23—99.47% copper and the average native copper is about 99.85%, a purity which was not easily obtained by smelting copper before the seventeenth century, when 97% was the average.

The earliest mines drove irregular galleries into the rocks looking for malachite and azurite and leaving the pyrites in place. But soon the sulphidic ores were worked too. Early slags contain from 0 to 3.6% of copper, the ores worked upto 60%. There is a great similarity between the slag of Enkomi (with 5.8% of copper) and that found at Ugarit (with 1.9%) and also between the by-products found at these two sites. It would seem that ores and black copper were exported from Cyprus to Ugarit and worked there as well as at well as at Cyprus itself by the same processes. Chalcopyrite was worked according to local geologists, roasted and smelted. A piece of matte found at Ugarit contains 35% of copper, the blue metal contains 84.1—87.2% of copper, 12.7 to 14.1% of iron and 0.2—0.5% of sulphur and the re-fined copper 98% of copper and traces of iron, tin, lead, zinc and sulphur (0.3%). Further analyses have proved that the same processes were used at Skouriotissa, Enkomi and Ugarit and that the working of sulphidic ores was therefore understood well before the sixteenth century B.C. This is very important in view of our conclusion that the working of sulphidic ores (our stage V) was well understood by the Amarna Age and then gradually became general practice until it superseded the working of oxidic ores by the Roman period. Possibly this smelting of pyrites was indeed started in Cyprus aided by the earlier smelting of galena in Asia Minor which always stood in close contact with Cyprus.

When geologists of the Cyprus Mines Corporation were prospecting (148) they found, apart from Roman galleries, shafts and slag heaps, open cast trenches in the northern hill near Apliki dated by Late Bronze Age pottery. In the houses nearby sherds, tools, tuyères and silicious rock used as flux were found. The remains of another house of the same Late Cypriot II period (1350—1300 B.C.) contained a furnace of the type found in Iron Age Megiddo, as well as slag of the common Cypriot type. A Boghaz Keui text of the same period states that "from the city of Alaśia from Mount Tagatta (^{alu} a-la-śi-ia-śum har-sag tag-ga-ta-śum) copper has been brought" which points to copper exports to the Anatolian mainland too, and a bronze stand found at Kurion shows a man carrying a hide-form ingot on his shoulders (Fig. 17).

The Egyptian records first mention Cyprus in the annals of Thoth-mes III but by the Amarna Age contacts are very frequent. The Amarna

letters contain the correspondence between the king of Cyprus and
Amenhotep IV (149). The earliest letter (No. 33) contains a message
to the Egyptian king on the occasion of his coming to the throne,
mentioning a gift of ten talents of copper already sent and promising
some 200 more. The next letter mentions 100 talents of copper sent
to Egypt in exchange for gold, horses, dresses, oil and timber! (No. 34)
and in letter No. 35 the Cyprian monarch regrets that he could not
send more than 500 talents of copper but "the hand of Nergal has
killed all the men of my country and so there is none who prepares the
copper". The Egyptian king is asked to send the Cyprian envoy together with his and he will send everything that is wanted and pay the
timber. Silver and oil should be sent to Cyprus. Fragments of another
letter (No. 36) mention 80 talents already sent, 70 ready for export
and 30 to be expected soon. "Now I have prepared much copper for
my brother and I will collect scores of vessels". Later on the copper
transports seem to have languished, but the Cyprian king assures his
Egyptian friend that this is due to the Lukki, the pirates who attack
the Cyprian coasts too, which goes to prove that they are not con-
spiring with him against Egypt (No. 38).

Since these days Cyprus remained an important centre of copper
production exporting to Egypt, Syria, Anatolia, Crete, and the Aegean
world. Earlier attempts to prove that this copper industry was initiated by the Phoenicians tried to derive the word Tamassos from a
Phoenician temes, to smelt, Tainaron from tannûr, oven and Serophos
from zarphat, to smelt but these attempts are absurd in the light of
modern archaeological evidence. The exploitation of the mines was
a monopoly strictly guarded by the native kings and the Ptolemies.
The Roman Emperors continued this tradition. The mines were worked
under Augustus as a gift of lease to king Herod (150), but Imperial
officials are in charge during the Empire (151).

Aristotle calls the copper ore of Cyprus chalkitis lithos, that is copper pyrites. The earliest methods used salts as fluxes, but very early
thuse of ferrugineous fluxes was appreciated.

Pliny mentions (152) that "copper was prepared from cadmea, It
is prepared also from another mineral called chalcitis in Cyprus where
copper was first discovered. Cyprian copper soon became very cheap".
But in his time already this copper was replaced in Rome by Spanish
copper, where the production soon outran that of the older production
centre. Still Cyprus remained important though we hear little of these
mines after the fourth century A.D. though mining was continued

under Byzantine rule. After a long period of neglect under Frankish rule (1192—1517) and afterwards under the Turks the mines have been reopened by modern industry.

We know nothing about early copper mining in Arabia and our knowledge from pre-classical *India* is scant too. In Mohenjo Daro and kindred sites copper and bronze occur from the lowest levels (153). As copper ore is unknown in Sind it must have been brought from other regions, the nearest of which are the mountain ranges of Baluchistan, where Sir Aurel Stein found a civilisation related to the

Fig. 17.
Cypriote bronze stand with man carrying ingot (After Casson)

Indus civilisation, often in an earlier stage but all using copper and bronze freely, at least in the explored surface strata. The amount of lead in the copper would point to Baluchistan and Afghanistan, but such ores do occur in Rajputana too. Because the copper also has an appreciable nickel content. Desch concluded that the ore was imported from Oman, but then nickel occurs in Chota Nagpur ores too! Sometimes 2 to 4.5% of arsenic is found probably from the working of local löllingite, a copper-arsenic ore. At Mohenjo Daro and other sites ingots, slags and remains of by-products have been found which lead us to believe that the furnace consisted of a circular brick-lined pit with a hole for the introduction of blast air, while the molten copper was run into a fore-hearth, a semi-circular depression in the ground.

The ingots weighing upto $2\frac{1}{2}$ lbs have a puckered surface, probably due to unequal cooling. The copper was either cast or hammered into sheet copper, the cire perduce process was known. Still the Indus tools and weapons show an exceptionally primitive character if compared with Mesopotamian forms of the same date. Copper axes were cast and then the cutting edge was sharpened by cold hammering. Copper plays its part in the Vedic Age even in ritual. At the dedication ceremony of a Kshatriya king the adhvaryu put a piece of copper into the mouth of a long-haired man sitting beside the king's hut, in order to remove evil spirits. It has often been supposed that copper objects mark the route of Indo-European invaders who had adopted earlier the civilisation already existing in the country (154). Though Mitra claims that there is no native copper in India but many places where copper and iron ores are associated, there are abundant signs of a Copper Age in Northern India. It is now generally agreed that the use of copper was introduced from the West by peasant communities of the Amri culture type, arriving in the Indus valley about 2800—2600 B.C. The Harappa culture had a fairly large range of equipment in copper an bronze and a good knowledge of metallurgy. Several objects found were hammered or cast from native copper (155), but in certain regions down south metallurgy was not always properly understood and bronzes may show season-cracks. In Southern India the Stone Age is immediately replaced by the Iron Age. The Chetri living on the foothills of the Awali Mountains of Rajputana and other primitive Asura tribes in Chota Nagpur still use their primitive methods of smelting copper from pyrites. They pound and wash the ore, mix it with cowdung and roast it, the roasting product is then resmelted with charcoal (156). Still it seems that the home production of India even in Hellenistic times was insufficient, though copper was required for coinage by the Indians and ancient Indian inscriptions frequently occur on that metal. That copper often came from Rome or its dominions by the way of the Red Sea (157). The copper which the Periplus (28, 36, 56, 49) says was exported from Barygaza to Ommana and Apologos in the Persian Gulf was perhaps surplus European metal exported to Malabar and Barygaza and thence re-shipped by the Indians to the Persian Gulf, probably when Rome and Parthia were at war. Pliny too has iron, copper and arsenic as products of Carmania shipped to the Persian Gulf and Red Sea ports for marketing.

Indo-Greek coins were frequently cast in moulds at fairly low temperatures and not die-stamped like modern coins and worked cold. The fact that some Bactrian coins contain some 20% of nickel has been the subject of violent discussions for over 90 years and even recently it has again been stated that this nickel must have 'been imported into Bactria from China (158). It is, however, certain that the Bactrians did not know how to produce "white copper" of cupronickel, nor did they import ores from China, but these coins were made from a particular local ore-body yielding such an alloy on smelting which was then used for minor coins equivalent to bronze and copper coins and never passed off as silver.

Tradition gave a very early date for the introduction of copper in *China*. The Emperor Huang-Ti (2704—2595 B.C.) was said to have opened the first copper mine, the Emperor Yü cast nine bronze tripods (2200 B.C.). But a careful archaeologist like Laufer put the introduction of copper in China at about 1500 B.C. and his opinion was largely confirmed by Andersons's excavations in Kansu where the earliest three strata were free of copper though the metal occured in the three later stages Hsin Tien, Ssu Wa, and Sha Ching. The earliest finds are small copper objects, then more numerous objects such as winged arrow heads follow. These copper objects are dated about 2200—1700 B.C. and the whole Yang Shao painted pottery civilisation is thought to be a cultural migration from the West. Creel proved that after this Copper Age the Shang culture introduces copper and bronze in general use shortly after 1400, the true Bronze Age starts after the Shang or Yin period which is the transitional period (159) as Dono proved by a series of analyses. As for Japan though the dolmen builders used native copper, 'there is no true Copper Age and copper and bronze do not come into general use before the ninth century A.D. (160).

Very little is known about the history of copper in *Persia* except for the sites that have been excavated in the last decennia. Anau I yielded copper and lead but no gold, silver or tin. Pumpelly states that because of its antimony and arsenic content the copper was of Central Asian origin, but then the local ores contain the same impurities. Upto Anau III copper is found together with a bronze of a variable low tin content, very often simply an impure copper and not a true bronze. In Tepe Hissar I (before 3000 B.C.) copper daggers were found, but Tepe Hissar II (3000—2500 B.C.) yield many more copper (or low tin bronze) tools and the Tepe Hissar III objects (2500 B.C.) ressemble those of the Kuban valley and those of Mohenjo Daro. At Tepe Giyân early copper was also found. In the early strata at Susa (3200 B.C.) gold, copper and silver were frequent. (161) Thin copper mirrors,

axes and blades were found and the art of casting copper and later
bronze was so well understood that many centuries later Ur Nina
sent to Susa for metal workers to carry out some work in his country.
It is interesting that, though the major discoveries in copper metallurgy
may not have been made there, Persia remained famous for copper and
bronze work for not only have we the famous Luristan bronzes, but
after the Arabian conquest of Iran the Persian copper-smiths travelled
far and they are now found all over Syria, Asia Minor, along the south
coast of the Black Sea, in Armenia, Kerman, Maghreb, Transoxania
and Ferghana.

Copper ores were plentiful in Persia and even at the present time
there is an important native copper industry at Kashan as there was
one at Mosul at the time of the Chalifate. But even in early times ores
travelled easily. Darius is said to have taken ores from Egypt and for
the Persian metallurgists there were plentiful supplies in the Afghan
mountains. Such long distance transports are testified by archaeology
for instance in the case of lapis lazuli, the "uknu" dear to the Sumerians
and Babylonians which could only be got from Badakshan or the region of Lake Baikal. But little evidence is available as to the ores and
methods of early Iranian metallurgists and this point should be given
more attention by future excavators in these regions.

This brings us to copper in *Mesopotamia*. The sources of ancient
Sumerian copper were the object of an investigation by the Sumerian
Copper Committee. Prof. Desch made many analyses of ores and objects for the Committee and at the outset he thought that the nickel
content of most Mesopotamian copper or bronzes would lead him to
the source of the ore. Most Egyptian copper objects did not contain
nickel or gold, but were very pure though sometimes they did contain
iron and arsenic. As nickel is no invariable constituent in copper ores,
therefore the Committee made a search for nickel-bearing copper ores
as the impurity might indicate the source of the ore. Native copper
does not contain nickel. Ore from Oman has the relatively high nickel
content of Mesopotamian copper, but the veins are thin. Still the slag
found in Oman contains no nickel which points to correct smelting,
Ores from Persia, the Black Sea region, the Sea of Marmora, Cyprus,
Egypt, and Sinai were shown to be free of nickel. In later reports, however, the Transvaal bronzes and ores with a high nickel content cropped
up though this source is impossible for supplies to Sumer. But the
sulphidic ore at Singhbum (India) has sufficient nickel and its outcrops
were probably worked early. Again the Abu Seyâl ore from Egypt

was found to contain nickel and though copper objects from Palestine were clearly derived from different sources than Mesopotamia, arsenical copper ores sometimes containing nickel were found in Armenia south of Lake Van and in Anatolia at Yenekoi south of the Sea of Marmora whilst the ore of Kastamouni was known to contain nickel. Such mixed ores seem to form a long band through Anatolia, Armenia, and Azerbaijan. Native copper was shown to contain no nickel but usually iron, gold, and silver. Thus after all the original theory that the Sumerians could only have got their nickel-bearing copper ore from Oman, which was supported by Peake (162) and Belaiew, was disproved by further data, which left the whole problem as it was. On the other hand it is not at all impossible that copper ores came from Oman, for as we pointed out lapis lazuli came from Badakshan and amazonite was fetched by traders from Central India and went from hand to hand until it reached Sumer. Oman also seems to coincide with the elusive Magan which was said to produce copper, diorite and dolerite as Oman does and from Magan Sargon was said to take his copper (163). A "KUR Má-gan-na" is also mentioned as a source whence comes in the ḤAR-RA: ḫubullu lexical list (164) and about 2000 B.C Gudea gets his copper from Magan and Meluḫḫa (165), but also from Mount Magda (probably up the Zagros river in Elam) and from the mountains of "Ki-maś, its soil he has chosen and its copper in baskets he has made to extract", which region has been identified with the mountain region east of the sources of the Tigris (166). Sargon II, for instance mentions mines in the mountain Ba-il-sa-pu-na, which may be Mount Segend near Lake Urmia. Other possible copper resources could have been found in northern Syria and in Arghana Maden, Armenia and N.W. Anatolia, but we will see that the region whence copper is imported varies all throughout Mesopotamian history. As long as our analytical techniques do not yet permit us to determine the ores from which the copper objects were made, we must remain content with the indications given in the archives.

When the hill-folk began to descend into the valleys of the Euphrates and the Tigris copper was still unknown there, the Hassuna culture of the early fourth millennium does not use it, but gradually the knowledge of the metal penetrates into the low lands, particularly after the discovery of smelting about 4300 B.C. The Ubaid people were acquainted with copper, though it still remains a rather rare material at first, but its use gains momentum about 3500 B.C. At Susa I bis true metal forms emerge immediately, objects being made by smelting very pure malachite (probably hand-picked) and "teemed" into open moulds. Weapons, and tools found together with a tholos-shaped kiln at Karkemiš go to show that the early Ubaid smiths had definitely conquered smelting copper ores and possessed the proper tools for working copper. Copper does not only occur in the AlUbaid graves but also in the earliest remains at Lagash, Kish, Nippur and Eridu. Probably Western Iran obtained its metallurgical knowledge from these Ubaid people whose influence spread far West and North.

During the following Uruk period (3000—2800 B.C.) there was a strong development of the copper industry and the metal came into general use, more difficult castings like that of the socketed transverse axe are attempted with succes. On the whole the number of types of copper objects grows quickly. In this period the cuneiform script was invented in its pictographic phase and as we find already signs for copper and gold in this script which was invented in the Uruk IV c stage, copper must have been a common thing in the earlier Uruk V period at least. It is also significant that these signs are written with a simple pictogram, that of copper being the picture of a copper vessel, of which there are several types mentioned already in the very early Fara texts. For bronze (ZABAR written ud-ka-bar; the Accadian siparru) a complex sign is used. It is astonishing to remark that later in Assyrian times the word siparru comes to be used for "copper" while the old word êru (Sumerian urudu) then denotes bronze. We can not see the reason, but it certainly confuses our translation of later texts, but in the earlier texts there seems no reason not to adhere to the strict separation of the two words. The Sumerians were much more formal in the use of names for natural objects and would hardly use a word in a loose sense like the Greeks used *chalkos*. They were well aware that bronze was an alloy, even if they did not known tin and bronze is called "what was made by the smith as an alloy" by the time of Sargon I. We can not understand Lutz' reason for stating that ZABAR originally meant shining ore and then copper, for which URUDU was used later and ZABAR was transferred to the alloys of copper and lead.

De Genouillac (167) mentions that at Telloh copper is as common as at Susa or Uruk and as the analyses show that the copper contained some iron and tin he supposed that mixed pyrites were already worked. This is, however, not probable, as there were no traces of sulphur found and the working of small surface deposits of complex ores might easily lead to the curious analyses that are sometimes found, but there remain exceptions to the general rule of fairly pure copper. Copper, however common already, still remained a luxury good and copper implements coincide with stone and polished stone tools. Some think that a scene picturing a man blowing into a furnace with a blow-pipe is depicted on seals of this period (168).

The following Djemdet Nasr period (2800—2700 B.C.) might well be called a Sumerian Renaissance. Copper metallurgy produces copper picks, double-axes, bowls, rings, tubes, mirrors, fishhooks, forks and socketed axes. Intricate casting of copper in animal form are attempted. This movement more or less culminates in Early Dynastic times. Then bronze seems to have come in general use as copper was already for some time. Early objects from Ur are as pure as native copper, but Desch consideres them manufactured from pure malachite. The melting and refining of copper must have been carried out with skill. No absorbtion of oxygen and embrittlement of the copper by the copper-oxyde formed could be proved and the floating layer of refining slag must have covered the copper in the furnace upto the right moment of casting. Not only is open mould casting known, but also closed moulds casting and the cire perdue process which was used for many of the elaborate copper reliefs of Ur. It often causes astonishment that these early metallurgists so freely cast copper which is still considered at present a difficult job especially in closed moulds as the molten copper is so viscous that it does not flow readily into all the ends of the moulds and often sticks to it on cooling. However, natural impurities of early copper often made casting much easier than would seem at first sight. Early Dynastic finds at Tell Asmar include statuettes of 99% pure copper cast by the cire perdue process and welded most professionally. Rickard states that the casting of copper had only just begun and says that the inequality and variability of the skill displayed in castings like the recumbent Ur bulls suggest an undeveloped art, but archaeology has by now disproved his statement. Hammering cold and annealing was practised on some of these reliefs like the Im-dugud relief (169) of Ur as was found by C. Elam and A. Scott. Hammering thin sheets of copper over a core was also practised. Filigrain, granulation and point-technique were well known and the skill of Sumerian metallurgists of the Early Dynastic is better and more widely developed than in Early Dynastic Egypt. Copper was already used in payments in the forms of bars, rings and bricks. Copper helmets were worn by the Sumerian army.

This highly developed metallurgy left little traces in religious texts.

Apart from such poetic expressions as "Your fame may shine like glistening copper" or "Your sorrow may flow like molten copper" we do not find direct associations between metals, colours and planets as often supposed even in Babylonian times! A special god of the copper-smiths as an emanation of Ea is mentioned and though the text is late (170), the legend is probably very old. The old fire-god Girru is mentioned as "the refiner of gold and silver the mixer of copper and *siparru*". A special god of copper, Nindara, who shone like it, came out of the earth where the metal is found "covered with solid copper like a skin".

In the period of the Sumerian Renaissance of the Ur III Dynasty (c. 2000 B.C.) the ensi Gudea imports copper from *kà-gal-ad*, the mountain of Kimaš (in the Zagros region), where it was dug from the mountain side (*ba-al*) and the ore was concentrated by sieving (*im-bi mu-na-ab-pad*). After smelting the cakes of copper were transported in baskets (*ušub*). Other texts of his reign mention *urudu-lah-ha*, that is copper refined by fire which serves to make bronze by alloying it with nagga (accad. *anaku*), a work of the smelter or SIMUG. It is possible that tin was already known and that the Sumerians mistook it for lead (*anaku*), as the Romans much later often mistook antimony for lead? In other texts (RTC 19 & 100) NAGGA-ZABAR (tin-bronze?) is mentioned. Three specimen of Ur III copper contained 0.78% of lead, 1.50% of iron and traces of arsenic, which experts considered to have been smelted from pyrites though the smelting was carried out quickly and the copper had not remained long in the furnace. This is of course most important and should be confirmed by further analyses. We have tentatively said that the smelting of sulphidic ores (our stage V) had become more common in the Amarna Age but it is quite possible that so intricate a process was developed only by many experiments and trials and that the foundation of the art was laid much earlier in imitation of the smelting of galena which as we saw was invented in the early half of the third millennium B.C. Connections between Anatolia, where this art was developed and Mesopotamia are particularly close in this period, when the Cappadocian letters testify that black copper and refined copper were exported from the inland of Asia Minor to Mesopotamia, to which correspondence we shall revert presently.

Texts from Umma belonging to this period throw some light on the organisation of metallurgy in these Sumerian cities.

The metal is delivered to a central storehouse (171) (AZAG AN) the

Table VI

Sumero-Accadian terms for copper metallurgy

Sumerian	Accadian	
URUDU NAGAR (dibira)	qurqur êru	smelter, bronze-smith cop-
simug	—	copper-smith
URUDU-SAHAR-HU-LAH-HA	și-it ḫurri	"what comes from] the mountains", native copper (ore)
URUDU-NÍG-SAHAR-RA	—	copper mineral (ore)
NIN-DA-ÁR-URUD-DIR	kirinnu	copper ore
URUDU-HU-LUH-HA	me-uš-ie	washed copper (native crude)
URUDU-SAHAR-KI (LÀ, ŚU)	—	crushed, broken ore
URUDU	sipparu	copper
URUDU ME-LUH-HA	—	copper from Dilmun
—	êru a-la-śu-ú	Cyprian copper
URUDU A-RA-LUM	—	copper from Aralu
ZABAR	êru	bronze
URUDU-AN-NE	—	tin
URUDU-LUH-HA	êru damqu	refined copper
URUDU-ZA-RI-IN	—	(brilliant) copper
URUDU-NÍG-TIL	—	(old) scrap copper
UDUN, UTUNU	—	crucible furnace
GIR$_4$, KÊRU	—	two-storied smelter
URUDU-BA$_6$-BA$_6$	ra-a-tu	fore-hearth
URUDU-A-HA-KUD-DA	nûnu	(metal) pig (lit. salmon, comp. German Luppe, Fr. saumon)
—	qalu, mesu, barru	alloyed copper
NE-KÚ	—	refining loss, wastage
URUD-DIR	—	scoria
URUD-UH	—	dross
KA + IM		blowpipe
—	nappaḫtu	bellows
URUDU GIZZAL	banû, epêśu	to cast
URUDU-Á-AŠ-GAR	nap-ta-qu	mould
URUDU-NÍG-DÉ-A	pitqum	cast copper
DÙ (DÉ)	pitqu	casting
URUDU-AMA-TUM	agarinnu	(mother of the axe) mould
DUB	tarâku	to hammer (copper)
—	nașraptu	crucible
BA-ZI-IR	—	blunted (copper tools ready for annealing)

purpose of which is defined in the texts by the addition "where is kept..." Here the copper-smiths get their orders and their material for which a receipt is written and kept. Here also the city's imports are stored. These texts range from the 34th year of Dungi to the ninth of

Bur-Sin, and comprise amongst others 'a receipt for 1 talent of imported copper, a delivery to the smith Ur-nigin-gar, a receipt for 0.6 talent of forged copper (URUDU-KIN) and a receipt of a present of 26.5 minae of copper for the ensi. From the latter text it would seem that quantities of 10 Kgrs of copper are still worth mentioning and this warns us again not to overrate the copper production of these early times.

We have a considerable amount of information on the state of copper metallurgy about 2000 B.C. from Ur III documents (172) which permit us to establish a table (Table VI) of the terms used by the later Sumerian copper-smiths, which goes to show how far they had mastered their craft. Dossin (173) believes that the very name of the river Euphrates means "river of the copper minerals" as he believes that most of the copper ore came from the Taurus and the Armenian mountains nearby (174) which is only partly true as the documents show. Here in the mines of Ergani Maden rich sulphidic ores were smelted (the slag still contains more than 4% of copper!) and the black copper was shipped to Tishmurna and Durhumit (near the mines and east of Boghazkeui and Kültepe) for refining. However, Ur received much of its copper from Dilmun (Telmun) between 2000 and 1700 B.C., it was indeed the "port of entry" of copper obtained in the present Bahrein, which was then a market place for parties coming from various regions of the coastal area of the Gulf to echange or sell their products, exporting copper ingots and objects, beads of precious stones, pearls and ivory (175).

In the days of the Third Dynasty (2000 B.C.) copper metallurgy was in full swing at Ur. The texts use the Sumerian "tibira" both for the merchant (tamkaru) and the metallurgist (qurqurru). The merchants get most of their copper from Magan but also from the West in exchange for products of the craftsmen of Ur (176). Certain towns in Sumer seem to have a special reputation in metallurgy, e.g. Bad-tibira (town of the smiths), Sippar (town of bronze?) and Eridu (town of copper?). The copper was imported to be delivered to the great storehouse, where the official issued quantities of copper to the guilds of the smiths to be worked into implements and tools. Sometimes the merchants were allowed to import quantities of metal at their own risk. The kings seem to have had a large store-house at Drehem (Pu-zuriś-Dagan). Limet describes no less than 163 different objects which the copper-smiths were able to manufacture on command. Sometimes large quantities of metal were issued, in the fifth year of Šu-sin no less than 20 talents of copper were given to the smiths, and other contracts speak of several hundreds of hacks or picks (177). Hence we meet a well-developed metallurgy at the end of the Sumerian civilisation, which disposes of all the tools and furnaces needed for the craft. The sign for copper, URUDU, may represent the cross-section of a mine, the word gradually came to mean metal in general and such terms as URUDU AN.NE or URUDU A-BÁR, which we meet in the texts, just denote tin and lead and not any alloy or special type of copper. The old crucible furnace (utunu) and the two-storied smelter (kêru) (in which alternate layers of charcoal and ore were smelted in the upper compartment, heated by the fire in the lower one) were both in use (178). The smith seems to have made his own bellows, for one document speaks of two big he-goats which a copper-smith receives "for leather for the bellows" (179). With a liberal air supply his furnaces could attain a temperature of 1100°C (180). Casting was an art well-understood, moulds are mentioned in several documents (181), wax is issued to a smith, who probably uses it for cire-perdu castings (182). The blow-pipe is also in use for certain types of work (183). Indeed, the Sumerian copper-smith had good reasons to thank his patron, the god Tibal or Tibira, for the skill which the god had taught him.

We have ample information on the trade connections with Cappadocia and Syria, which were already firmly established by this time (184). The Syrian copper-smiths were as skilled as their Mesopotamian brethern. Copper was shipped from the West into Mesopotamia in the form of oblong ingots, bars and blocks. Thus a text of the Larsa period (c. 1800 B.C.) (185) speaks of "...copper ingots of 4 talents, 4 copper ingots of 3 talents each, 11 shekels of oblong pieces of bronze...".

The documents from Alalakh (186) dating from the eighteenth century B.C. give many details on the copper and bronze objects made locally and they mention a fine of no less than 6000 shekels of copper. Further evidence can be culled from the archives found in the town of Mari on the Euphrates (187). The Mari tablets contain several texts which shed some light on the production of this copper. First of all there is the letter from Aplachanda of Carcemish to Iasmach-Addu of Mari running: "there are copper ores at Zirânim. They are abundant. Put your young men to watch over them. May they keep them for you alone, and as long as you stay there, may they bring them (the ores) to you very regularly". Then we have the letter which Kibri-Dagan, an official writes to his lord which says:

"On the abundant ore to be stored (at Terqa on the Euphrates) my

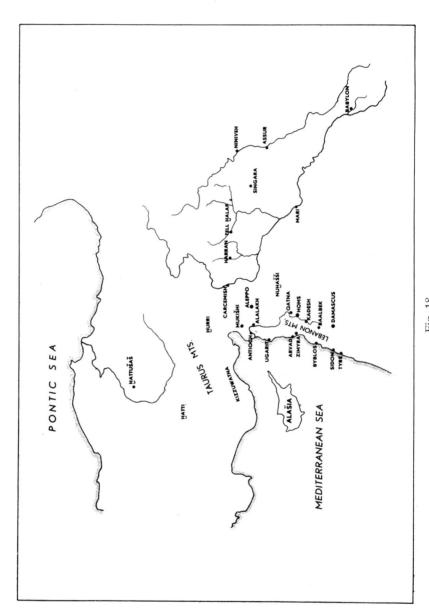

Fig. 18.

Map of Northern Syria and Mesopotamia about 1500 B.C.

lord has written me. On... I have laid my hands, but there is no responsible official who could check this material and store this ore in
the ware-house. May a responsible official, on whose order the ore
could be stored in the ware-house, arrive speedily and may he store the
ore".

The viceroy of Mari has further received the following instructions
from his father, the king of Assyria:

"On the matter of the gathering of copper ore, this is perfect. As
the porters bring the copper ore from a distance of ten or twenty double-
hours (100—200 km.!), tell the children of the great and the ušmû,
which are with thee, to gather the copper ore. With the help of a...
they shall remove the impurities and the dirt carefully. That the... and
the washed mineral, after careful cleaning, with the help of water be...
When the copper ore has been... the pounding and the picking will
take place...".

It is interesting to note, that here regional copper ores are reported,
collected and transported as such to the towns to be smelted and refined by the local smiths. In this case there was no need to import copper
in bars from the smelting centres in Cyprus and Asia Minor which delivered black copper to be refined by the local coppersmiths. Our
texts clearly describe the collection and transport, the storage, the
washing, pounding and picking of the ores thus finally yielding an
ore rich in copper for local smelting.

The word for copper ore used in these texts, šuripu, is literally to
be translated as "the fusible", and in certain texts it is no doubt used
for "ice". Dossin rightly takes it as a synonym for "šuchtum", copper
ore (and sometimes copper or bronze). The application of the term
šuripum to the smelting of copper ores is clear from a text which refers
to the "softening, smelting" (šurîpum) of such ores and from another
tablet found in room 108 of the palace of Mari which mention "14
shekels of silver and 10 grains of gold for a fount (šurîpum) of bronze
which Iar'ib Abba has made". From room 115 of the same palace
comes a note of Iarim-Lim to his lord reading: "On the subject of the
bronze object on which my lord wrote me, I went to inspect it and...
three days ago the bronze was cast. In order that it reaches my lord
immediately, this selfsame night I sent the piece of bronzework to
Mari".

At Mari a "bît šurîpum", or "house where the copper ore is worked"
was actually found (188). An antechamber opening to a long corridor
connects three narrow oblong rooms (Nos 216, 217 & 218) in which

there are benches with a row of holes on one side which served as hearths for crucible smelting of copper ores. An abundance of charcoal, copper ore and broken crucibles was found on the spot.

What the smiths made from this locally refined copper is quite clear from the many lists of copper objects from Alalakh and notably from two interesting texts from Mari. One of these refers to copper nails: "To Iasmach-Addu say this: Thus speaks thy father Shamshi-Addu: On the matter of the manufacture of 10.000 nails of 6 shekels each (by weight!). I have written to Lâ'um and to Mašiya (whom we met earlier in connection with the casting of a silver statue, he must have been an expert metallurgist!). They have written me thus: There is no bronze available, we will not be able to make 10.000 nails. Now we can make 5.000 nails only. For the 5.000 nails we need 8 talents and 20 minae of bronze. On the market 2 minae of bronze cost one shekel of silver; for 8 talents and 20 minae we need therefore 4 mana and 10 shekels of silver. Give this money, that the bronze be bought and the 5.000 nails be made!".

A second text from Mari refers to spear-heads: "...On the matter of the lances on which you wrote me in these terms: Here there are no lances, the... and the smiths shall be ordered to make lances!... On the matter of the copper destined for the manufacture of nails... on which you wrote me. I have sent the copper, have the nails made... and store them".

Further letters mention the manufacture of a bronze-plated war-chariot for the king, consuming no less than 18 minae of copper, and 28 minae of copper are used for "the statue of the king", that is to be sent to Aleppo, this copper belonged to Dagan of Terqa.

Four passages in these texts refer to *erû misû -ala-šu- u*, that is refined Cyprian copper used in the palace refineries. These imports of refined Cyprian copper become very common in the fifteenth century, exports of copper and bronze to Syria are common in Mesopotamian texts since the sixteenth century.

However, during the Old Babylonian period (1800—1500 B.C.) the copper produced in Syria and adjoining countries north-west of Mesopotamia goes to Assur and thence into Babylonia, where it is not yet popular because of its price. In the south one shekel of silver will buy 4—6 minae of copper (189) whereas the price at Mari is one shekel of silver for 4 minae of copper and in Anatolia 1 to 1. This copper could hardly compete with the copper from Magan which at Ur fetched only one shekel of silver for 8 minae of copper! Hence this

copper dominated southern Mesopotamia until well in the sixteenth
century B.C. when the West finally wins through. We see this clearly
in the texts from Alalakh dating back to the fifteenth century B.C.
(190).

During this period copper has taken the place of silver as a medium
of exchange. It is usually weighed in local "talents" (in kakuru of 1800
shekels or half a Babylonian talent of 30 kgr), its value is about 1/45th
of that of silver. The copper is received in bars and handed over to the
smiths to be worked into vessels, rings, baskets, braziers, door-panels
and parts of furniture, tools and weapons. In certain cases we are sure
that copper metal is actually meant. Thus we have a note on "3 talents
of copper, and 1200 shekels for the smiths of Berâšena, 7.000 shekels
of copper for Bentamušuni", 400 shekels of the sum here being for
arrow-heads to be made by one person. Then there is a note on "7
talents of copper for the smiths to make 2000 copper baskets for the
town of Nichi", and another reading "4 talents of copper for the men
of Berašena. 4000 shekels of copper for arrow-heads and 600 shekels
for copper doors". A receipt for weapons includes "copper made into
bars (ZAG. ipiša) and 30 copper eriga delivered to Šuwa". Then there
are the texts on copper objects such as the note on 4 bronze drinking
vessels weighing in all 4200 shekels and a list of bronze utensils, e.g.
2 picks of 400 shekels each, or the note on two loads of bronze chains
weighing 2750 shekels of bronze, which have been sent to the town of
Zalche. Bronze (ZABAR) is employed in the manufacture of most
weapons, bows and chariot fittings.

In many cases, however, the words "shekels of copper" refer to
currency. Thus the king awards Šatuwas 6 talents and 2 bronze daggers,
4 talents of copper belong to Echli, 18 talents of copper for several
towns, 20 talents of copper to defray the expenses of Birriaššuwa, son
of Irip-seni for his journey to the country of the Hittites, 550 talents
of copper for Aššurbani or the 4 talents of copper "the excess of the
money which Echli sent in and 1 talent of good copper and one sikarnu
debited against Ewa". All this is undoubtedly *money*, not metal.

In none of these texts the source of the copper or its ores is given,
local sources may have been exploited but the larger part of the copper
used must have been imported from the north or from Cyprus. The
latter country was a very important supplier of copper, its oxhide-
shaped bars of copper being found all over these parts.

We do not yet quite know the part played by the country of Subartu
in the foothills of the Armenian mountain and the region of Lake Van,

Urartu, but this is certain that these mountain regions, rich in metals, must have played a large part in the evolution of metal craft in the alluvial Mesopotamia (191). Possibly the Subareans and the inhabitants of Urartu were not only trading in metals and ores but also worked as metallurgists in Assyrian and Babylonian towns. A texts of the end of the Hammurapi Dynasty (192) mentions "25.3 minae of copper (ore?) that they have added for the Subarean".

Subartu, Urartu and all the Armenian mountains kingdoms play a large part in the supply of Assyria. In Assur there was a special gate and a quarter of the metallurgists. The copper of the North and West were often brought back as booty by the Assyrian armies. The Assyrian records (193) mention that Tiglath Pileser I took 180 vessels of bronze and 5 bowls of copper from the Muški and Kutmuhi (Commagene) and from Urratinaš 60 vessels of bronze, bowls of copper and great cauldrons of copper (194). Tukulti Ninurta II received 130 talents of copper as a tribute from the Lakean Hamataia, 30 copper pans from Harâni the Lakêan, 40 copper pans from the city of Sirku and 50 copper vessels from the city of Katni (195). Assur-nasir-pal took vessels of copper from the land of Kutmuhi, the city of Katni and vessels, cups, dishes and a great hoard of copper from BîtAdini, vessels of copper from the land of Hanibalgat and the land of Nairi and bowls, cups, copper utensils and a copper wild-ox from the land of Zamua (east of the Tigris (196). Also "at that time I received copper, tabbili of copper and rings of copper from the land of Sipirmena", from the land of Kirhi in Kutmuhi and as a tribute of Ahuni of the land of Adini whilst the tribute of Sangara, king of the land of Hatte (the Hittites)! consisted of wild-oxen, vessels, bowls and a brazier of copper together with 100 talents of copper (197).

Shalmaneser II received a tribute of copper from Hattina, from Sûa the Gilzanite and Karparunda of Hattina and again "from... of the Hattinites 300 talents of copper and 1000 copper vessels, 90 talents of copper from a prince at the foot of Mount Amanus, and from Sangara, prince of Karkemiš 30 talents of copper." (198)

The booty of Sargon II taken from the temple of Khaldia in Musaṣir was no less than 3600 talents of crude copper, 25.212 shields of bronze, great and small, 1.514 lances, 305.412 daggers, 607 basins, all of bronze" together with many undefined objects of bronze (199).

These few quotations will go to show the enormous importance of these regions for the copper supply to Mesopotamia. The Assyrians themselves were as skilled in bronzework as the Sumerians, from the monuments we know that they were able to run vast quantities of molten bronze into a single mould.

The importance of copper trade is also shown by the records of a Babylonian banking-firm which deals in gold, silver, copper, bronze and lead but not yet in iron (1395—1242 B.C.) (200).

Here again though bronze and iron are available the use of copper weapons continues into the Persian period.

A few data are also available on the prices of copper in different periods. We have mentioned that it served as a medium of exchange in the form of rings, blocks or cast animal figures which were at the same time weights. In the Sumerian period Telloh texts give a silver-copper ratio of 1/240, Singašid states that he fixed this ratio at 1/600—700, which is too good to be true, as the ratio of Hammurabi's period is 1/120—140. The earlier Dynasty of Agade (Sargon I) gives a ratio gold/silver/copper of 1/8/200. The Cappadocian tablets distinguish different qualities of extra refined copper for which the silver/copper ratio of 1/25 and 1/55 is given, but the ordinary copper is usually sold at an average ratio of 1/45—60.

In the Assyrian period a ratio of silver-bronze is given at 1/185 and therefore Sargon II's statement that silver and copper had equal value in his time is undoubtedly a boast, as is Shamsi Adad I's low price. In the sixth century B.C. the silver/copper ratio was about 1/80. The regions south and east of the Upper Zab seem to have played no part in the copper supply of Mesopotamia. But in the mountain region of Armenia, which is practically unexplored, further excavations will undoubtedly throw a wealth of light on this question as we are practically certain that even from prehistoric times onwards a metallurgical centre existed here, the influence of which can not yet be estimated.

Another region yet insufficiently explored (though several unobtainable but recent publications in the Russian language are announced) is Transcaucasia and Caucasia. *Transcaucasia* is a region particularly rich in copper ores. Jessen counted no less than 418 outcrops of some extent especially in the Middle Caucasus, Araxes and the adjacent Pontic regions. The ores contain an average of 10 to 20% of copper and native copper is quite common; nuggets of upto 4 lbs have been found. Both fuel and water are plentiful and make these mountain ranges the ideal centre for metallurgy. In the Northern end of the Caucasus range there are but few mines. Most early copper objects found in these regions contain the same impurities arsenic, lead, antimony, silver and nickel in about the same proportions, which suggests that the ores of the Araxes region were those exploited in Antiquity.

It has been observed that Mesopotamian metal types have greatly influenced Caucasian types, which is quite clear when we remember that Transcaucasia is situated on important crossroads from east to west and from north to south and that Mesopotamia has always tried to dominate these important mountain regions and their valuable ores by more or less succesful inroads and conquests. Sumerian and Assyrian rulers were ever engaged in breaking any growing power in these regions.

The archaeology of Transcaucasia has been discussed by Hančar who distinguished three phases. In the earliest Načlik period (from 3300 to 2400 B.C.) the inhabitants were mainly engaged in hunting and primitive agriculture; they imported their copper from the south. In the following Kuban period (Childe's Kuban period) (2400—1800) contemporary with Troy II and Tepe Hissar III the import of copper objects seems to cease and a local copper industry starts which has connections with the south, the west (Troy II) and the east (Hissar III). This industry rapidly grows in importance; casting and hammering are learned and copper, either pure or with 0.25—1.25% of tin (no intentional alloy!), is used. The connections with the Near East are then suddenly cut short at the end of this period.

In the following period (Childe's Middle Kuban period) (1800—1200) the metal industry developes quickly, casting in valve or closed moulds is learnt and the local smith already admitted to the ranks of the barrow builders in the former period now attains the height of his skill. Caucasian metal industry now greatly influences the tribes of the Caspian steppes and at a time trade with the Danube valley seems to have existed!

Metal forms of Transcaucasia and Armenia have always exerted a great influence on the metallurgy of the Near East and especially on *Asia Minor*. Though Herzfeld is probably exaggerating when he says that Khaldic metal objects are found from the Oxus to Etruria, it is quite certain that metal objects from these regions were found in Byblos, Cyprus and the Balkans at an early date (Hubert). The influence of Transcaucasian and Pontic metallurgy on Troy is obvious and Frankfort has proved that metallurgy had a bad influence on the quality of the pottery in that town.

Very early sites of Asia Minor like Sakcegözu (201) yield copper even in the deepest strata and in the Ib period of that site bronze is already found. It seems that the earliest invaders of Asia Minor were already acquainted with copper and by 3000 nearly every site in Asia Minor shows copper that has been reduced from ores and casting is well understood. Still native copper occuring in Asia Minor too us used, as some contend even in Phrygian times (202). Though Virchow has ascribed the invention of copper metallurgy to the Pontic tribes, the famous Chalybes and Tibareni, this statement is not true as we have seen. Nevertheless the Pontic region is a most important secondary centre of metallurgy, where many other important discoveries were made. It seems certain that an important copper production existed in this regions by the time of the Cappadocian letters at the end of the third millennium B.C. These letters mention especially the towns of Haburata, Tišmurna and Wašhnia. The Assyrian merchants engaged in metal trade in Anatolia had trade communities of local branches in several of these towns and did not engage in private trade but each merchant seems to have delivered periodically certain fixed quantities of copper to the central office and storehouse of his particular town. In this "bît karim" his merchandise was received and he was credited for his deliveries on a special personal account (qâtum) for the amount of refined copper equivalent to the amount he had brought in. Other accounts in silver, etc. were run to his name. There were two qualities of copper, the "bad" (probably black copper) and the "good" copper (refined copper), for one text gives a clear definition of the two kinds: "You wrote as follows: Tell me how much good and how much bad copper there is. Bad copper there is, I am waiting for the good kind and how much will be won by refining". Again of the "good" copper there were two qualities distinguished by their price. The cheapest kind was the *erûm haburatai*, valued at a silver-copper ratio of 1/55, and then the better *erûm šikum* valued at 1/25, the average of the prices mentioned for refined copper is 1/45—60 and the amounts mentioned in these letters are 130, 40, 180, 78, 100 minae, etc. (203). Another letter mentioning the refining of copper runs: "Make good copper, so that they buy it from me". The copper was probably traded in bars or cakes. These cakes had not as is often stated the form of a double-axe in honour of the thundergod but they are in the form of a hide, probably they were used as money and the connection of early forms of money with cattle is well known from Rome and other countries. There is no question that a hide is represented and not an axe for the edges are not convex but concave!

Still very little more is known of these highdays of copper metallurgy between 2400 and 2000, except that it would seem that attempts were made to work sulphidic ores as the sulphur content of some copper objects would go to prove. This should, however, be confirmed. Tools or furnaces are not mentioned in the excavations, but then these have still been carried out very spuriously in the Pontic region and any careful investigation is sure to bring further evidence. A second apex of mining and metallurgy was reached between 1500 and 1200 B.C. By then the demand had reached such proportions that import of copper from Cyprus ("from Mount Tagatta") was growing. A ship found on the bottom of the sea near Anatalya dating from the earlier part of this period had a load of bars of copper on board wich seemed to have served as money too. The Hittite lawbook (1300) gives a copper-silver ratio of 1/240, which is higher than that in Babylonia. Much old metal was recast in this period as is proved by the many hoards found. By 1500 all the aspects of copper metallurgy were perfectly understood in Asia Minor and when the copper industry revived after the troubled times between 1200 and 800 A.D. to flourish in the Iron Age between 800 and 550 there were no new technical discoveries to be made.

Quiring states that the types of shafts with a circular descending staircase as found at Kedabeg and Arghana Ma'den (where Assurnasirpal II got his ore) date from the Assyrian period, but then his typology of early mines is still rather theoretical and remains to be proved. That the copper mines of Western Asia Minor were exploited in late Babylonian times is proved by the fact that Nabonidus imports copper from Jamana (Ionia) in 550 B.C.

Crete received its first metallurgical impulses from the Anatolian mainland. Copper becomes common at the beginning of the Early Minoan I period about 3000 B.C. before gold and silver, and remains the most important metal until replaced by bronze about 2000 B.C. There is no doubt that Crete itself could but supply a secondary copper industry. There is a little copper ore in the west coast eparchies of Kydonia and Selinos and on the island of Gavdos in the south-west (204). The supposed copper mines described by Mosso at Chrysokamino do not contain ores, but were probably smelting places. But even the Curetes would have found the methods described by Mosso impracticable. The slags, ore, pieces of crucibles, etc. are of Middle Minoan date (205), their real source is the East, probably Cyprus. Contacts with this island were always close and there is no doubt that the principal impulses for the development of Minoan and Aegean metallurgy came from the East along the traderoutes along the south coast of

Asia Minor rather than by the way of Troy. In Troy the earliest settlement has yielded some copper (very hard through accidental impurities) and even bronze, but the true metal culture starts in Troy II when
the town becomes an important trade centre between Asia and Europe.
Though they practise open mould casting, spinning of copper vessels,
hammering and other techniques the Troian metallurgists were not
very skilled or advanced, but then Troy was a trade centre not a metallurgical centre though there are plenty of ores in the neighbourhood
which were certainly exploited in classical times. These local smiths

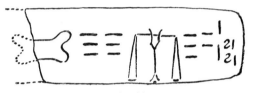

Fig. 19.
Tablet from Knossos, Crete, showing typical copper
or bronze ingot (After Head, Corollo Numismatica)

worked according to Asiatic traditions (206). We do not have a large
series of analyses of Troian metal objects, still we know that the metallurgical tradition is absent in Troy III to reappear in Troy IV when
copper (probably mostly native) is used along with stone and bone for
pins, awls and chisels or other implements but bronze seems to have
been unknown for some time. Copper and bronze then become more
frequent again in Troy V when the old traditions and contacts seem
to have been re-established (207). Hence it seems that this centre,
however important it was for the spread of copper and bronze metallurgy to Central and Western Europe, did not play a part in the development of Aegean metallurgy.

There is a close connection between Egypt and Crete, a flat copper
axe of late Neolithic date indicates this, but the connection is broken at
the end of the Old Kingdom to be resumed under the XIIth Dynasty,
to be interrupted again by the Hyksos invasion and resumed in the
XVIIIth Dynasty. Small specimen of votive axes (pelekeis) may have
been used as weights or currency or probably both. Nineteen large
bars in hide-form of Late Minoan date (1600—1250) have been found,
each weighing 28.8 Kgrs, that is a Babylonian or Cretan talent. Forrer
supposed that the Babylonian mina was the basis of Cretan weights
but the supposed relations are doubtful and the Minoan weight system

still obscure. These ingots punched or incised with Minoan signs are found in Sicily, Sardinia, and elswhere in the Mediterranean, and they were imported in Egypt as Egyptian wall paintings prove. They were also found in Dalmatia, Mycene, and Euboea, and thus prove the extent of Minoan trade relations. We have already mentioned that their form has nothing to do with the Homeric *pelekeis*, but that they are blocks of copper in the form of a hide, cast in an open mould. They also occur on account tablets found in different sites of Crete. In Mycenaen times they are still in common use (208). Seltman believed that this ox-hide-

Fig. 20.
Tribute from Punt and Crete shown in the tomb of Rechmire. The ninth man from the left, bottom row, carries an ingot
(After Wreszinky, Atlas I, 15)

shaped ingot weighing one talent of copper represented the value of an ox (209), but probably the shape of the ingot is a purely utilitarian one, which is easy to carry and to load and ship (210). Both ingots of this shape or "bricks" of copper have been discovered in various Mycenaean excavations (211), the ingots figure on the Knossos and Pylos tablets as weight symbols and as indications of quantities of real ingots, which weigh slightly short of 30 Kg. each (212) (Fig. 19).

The smiths of Crete were famous in Antiquity, as the Curetes were said to be their ancestors, and their art had its influence on the Greek mainland and the Cyclades, where copper occurs on Paros, Syria, and Siphnos, but most metal objects are ostentably imports.

In *Greece* chalcolithic *button* seals have been found but in the Early Helladic period copper was mined or imported, distributed and worked. Anatolian settlers probably brought their knowledge to Early Macedonia, as is proved by a crucible found at Saratse, but long after the metal still remains rare. The Mycenean civilisation derived its knowledge of metallurgy from Crete. An axe found near Saloniki and dated about 1300 B.C. (213) was proved to have been made from cast copper and hammered cold. The sources of slags at Mycenae and other prehistoric sites have not been discovered, they were possibly derived from small local deposits now exhausted. The copper mines of Euboea gave out in Strabo's time, but copper seems to have been exploited in the Othrys range in Hellenistic times. Still in the Homeric world metals formed a valuable part of private property.

Though most of them were derived from local sources from the mainland and some of the islands, there were more important mines in Macedonia, Thessaly and other parts of the Balkan peninsula (214) which served not only the Mycenaeans but also classical Greece, as did Cyprus and South-eastern Asia Minor (215). Cyprus is mentioned in the Pylos and Knossos tablets as ku-pi-ri-jo, which is sometimes part of a man's name. Homer says that the ships from Lemnos brought wine, chalkos, iron and hides (216) and "chalkos" is mentioned in the Iliad and Odysey well over 400 times (217), where "polychalkos" is as good a term for riches as is "polychrysos", though the latter term is used twice as often as the former. There is no doubt that bronze and copper are the metals from which tools, armour and weapons are shaped.

In Greek too there is but one word for bronze and copper, "chalkos", which appears in the Pylos tablets as "ka-ko". It would seem that copper and bronze were still relatively expensive in the Mycenaean world if we read that "Glaucus made exchange of armour with Diomedes, giving golden for bronze, the worth of an hundred oxen for the worth of nine" (218). In the Odyssey Mentes, king of the Taphians, probably non-Achaeans, living near Ithaca, carries a cargo of iron which he wanted to exchange for copper at Temese (Tempsa in Bruttium or more probably Tamassos in Cyprus where Greek settlers lived already) (219) but this passage is certainly a poetical lapse. Both poems confirm what the tablets told us, that bronze was used for plates on corslets, helmets, bits for horses and weapons. The copper in the shaft-graves at Mycenae was almost pure copper (98.5%) the bronze swords had about 13% of tin, no details of their metallurgy appears in the tablets and little emerges from Homer.

The copper and bronze metallurgy of the classical period is of course well-known, the details have been collected long ago by Blümner and Miller (220). There was a strong tendency towards specialisation in metal industry, factories of special weapons are known to have existed. Special markets and hours of sale were fixed for the producers of metal objects and among the famous centres of copper and bronze industry we mention Corinth, Delos, Chios, Samos, Cyzicus, Rhodes and Pergamum. Under Roman rule the "Roman gave order that gold and silver was to be worked by the state only, but iron and copper remained free. The charges imposed were only half of what the "Macedonian kings imposed formerly" (221).

Recent analyses have informed us on some aspects of Aegean copper (222). The copper from local resources used in prehistoric Greece was and arsenical copper with some 2.5% of arsenic and traces of lead, iron and nickel, such as used both in prehistoric Central Europe but also in Mesopotamia. This type of arsenical copper can acquire a considerable hardness when forged cold. Later bronze was introduced not only for utilitarian purposes but also for statuary bronzes. The Greeks usually stuck to a tin-copper bronze with good casting and working properties, whereas in Roman bronzes lead is always present in considerable proportions and the tin content is lowered accordingly, a practice which Pliny mentions in his thirty-fourth book. The same can be said about Greek and Roman coins. Roman coinage of the third century A.D. may have 30% of lead, whereas the tin content has fallen to 3—4%! In certain cases however, the Greeks made specific alloys. A rectangular sheet of metal, consisting of two layers of a white alloy covering the two side of sheet copper, was recovered from the Alpheus river. The white alloy consisted of 53% of copper, 33% tin and 14% lead. It would have cracked under hammer blows and probably the sheet copper was hammered by the usual repoussée technique and then coated on both sides with the white alloy by dipping the cleaned, cold copper into the molten alloy, which had a very low melting point of 300°C, which would avoid all distortion of the copper. Then the white alloy could be finished by tooling and polishing giving the vessel the look of polished silver.

Techniques came and went with fashion (223). Hammered relief was used throughtout Greece and Rome in Antiquity, though it was not popular during the Golden Age of Greece. Introduced in the fifth century (second half) it is fairly common in the third century. Cast low relief was always used, hollow cast relief (both high and low) came into fashion in Hellenistic times only. Commercial duplication of utilitarian metal objects with the aid of moulds, which were also matrices, and from repoussé reliefs with the aid of clay impressions were in common use. Pliny tries to explain that Pheidias invented repoussé and that Polykleitos developed it. There is little truth in the statement that pottery often had metal prototypes, but in later periods metalwork and pottery have more correspondence as more lathe-turned and cast metal vases are turned out and there were strong cross-currents in Hellenistic and Roman times.

Copper metallurgy came fairly late to Italy by the overland route. Copper is being hammered and cast in Northern Italy about 2000 B.C. In *Italy* many mines of copper, silver and lead have been located in the Campagliese (224), though copper furnaces have not yet been identified. The Etruscans have also exploited mines in the Locrian Temesos and in other places in Italy. Many of these mines were taken over by the Romans who succeeded in lowering the limit of exploitation from an average of 125 M to about 200 M by proper draining. The metallurgical centre of the Etruscan territories was Populonia (Pupluna, town of mines and metals?), which together with Volterra had the right to coin pieces with the image of Vulcan and the emblems of smiths. Sulphidic ores were pre-roasted as the examination of copper-slags has shown. After roasting and smelting refining followed by "liquation", adding some 8% of lead to the black copper to absorb the impurities, as Pliny (225) told us. Much attention has been given of late to the composition and manufacture of Etruscan bronze mirrors, which during the fourth and third centuries consist mostly of 83—87% of copper, 15—12% of tin, cast, hammered and reheated to about 600°C before polishing and finishing (226). Furthermore copper and leaden objects have been recovered from shipwrecks and analysed to give us a good picture of what Greek and Roman metallurgist could make (227). Copper nails, probably of Iberian origin, and from 86 B.C., were 98.5% pure and probably smelted from sulphidic ore. Earlier copper nails (200 B.C. ?) found near Marseilles were 98.5—99.0% pure.

In Central Italy blocks of copper of a specified weight (aes rude) were common from the ninth century B.C., gradually developing to bars or blocks, well shaped and with pictures of an ox or a pig stamped on. "King Servius was the first to coin copper, uncoined copper being used at Rome before that time according to Timaeus. The device employed was the figure of an animal (pecus), from which it is called pecunia" (228). In Etruria copper bars were in circulation very early and continued to be used for judicial and religious purposes after coinage was in use, finds of over 10.000 pieces are known (229). "We have shown for what a long time copper was the only material used in coins by the Roman people and the fact that, in a distant past, a guild of copper-smiths was third among those established by Numa, proves that the importance dated back to the foundation of the city"

(230). The gradual reduction of the bronze as from 1 ounce in 200 B.C. to half an ounce in 100 B.C. may indicate a corresponding rise in the price of copper as against silver, because of the heavy indemnities of the conquered countries. The ratio of silver-copper rose from 1/110 in 200 B.C. to 1/70 in 150 B.C. when it was 1/60 in Egypt!

Under the Republic copper mines were still worked between Populonia and Volterra, so that Etruscan bronze is more or less a home product. However, after Cato organised the newly acquired mines in Spain, which were far richer in metals, Etruscan mining began to decline. This may have been due to disfavour of the Spanish equestrian contractors with private mining in Etruria (Frank) or the Senate wished to preserve Italian copper supplies. A Senatus consultus was imposed on mining in Italy in the second century B.C.

In the Early Empire the old copper mines at Tempsa were abandoned. Roman copper coins were exported as bullion to Silezia, East Prussia, and the Baltic States ,and there is a connection between the copper alloys of these countries and Roman coinage. Exports of copper from the Roman Empire to the East developed at the same time (231).

The manufacture of bronze and copper ware seems to have developed a real factory system at least in Capua at the end of the Republic and in the Early Empire. Great quantities of this ware, quite uniform of workmanship, are found throughout Italy and everywhere in Germany, Sweden, and even in Finland. Gaul was another province where certain quality wares were produced. Capua was the centre in Cato's days and in Pliny's time (232). The metal was alloyed with proper proportions of tin and zinc and cast, polished, carved or forged. Copper nails of the Nemi ships are equal to the best quality of refined copper now available (233). They are rather brittle but hard and forged hot after annealing.

The old copper producing centres lost their importance to Baetica, Lusitania, Narbonensis, and England. The Italian copper industry shows a generous investment of capital and far-reaching division of labour. Plain kitchen utensils and farm implements required the service of many individual shops. These coppersmiths combined the functions of craftsmen and salesmen, often melting down articles of stock to supply materials of immediate need.

In Rome itself we find some individual aerarii as well as a guild of copper-smiths and at Milan there was a very large Collegium Aerariorum with 12 centuries of members.

There were different mining laws for gold, silver, and copper mines,

30910

who ranged together, and iron mines, where the different metallurgy and greater production required a different form of organisation to produce at the lowest cost.

Spain was the most important copper-producing province, and the metal was produced since prehistoric times. Though Quiring gives very early dates judging by his theory of the analogy of architectural and mining details, Schulten is of the opinion that regular copper production in Spain is not earlier than 2400—2000 B.C. The ore bodies of Murcia and Almeria contain small quantities of native copper which were collected by the aborigines in the Copper Age (El Garcel). Like its counterpart in Sicily the Spanish Bronze Age was due to the impact of influences on the peninsula from the Eastern Mediterranean which gave rise to a copper industry in the south-east (Algarve, Los Millares, El Agrar). Malachite and azurite are mined to depth of 125 M. Gradually the mines of Cerro Muriano (Cordoba), Villaneuva del Rey, Rio Tinto and Huelva are drawn into the process, and flint tools prove that this exploitation took place at least at the end of the Bronze Age and in the Early Iron Age. The Huelva district and Eastern Portugal contain no less than 30.000.000 Tons of slags of which at least one tenth is of the pre-Roman type and derived from the reduction of oxide ores. Gradually the knowledge of copper metallurgy spread from Almeria and Portugal northwards, though during the Bronze Age long distance trade with the East languished and was perhaps totally interrupted during part of the period. As tin was rather scarce the smith had to be content with copper and bronze objects. In the Iron Age an intense exploitation with the accompanying deforestation set in. Tartessian copper reached Greece in the VIIth century B.C. On the North-western mountain divide of Asturias and Leon most mines belong to this period, though many just like those in Galicia were mainly worked in the Roman period.

Though the Romans still worked malachite in the first two centuries B.C., they exploited the large sulphidic ore-bodies under the Empire which had been worked for precious metals only before that date. The copper ore of Baetica contains upto 25% of copper and the Huelva outcrops contain gold and silver. There is little evidence of Roman exploitation south of the Guadalquivir, the distribution of the more important Roman mines coincides with the ore bodies worked today. Roman technology was not afraid of difficult problems, chalcopyrite and grey copper were treated, liquation practised and the purified copper refined. Pliny and Strabo were not the only classical authors to wax enthusiastic over the rich copper ores, they are also mentioned by Justin and Florus (234). Roman conquests were often economic acquisitions and Roman policy had a good eye for mining prospects.

The rich mines of the Sierra Morena fell to the state when Tiberius had the proprietor of the Aes Marianus, Marius, murdered, (235). We have a wealth of details on the rich Metallum Vipascense at Ajustrel because of the Lex Metalli Vipascensis which contain mining regulations for taxation purposes. Mining dumps and rock piles were taxed. The laws distinguish the following phases of mining: mining, cleaning, crushing, smelting, preparing, breaking up, separating and washing.

Though there may have been some exploitation of malachite in the Midi (dépt. Hérault) in the Bronze Age (236), Gaul was not rich in copper ores and even in Roman times there were no mines worth mentioning.

When discussing *Britannia* Caesar says: "They use imported copper or bronze (237)" but then he must refer to imports of copper objects for pre-Roman mining of copper is proved by the finding of rilled hammers and many other signs. Pits sunk in the sandstone impregnated with copper on Alderley Edge (Cheshire) contained most primitive tools very similar to those found near Lake Superior. Other pre-Roman mining sites were in North-west Wales, Carnavon, Anglesey and Shropshire. The Romans have continued many of these mines, large quantities of bun ingots, flat round cakes of copper, have been found about 11—13" in diameter and $2-2\frac{1}{2}$" thick (238) weighing about 30—50 lbs and many were inscribed with abbreviated personal names (conductores of company?). The copper is mostly 98.5% pure, but often over 99%. Recently a special volume has been written on the prehistoric and early metallurgy of the British Isles (239) and a series of studies (240) deal with the early Irish metallurgist from Ireland, belonging to the Beaker folk, who used mixed ores and even sulphidic ores to produce smelted copper. They are supposed to have had contacts with the Halle-Saale region of Central Europe but their products have some special features.

The origin of copper metallurgy in *Central Europe* was the cause of a violent controversy between Witter (and his school) and the other European archaeologists. Witter (241) did excellent work in analysing many prehistoric metal finds and ores in Central Europe, publishing them in two larger handbooks. However, he was convinced that "the metal is an image of the composition of its ore" and this led him to the conclusion that by 2500 B.C. metallurgy developed in Central Europe independently from the Ancient Near East on lines different from other countries because of the peculiar composition of its ores, containing arsenical compounds and thus easily detected by their smell when broken. Their content of gold and other precious metals pointed to a relatively small region, the Halle-Saale region, in Central Europe where the development of metallurgy along the lines of copper-tin and copper arsenic alloys took place, beginning as early as the "Schnurkeramische Periode". His views were more or less adopted by Oldeberg, who published a careful surveys of the analyses of over 740 metal objects ranging from the Copper Age to the days of the Vikings from Swedish museums (242). Witter's close friend and co-worker H. Otto was more careful (243) stressing the fact that Bronze Age metal objects from European sites can be arranged in no less than seven types accoording to the metal used:

1. pure copper with only traces of impurities such as silver (0.05%),
2. crude copper with up to 2% of silver,
3. arsenical copper, mostly from the northern valley of the Erzgebirge,
4. copper with silver, arsenic and antimony,
5. copper with silver, nickel, arsenic and antimony,
6. copper with silver, arsenic antimony and less than 10% of tin,
7. copper with nickel, arsenic, antimony and more than 10% of tin.

Otto holds that only by a close study of both the chemical composition and the typology of the objects analysed chronological series and commercial traderoutes or adoption of techniques can be established. Later spectral-analytical research has confirmed Otto's doubts, it is very difficult to assign the metal of which such objects are made to a particular mine. Arsenical copper for instance is hardly typical for Central European metal objects, it is found in the Aegean and the Ancient Near East quite frequently and in fact quite normal in objects made from copper hailing from Anatolia and Armenia. Hence Childe was perfectly right in rejecting Witter's conclusions which were partly due to "imperfect knowledge of the prehistory and early history of the Ancient Near East". Childe (244) had himself demonstrated the value of comparison of metal types for the investigation of diffusion of metal techniques and the more research was done on ancient metal objects the more convincing his arguments proved.

It is now generally accepted that by 2500 B.C. the rudiments of metallurgy had penetrated into Europe via the Danube valley and

Troy and that at that date both in Central Europe and Hungary native copper and smelted copper were coming into use. By 2200—2000 B.C. the Carpathians, Slovakia, the eastern Alps, the Balkans, Bohemia and Saxony were producing copper lavishly, somewhere around 2100 B.C. copper metallurgy started in Poland and by 2000 B.C. in northern Italy, then spreading slowly north and west. In Spain- metallurgy came probably as early as 2500 B.C. by way of the sea and around 2400—2000 B.C. gold, silver and copper were being produced on a fairly large scale in Almeria and Andalusia.

Of course the Romans did not work many mines in Central Europe, there are a few small Roman prospects of poor impregnations of malachite and azurite in Baluberg (Wallerfangen) and Kordel, both in Rhineland, which were worked for a short period only (245).

The mines of the Eastern Alps played their part in the development of metallurgy in Central Europe and their influence was even felt in the Mediterranean world. These mines have been the object of sustained, intelligent and succesful reseach by Pittioni and many others (246). Modern methods have been applied to this research and Pittioni and Voce have succeeded in reproducing procedures employed by prehistoric metalworkers. They cast a shaft-hole axe of unalloyed copper in a closed mould, cut copper rods with stone chisels and made successful castings in a prehistoric bronze mould such as armchair antiquaries thought could be used only for making the wax models for cire perdue castings. Gordon Childe in his review of this work correctly said that:

> "Metalworkers have undoubtedly been pioneers in discovering and applying fundamental facts and principles from which our sciences of geology, chemistry and even physics have sprung. But miners, smelters and smiths were illiterate in all societies before the classical Greek—and in many since. So the only way of finding out what chemistry or geology they knew is to find out what knowledge they used; that means what processes they consistently and successfully employed. Only a minute scrutiny of their products, their equipment and the refuse they have left by one with practical experience of the sort of operations involved can recover the outlines of this preliterate knowledge that yet lives implicitly in our systems of sciences".

The search of copper reached this region from other areas, probably from the Eastern Balkans. Copper slags used to temper Early Bronze Age sherds from valley settlements suggested that smelting had already started by then, but these settlements are so far removed from the mountain mining sites as to raise doubts whether the ore smelted in such crucibles were not derived from some other source, perhaps lumps collected from river gravels or copper imported from Hungary. During the Early Bronze Age (1700—1300 B.C.) open cut workings with small shafts were worked. The highdays of the exploitation fell in the Late Bronze Age and the Early Iron Age (1300—800 B.C.). Sherds in the dumps were reminiscent of Hallstatt C forms and this inspired Pittioni to investigate whether exploitation did not continue into the First Iron Age.

Anyway the Austrian ores of the Grauwacke zone were systematically exploited from the beginnings of the Bronze Age and contributed substantially to prehistoric Europe's wealth in copper. It is remarkable that the prehistoric miners took only sulphidic ores, notably copper pyrites of special formations only, other strata with the same type of ore remaining untouched. Over a thousand years, for exploitation, though on a much lower scale, continued into Roman times, Mitterberg alone produced something like 20.000 Tons of copper, the total yield of the Eastern Alps being about the fivefold, e.g. five waggon-loads of raw copper per year. Some 180 smelting sites are now known, produced from the various systems of shafts and galleries (247). The copper was put into circulation in the form of circular cakes, flat during the Early Bronze Age, but later mostly cap-shaped.

The specific impurities of this copper are nickel, cobalt, lead and silver. Investigation of the various metal objects and their composition has already led to remarkable conclusions. Judged from the metal impurities, the objects hitherto accepted as imports from Italy seem to have been made from the same sort of metal (i.e. metal from the same kind of ores) as the admittedly Central European Hallstatt types. This is true for instance of the celebrated pail cover from grave 696 decorated with embossed animal figures, though a technical and stylistic reconsideration of the lid leaves Pittioni still convinced that the pail is a Venetic product. Either the East Alpine copper was exported to Este, or the local smiths drew on some unidentified source of very similar ore!

In the rest of the Hallstatt bronzes the impurities detected — notably the presence of traces of nickel, lead, arsenic and antimony — agree very well with those characteristic of East Alpine ores. An exception is constituted by traces of zinc in some 40% of the artifacts, an element of which no trace is found in the copper ores. Pittioni suggests that this impurity may be derived from the tin which was alloyed with the copper. Further examination will show whether the East Alpine lodes did in fact supply the copper for the Hallstatt bronzes, where the arsenical copper from Western Hungary went and whether Tyrolian copper really travelled to Scandinavia to be worked there as some believe.

9. *Nomenclature of copper*

A few words remain to be said on the nomenclature of copper. Our word "copper" is derived from the name of the island Cyprus. The earlier Latin authors speak of "aes rubrum" or "aes cyprium" (Pliny). Vitruvius, Scribonius and Largus have "aes cyprinum", Pollio and Palladius "cyprius", Vegetius "cuprinus", the Edict of Diocletian "cuprum", Solinus "cyprum" and there is the Byzantine "koupron". From Spartian (fourth century A.D.) onwards "cuprum" is the general term, whence our words "copper, cuivre, Kupfer, koper, etc.".

The Italian "rame", Spanish "alambre", French "airain" all stem from the Latin "aeramen, aerementum" (copper ware).

The Sumerian and Accadian languages were the only ancient tongues disposing of separate words for copper and bronze from the beginning. The Hebrew "nechôšèt", the Greek "chalkos" and the Latin "aes" mean either copper or bronze. The Latin "aes" is derived from one the Indo-European words for copper "'ayos". Both this word and 'raudha or 'roudhos are probably words used by the Aryans only and not by all the Indo-Europeans (248). Pokorny has suggested that 'ayos may be derived from *Alašia*, the copper land Cyprus (249). In the different Aryan languages, however, the words derived from this original acquired widely varying meanings. The Latin *aes* was used for copper, bronze, and brass, but the Gothic *aiz* (Old High German *êr*, German *Erz*) meant both ore and later metal especially iron, the Old Slavonic *âr* came to mean *ore*, the Sanskrit *ayas* is used for iron only! (250). There are no archaeological proofs for Pokorny's contention, no direct connection between Cyprus and the early Aryans.

The derivation of the other word 'roudhos from the Sumerian *urudu* is more firmly established. We should remember that the Sumerian *urudu* is a very early word for copper, being written with a simple pictogramm and occurring in the oldest texts in Sumer. It is also used in the Sumerian language to determine copper vessels or metal vessels in general (251). Then we must remember the early Sumerian influence on Transcaucasian metallurgy and the influences which the latter had at a later date on the tribes of the Northern steppes and which we can find even in the Danube valley. The Hero-smith of the Kalevala, Ilmarinen, has copper weapons of the type which the Finns believe to have brought to their country from the "Ural mountains", but which show affinity to Transcaucasian models. In this case at least a chain of archaeological evidence goes to support Ipsen (252). The root 'roudhos is said to mean "red" and the name "red metal" would suit copper perfectly. The Sanskrit *rudhira*, the Old Persian *ruad, rodh* (New Persian

Fig. 21.
The typical round bronze (and copper) ingots of Central Europe.
Specimen from Ittersee (After Franz)

roy), the Greek *erythros* (refined copper is called *chalkos erythros*), the Lat. *ruber*, Gothic *raudo*, Old Norse *raudhr*, Finnish *rauta, ruda*, and the Basque *urreida* all mean either copper or red or both. The connection between the Basque *urreida* and the Sumerian *urudu* or its Indo-European equivalent is not clear. It is not impossible that the Sumerian word or a derivative reached Spain by the way of the Mediterranean. Spengler has correctly remarked that the names of materials and objects of trade are apt to be adopted by those come in contact with them, trade names easily form part of some "pidjin" language. *Urudu*, the oldest word for copper, may easily have passed into the lingue franca of the Mediterranean.

The third word, *chalkos*, has been the subject of much speculation. Many philologists have contended that this word was a loan-word from some Asiatic language and that the "Greeks as the most advanced Aryans were ignorant of copper" (253). Lenormant connects chalkos with the Phoenician "ḥalaq" (to polish, to work), Eisler with the Aramaic ḥalḥi ("belonging to the heaven) (a rather illogical connection for copper, as gold is the sun metal and there is no meteoric copper), Dussaud (254) derives it from the Khaldi, the inhabitants of Urartu.

Kretschmer believes it to be a third Indo-European word for copper, connects it with the Greek name of the murex "chalkè". But the Greek for murex is kalchè! Still he points to other words like the Lithonian gelezis and the Slavonian želežo which mean iron and therefore he says that the word originally meant copper or "red metal" and then came to mean iron. Curtius at a time connected chalkos with the Semitic ḥalaqa (to work) and said that chalkeus first meant "a worker in copper", then "one who cast copper", then "copper-smith" and finally "(iron") smith".

Liddell-Scott give a later view of Curtius comparing chalkos with the Sanskrit hrik-us, hlik-us (tin), Slavonic zel-ezo, Lithaunian gel-eziz (iron) and thinks that the Sanskrit ghar (lucere) has the same root. Chalkos has the specific sense copper and metal in general in Greek only. F. Muller derives the word from a root ghel (âˣ): yellow, blonde (compare the Latin helvus, gilvus, flavus, the German gelb) and he therefore supposes that the original meaning was "yellow metal" and that chalkos is really the third Indo-European word for copper.

We can not enter the battlefield of philologists but the last two authors seem to give serious links worth pondering over. We must add that the Greeks used the word chalkos in the general sense of "metal" fairly often, but we should hesitate to join some authors in believing that this was the original meaning. This might of course be true for a civilisation in which apart from copper and copper alloys no other useful metal was known. The knowledge of gold and silver would no prevent such a terminology as the precious metals do not serve any practical purpose in such a community. But we know of no passage in which this word chalkos means metal in general, however, several places give chalkos with some colour determinative added to denote some variety of copper. Thus we find "chalkos melas" for "black copper" "chalkos leukos" and "chalkos erythros" for refined copper, the latter expression occuring only once in Homer, (Iliad, Book IX).

But these matters of philology must be left to competent authorities, though may be these riddles are as dark of the properties of lapis lazuli about which Al Mustatraf says:

> "Aristotle says that wearing it in a ring enhances a man's dignity in the eyes of the people and that it is useful in cases of sleeplessness — but Allah knoweth best".

BIBLIOGRAPHY

For further literature we refer the reader to our Bibliographia Antiqua, Philosophia Naturalis, section 2 (Leiden, 1942 and Suppl. I (1952), Suppl. II (1963)).

1. CARPENTER, H. C. H., *Note on the extraction of native copper at Calumet*, (Lake Superior, U.S.A.) (J. Inst. Metals XII, 1914, 230)
   HURST, V. J. and LARSON, L. H., *On the source of copper at the Etowah site, Georgia* (American Ant. 24, 1958, 177—181)
   LILLEY, E., *The use of copper by the American aborigines* (Proc. Indiana Acd. Sci. 46, 1937, 53)
   PHILLIPS, G. B., *The primitive copper industry of America* (J. Inst. Metals, XXXIV, 1925, 261—270; XXXVI, 1926, 99—106)
   PRENDERGAST, D. M., *Metal artifacts in Prehispanic Mesoamerica* (Amer. Ant. 27, 1962, 520—545)
   RICKARD, T. A., *The use of native copper by the Indigenes of North America* (JRAI, 64, 1934, 265—287)
   RICKARD, T. A., *Man and Metals* (London, 1932, vol. I)
   SCHMIDT, E., *Die prähistorischen Kupfergeräte Amerikas* (Arch. f. Anthr. XI, 1879, 65)
2. FORBES, R. J., *Studies in Ancient Technology* (Vol. VIII, p. 13) (Leiden, 1963)
3. BERGSØE, P., *The gilding process and the metallurgy of copper and lead among the pre-Columbian Indians* (Kopenhagen, 1938)
   BRUCH, C. F., *Precolumbian alloy objects from Guerrero, Mexico* (Science (USA) 138, 1962, 1336—1337)
   MEIGHAN, CL. W., *Prehistoric copper objects from Western Mexico* (Science 131, 1960, 1534)
   QUIRING, H., *Herkunft und Beginn der altamerikanischen Hochkulturen* (Forschungen und Fortschritte 26, 1950, 7/8, 81—85)
   RIVET, P. and ARSANDAUX, H., *La métallurgie en Amérique précolumbienne* (Paris, 1946)
   Anon., *Mexican and Ecuadorian copper and bronze axes* (Nature 131, 1933, 279)
   WHARTON, C. L., *Metallographical study of primitive copperwork* (Amer. Ant. I, 1935, 109—112)
4. FORBES, R. J., *Studies in Ancient Technology*, Vol. VII (Geology and Mining), p. 115 (Leiden, 1963)
5. PLINY, *Nat. Hist.* XXXIII. 98
6. DIOSCORIDES V. 104; V. 115
7. PLINY, *Nat. Hist.* XXXIV. 117—123
8. DIOSCORIDES V. 117
9. FORBES, R. J., *Studies in Ancient Technology* (Vol. VIII) (1963), p. 266, 270

10. STRABO, III. 4. 15
11. PLINY, *Nat. Hist.* XXXVI. 137
12. ANDRAE, J., *Bergbau in der Vorzeit I* (Leipzig, 1922)
13. LUCAS, A., *Copper in ancient Egypt* (JEA XIII, 1927, 162)
    LUCAS, A., *Ancient Egyptian Materials and Industries* (London, 1962)
14. STRABO, 17. 2. 2. cap. 821
15. DIODOR, I. 33
16. STRABO, 17. 3. 11. cap. 830
17. QUIRING, H., *Vorrömische und römische Bergwerke in Nordmarokko*
    (Z. Berg-, Hütten- und Salinen-wesen 88, 1940, 213—218)
18. DIODOR, I. 15
19. ORTH, PW. (suppl. Bd. IV, 113)
20. DEUT. 8. 9; Job 28. 2
21. GLUECK, N., *The other side of Jordan* (New Haven, 1946)
    GLUECK, N., *Rivers in the desert* (New York, 1959)
22. EUSEBIUS, *Hist. eccl.* (VIII. 13. 5; mart. Palest. XIII. 1)
23. WAINWRIGHT, G. A., *Alashia: Alasa and Asy* (Klio XIV, 1915, 1)
    KNUDTZON, J. A., *Die Amarnabriefe* (VAB vol. II, Leipzig, 1915)
24. STRABO, 15. 2. 4. cap. 726
25. STRABO, 15. 1. 69
26. STRABO, 11. 8. 6. cap. 513
27. HANČAR, FR., *Urgeschichte Kaukasiens* (Berlin, 1937)
28. EUSEBIUS, (mart. Palest. XI. 6; XIII. 2)
29. HOMER, *Odyessey* I. 184; THEOPHRASTUS, *On Stone* cap. 25; GALEN,
    De simpl. med. 9. 3. 21; DIOSCORIDES V. 10; PLINY, *Nat. Hist.*
    V. 98; VII, 195; XXXIV, 2; ISIDORE, *Orig.* XIV. 6. 14;
    STRABO, 3. 4. 15; 6. 1. 5; 14. 6. 5
30. PLINY, *Nat. Hist.* XXXV. 12; PAUSANIAS, VIII. 14; X. 38
31. STRABO, 13. 1. 51. cap. 607
32. THEOPHRASTUS, *On Stones* cap. 25; POLLUX, V. 39
33. PLINY, *Nat. Hist.* XXXIV. 9—10
34. STRABO, 10. 1. 9. cap. 447
35. DAVIES, O., *Prehistoric copper mines near Burgas* (Man, vol. 36,
    1936, no. 119)
    DAVIES, O., *Bronze Age Mining round the Aegean* (Nature 130,
    1932, 985)
    GAUL, J. H., *Possibilities of prehistoric metallurgy in the East Balkan
    peninsula* (AJA 46, 1942, 400—409)
36. ACHIARDI, G. D., *L'industria mineraria e metallurgica in Toscana al
    tempo degli Etruschi* (Stud. Etr. I, 1927, 411)
37. ARISTOTLE, *De mirab. ausc. cap.* 93
38. STRABO, 6. 1. 5. cap. 255
39. PLINY, *Nat. Hist.* XXXIV. 3—4
40. STRABO, 3. 2. 8. cap. 146—147
41. STRABO, 3. 2. 3. cap. 142
42. PLINY, *Nat. Hist.* XXXIV. 4
43. AGRICOLA, GEORG, *De Re Metallica* (Engl. trans. H. C. and L. H.
    Hoover, New York, 1950) (German Transl. Berlin, 1928)

44. BIRINGUCCIO, V., *The Pyrotechnia* (transl. C. S. Smith and M. T. Gnudi, New York, 1943)
45. THEOBALD, W., *Des Theophilus Presbyter Diversarium Artium Schedula* (Berlin, 1933)
46. THEOPHRASTUS, *Hist. plant.* V. 9. 3; THEOPHRASTUS, *On Stones* cap. 16; PLINY, *Nat. Hist.* XVI. 23
47. TÄCKHOLM, U., *Studiën über den Bergbau der Römischen Kaiserzeit* (Uppsala, 1937)
48. DIOSCORIDES, V. 75
49. PLINY, *Nat. Hist.* XXXIV. 100
50. LUSCHAN, VON, Z. f. Ethn. 41, 1909, 37
51. PLINY, *Nat. Hist.* XXXIV, 101
52. PLINY, *Nat. Hist.* XXXIV. 94
53. BAILEY, K. C., *The Elder Pliny's Chapters on Chemical Subjects* (London, 1929/32, 2 vols.)
54. DIODOR, V. 36
55. PLINY, *Nat. Hist.* XXXIV, 94—98
56. PLINY, *Nat. Hist.* XXXVI. 137
57. PLINY, *Nat. Hist.* XXXIV. 94
58. ANDRÉE, R., *Die Metalle bei den Naturvölkern* (Leipzig, 1884)
59. THOMPSON, R. C., *Dictionary of Assyrian geology and chemistry* (Oxford, 1936)
60. GOWLAND, W., *The art of metal working in Japan* (J. Inst. Metals IV, 1910, 4)
    GOWLAND, W., *The metals in Antiquity* (JRAI XLII, 1912)
61. ZSCHOCKE, K. & PREUSCHEN, E., *Das urzeitliche Bergbaugebiet von Mühlberg Bischofsofen* (Wien, 1932)
    PITTIONI, R., *Prehistoric copper-mining in Austria, problems and facts* (Seventh Ann. Rep. Inst. Archaeol. Univ. London, 1951, 16—43)
62. KELSO, J. L., *Ancient copper refining* (BASOR 1951, no. 122, 26—27)
    THOMPSON, G. C., *The mining, extraction, refining and casting of copper* (Man 1956, pgs. 1431—1432)
    STORTI, C., *Metallurgia del rame* (Sibrium V, 1960, 208—215)
63. COGHLAN, H. H., *Prehistoric copper and some experiments in smelting* (Trans. Newcomen Soc. XX, 1939/40, 49—65)
    COGHLAN, H. H., *Some experiments on the origin of early copper* (Man 39, 1939, 92)
    COGHLAN, H. H., *Some fresh aspects of the prehistoric metallurgy of copper* (Antiq. J. XXII, 1942, 22—38)
    COGHLAN, H. H., *Native copper in relation to prehistory* (Man 51, 1951, 156)
    COGHLAN, H. H., *Notes on the prehistoric metallurgy of copper and bronze in the Old World* (Oxford, 1951)
    COGHLAN, H. H., *Research upon prehistoric copper metallurgy in England* (Archaeol. Austriaca, Beiheft 3, 1958, 57—69)
    COGHLAN, H. H., *Il rame nativo nel mondo antico* (Sibrium II, 1955, 17—26)

COGHLAN, H. H., *Prehistorical working of bronze and arsenical copper* (Sibrium V, 1960, 145—152)

COGHLAN, H. H., *A note on native copper: its occurence and properties* (Proc. Preh. Soc. XXVIII, 1962, 58—67)

DERKOSCH, J., MAYER, F. X., und NEUNINGER, H., *Spektral-analytische Untersuchungen von urzeitlichen Kupferfunden* (Mikrochimica Acta 1956, 11, 1649—1661)

CHILDE, V. GORDON, *Review of Coghlan's Notes in prehistoric metallurgy of copper* (Antiquity XXVI, 1952, 162—165)

MARÉCHAL, J. R., *Les origines de la métallurgie du cuivre* (Paris, 1958)

OTTO, H., *Die chemische Zusammensetzung von bronzezeitlichen Bronzen* (Naturw. Rundschau II, 1949, 106—110)

SALIN, E., *Le cuivre à travers les ages* (Cuivre, Laiton, Alliages I, 16, 1953, 40—43; I, 17, 1953, 36—39; I, 18, 1953, 36—39)

64. WITTER, W., *Die älteste Erzgewinning im nordisch-germanischen Lebenskreis* (Leipzig, 1938, 2 vols.)

WITTER, W., und OTTO, H., *Handbuch der ältesten vorgeschichtlichen Metallurgie in Mitteleuropa* (Leipzig, 1952)

BLANCE, B., *Early copper working in Europe* (Antiquity XXXIII, 129, 1959, 61—63)

65. FORBES, R. J., *Studies in Ancient Technology*, Vol. VIII, (1963), p. 25

66. MAN 1948, 3 & 17; 1951, 234, 1953, 150; 1954, 21

67. LAMARRE, H., *La cachette de fondeur de Longueville* (Seine et Marne) (Revue Archéol. XXIII, 1945, 98—115)

BRAILSFORD, J., *A founder's hoard from Dartford, Kent* (Proc. Preh. Soc. XIII, 1947, 175—177)

68. MAN, 53, 1953, no. 150; 54, 1954, no. 21

69. VOCE, E., *Scientific evidence concerning metal-working techniques* (Man, 61, 1961, 68—71)

CHADWICK, R., *The effect of composition and constitution on the working and on some physical properties of tin bronzes* (J. Inst. Metals LXIV, 1939, 331—346)

70. *Bureau of Standards Circular no. 73* (Washington, 1922)

71. SCHNEIDER, W. G., *Hardening copper and outdoing the ancients* (Iron Age) (New York, 124, 1929, 96)

72. FINK and POLUSHKIN, *Microscopical examination of ancient bronze and copper* (Iron Age (New York) 137, 1936, 34)

73. CARPENTER, H. C. H., *An Egyptian axe of great antiquity* (Nature 130, 1932, 625)

74. SMITH, G. ELLIOT, *The invention of coppermaking* (Man 16, 1916, 26)

75. LUCAS, A., *The origin of early copper* (JEA 31, 1945, 96—97)

76. DIJKMANS, G., *Histoire économique et sociale de l'Egypte* (Paris, 1930, vol. I, 200—213)

77. HERODOTUS, IV. 168

78. STRABO, 17. 2. 2. cap. 821

79. CLINE, W., *Mining and metallurgy in Negro Africa* (Paris, 1937)

RICKARD, T. A., *Curious methods used by the Katanga natives in smelting and mining copper* (Eng. Min. J. vol. 123, 1927, p. 51)

80. DART, A., *Prehistoric copper mining in South Africa* (Nature 123, 1929, 495)
81. WOLF, W., *Die Bewaffnung des altägyptischen Heeres* (Leipzig, 1926)
82. WILKINSON, J. G., *Manners and customs of the Ancient Egyptians* (London, 1842)
83. PAUSANIAS, II. 3. 3.
84. CARPENTER, H. C. H., *The metallography of some ancient Egyptian implements* (Nature 125, 1930, 859)
85. *BGU* 197; *SPP* XXII, 48
86. DIODOR, I. 15
87. SEBELIEN, J., *Early copper and its "alloys"* (Ancient Egypt 1924, 10)
88. GARLAND, H., and BANNISTER, C. O., *Ancient Egyptian metallurgy* (London, 1927)
89. LUCAS, A., *Notes on the early history of bronze and tin* (JEA XIV, 1928, 97)
90. MÖLLER, G., *Die Metallkunst der Aegypter* (Berlin, 1925)
91. ERMAN, A., *Reden, Rufe und Lieder...* (APAW no. 15, 1919)
92. MONTET, P., *Les scènes de la vie privée dans les tombeaux égyptiens de l'ancien Empire* (Paris, 1925)
93. SETHE, K., *Copper works of art of the oldest period of Egyptian history* (JEA I, 1914, 233)
94. CLÈRE, J. J., *Sur un nom du Wadi Maghara* (Sinaï) (JEA 24, 1938, 125—126)
95. MURRAY, G. W., *A New Empire copper mine in the Wadi Arabah* (ASAE 51, 1951, 217—218)
96. *JEA* XIV, 1928, 189
97. PLINY, *Nat. Hist.* XIII. 23, 45; XXXIII. 5. 30; THEOPHRASTUS, *Hist. Plant.* IV. 8. 3
98. PETRIE, SIR. W. FLINDERS, *Researches in Sinai* (London, 1906)
    WEILL, R., *La presqu'île du Sinai* (Paris, 1908)
99. *AR* I. 726
100. DAVEY, *Turquoise in the Sinai peninsula* (Trans. R. Geol. Soc. Cornwall 16, 1928)
101. Weill, R., *Les mots bi3...* (Revue d'Egypt. III, 1938, 69)
102. LEPSIUS, C. R., *Les métaux dans les inscriptions égyptiennes* (Paris, 1877, 45)
103. *AR*, II. 459, 460, 462, 490
104. *AR*, II. 493
105. *AR*, II. 471, 491. 509
106. *AR*, II. 45
107. *AR*. II. 45, 614; III. 217, 537
108. *AR*, II. 755
109. *AR*, III. 274
110. *AR*, III. 403
111. *AR*, IV. 408
112. WEISZ, H., *Studies of Egyptian bronzes* (J. Chem. Educ. 32, 1955, 70—72)
113. DUNHAM, Dows, JEA 28, 1941, 76

114. DUNHAM, DOWS, *Two pieces of furniture from the Egyptian Sudan* (Bull. Mus. Fine Arts XLVI, 1948, 98—101)

YOUNG, E., *A note on a hitherto unknown technique in Egyptian bronzeworking* (JEA 45, 1949, 104—106)

115. FINK, C. G., and KOPP, A. H., *Ancient Egyptian plating on copper objects* (Metrop. Mus. Studies IV, 1933, 163)

116. BARROIS, A.-G., *Manuel d'archéologie biblique* (Paris, 1939, I. 363—373)

117. PERROT, J., *Palestine, Syria, Cilicia* (In: Braidwood and Willey (edit.), Courses toward Urban Life, Edinburgh, 1962, 158)

118. MALLON, A., KÖPPEL, R., NEUVILLE, R., TELEITÂT GHASSUL (Rome, 1934)

119. VINCENT, H., *Les fouilles de tell ed-Douwier*: *Lachiš* (Revue biblique 48, 1939, 265

J. L. STARKEY, *Palest. Expl. Quart.* 66, 1934, 164

120. DOSSIN, G., *Debir* (Museion LXI, 1/2, 1949, 37—41)

121. KELSO, J. L., *Some sixteenth-century copper objects from Tell Beit Mirsim* (BASOR 1943, no. 91, 28—36)

122. GRANT, E., *Rumeileh*: *Ain Shems III* (Haverford, 1934, 20, 52)

BEA, A., *Archäologische Beiträge* (Biblica 21, 1940, 432)

FRANKEN, H. J., *The Excavations at Deir 'Allâ in Jordan* (Vetus Testamentum vol. X, 1960, 4, 386—393; vol. XI, 1961, 4, 361—372; vol. XII, 1962, 4, 378—382)

123. GLUECK, N., *Explorations in Eastern Palestine* (AASOR XV, 1934/35, 1—202) (AASOR 25, 1951, 346)

GLUECK, N., *The other Side of the Jordan* (New Haven 1945, 56—88)

WRIGHT, G. E., *More on King Solomon's Mines* (Biblical Archaeologist 24, 1961, 59—62)

MECQUENEM, R. DE, *Les mines de cuivre du Roi Salomon* (Techniques et Civilisations V, 1956, 2, 65—67)

KELSO, J. L., *Ancient copper refining* (BASOR no. 122, 1951, 126—128)

SOKOLOFF, V. P. and SEROUSSI, A., *Observations at an ancient smelting site in the Negev* (Science (USA) 123, 1956, no. 3197, 587—588)

FORBES, R. J., *King Solomon's Copper Mines* (Technion Yearbook XIV, 1957, 135—137)

ROTHENBERG, BENO, *Ancient Copper Industries in the Western Arabah* (Pal. Explor. Quart. Jan./June 1962)

124. *AJA*, 45, 1941, 117

125. EUSEBIUS, *mart. Palest.* XIII. 1

126. *Syria* XX, 1939, 14—16

127. *Bull. Metrop. Mus., sect.* II, Nov. 1934

128. BRAIDWOOD, R. J., BURKE, J. E. and NACHTRIEB, H. H., *Ancient Syrian copper and bronzes* (J. Chem. Educ. 28, 1951, 87—96)

129. SCHAEFFER, C. F. A., *La contribution de la Syrie ancienne à l'invention du bronze* (JEA 31, 1945, 92—95)

130. Dussaud, R., *Les découvertes de Ras Shamra et l'Ancien Testament* (Paris, 1937)
131. Buchholz, H. G., *Keftiubarren und Erzhandel im zweiten vorchristlichen Jahrtausend* (Präh. Z. 37, 1959, 1—40)
132. Wainwright, G. A., *Alashia: Alasa and Asy* (Klio XIV, 1915, 1)
133. Casson, St., *Ancient Cyprus* (London, 1937, 122, 136, 145, 153)
134. *In Reallexikon der Assyriologie*, Bd. I, 1932
135. Dossin, G., *Les noms de l'isle de Chypre* (Bull. Class. Lett. Acad. R. de Belgique, 5e sér. XXXV, 1949, 310—315)
136. Davies, O., *The copper mines of Cyprus* (ABSA XXX, 1928/29, 74)
137. Odyssey, I. 184
138. Diodor V. 55; Strabo, 14. 2. 7
139. Dikaios, P., JHS 65, 1945, 104
140. Robertson, JHS 59, 1939, 208; Megaw, JHS 77, 1957, Suppl. 24 ff
141. Schaeffer, Cl., *Missions en Chypre* 1932/35 (Paris, 1936, 94)
    Schaeffer, Cl., *Enkomi-Alasia* (Paris, 1952, 28)
142. Buchholz, H. G., *Keftiubarren und Erzhandel im zweiten vorchristlichen Jahrtausend* (Präh. Z. 37, 1959, 1—40)
    Buchholz, H. G., *Der Kupferhandel des zweiten vorchr. Jahrtausends* (Minoica, Festschr. Sundwall, 1959, 92—115)
    Landsberger, B., *Assyrische Handelskolonien* (AO vol. 24, 4, 1925, p. 20)
143. Pliny, *Nat. Hist.* VII. 57; Homer, *Iliad* XI. 20
144. Galen, XII, 214, 219 K; Ps. Aristoteles, *de Mirab. Ausc.* 43
145. Strabo, 14. 6. 5. cap. 684
146. Ovid, *Metamorph.* X. 220. 531
147. Pliny, *Nat. Hist.* XXXIV. 2. 94
148. Taylor, J. du Platt, *Mines where the Mycenaeans got their copper discovered in Cyprus* (ILN 24/2/1940, 251)
149. Knudtzon, J. A., *Die Amarnabriefe* (VAB II, Leipzig, 1915)
150. Josephus, *Antiq.* XVI. 4—5
151. Galen, XII, 266 K, 234; XIV. 7
152. Pliny, *Nat. Hist.* XXXIV. 2
153. Mackay, E., *The Indus Civilisation* (London, 1935, 106, 114, 121)
    Marshall, J., *Mohenjo Daro and the Indus Civilisation* (London, 1932, 30, 38, 105, 481, 507, 674)
    Wheeler, Sir Mortimer, *Early India and Pakistan* (London, 1959)
    Gordon, D. H., *The early use of metals in India and Pakistan* (JRAI. LXXIX, 1949/52, 55—78)
154. Mitra, P., *Prehistoric India* (Calcutta 1927, 247)
155. Caley, E. R., *Results of the examination of metal specimens from an excavation of Shamsi Gar, Afghanistan* (Ohio J. Sci. 55, 1955, 311)
    Sankalia, H. D., *Flat bronze axes from Jorwe, Deccan* (Man 55, 1955, 1, 1—3)
    Paramasivan, S., *Investigations on ancient Indian metallurgy* (Proc. Indian Acad. Sci. XIII, 1941, 87—93)
156. Mitra, P., *Prehistoric India* (Calcutta, 1927, 247)

157. WARMINGTON, E. H., *The commerce between the Roman Empire and India* (Cambridge, 1928)
WHEELER, SIR MORTIMER, *Rome beyond the Imperial frontiers* (London, 1954)

158. CALEY, E. R., *The earliest use of nickel alloys in coinage* (Numismatic Review I, 1943, 17—19)
CHENG, C. F., and SCHWITTER, C. M., *Nickel in ancient bronzes* (AJA 61, 1957, 351—365)
SCHUYLER, V. R. CAMMANN, *The "Bactrian Nickel Theory"* (AJA 62, 1958, 409—414)
PARAMASIVAN, *Metallography of Indo-Greek bronze coins from Taxila* (Current Science XI, 1942, 190—192)

159. DONO, I., *The chemical investigation of the metallic culture in the Orient* (J. Fac. Sci. Imp. Univ. Tokyo, sect. i, III, 1937, 287—327)
DONO, Ts., *The Copper Age in China* (Bull. Soc. Japan VII, 1932, 347)
ANDERSON, R., *Excavations in Kansu* (Mem. Geol. Survey China, 1929, A. No. 5, 18)
WATSON, W., *China before the Han Dynasty* (London, 1961, 79)
COLLIER, H. BRUCE, *Black copper of Yunnan* (J. Chem. Educ. 17, 1940, 19—21)
HUYSER, J. G., *Oud-Javaansche koperlegeeringen* (Cultureel Indië I, 1939, 227—231, 257—259, 292—297)
GETTENS, R. J., *Corrosion products of an ancient Chinese bronze* (J. Chem. Educ. 28, 1951, 67—71)
CHUAN, LIANG SHU-, and NAN-CHANG KAN-, *The composition of some early Chinese bronzes* (J. Chin. Chem. Soc. 17, 1950, 9—17)
MERCIER, R., *Etude de procédés de fonderie artisanale au Viet-Nam* (Bull. Soc. ethn. indochin. n.s. 31, 1956, 2, 157—169)
PLUMER, J. M., *The Chinese bronze mirror* (Art Quart. VII, 1944, 91—108)
WILLETTS, *China* (Pelican books, London, 1958, 108—124)

160. GOWLAND, W., *Metals and metal working in Old Japan* (Trans. and Proc. Japan Soc. (London) XIII, 1915, 20)
KIDDER, J. E., *Japan* (London, 1959, 110)

161. MECQUENEM, R. DE, *L'emploi des métaux par les civilisations Susiennes* (Métaux et Civilisations I, 1946, 4, 77—88)

162. PEAKE, H., *The copper mountain of Magan* (Antiquity II, 1928, 452)
BELAIEW, N. T., *On a Sumerian copper bar in the British Museum* (Semin. Kondakovianum V, 1932, 165—180)

163. II R. 51, no. 1, 1. 17

164. LANDSBERGER, B., JNES XV, 1956, 146—147, line 23

165. CYL. A., XV, 8; STATUE D, IV, 7—10; MATOUŠ, L., LTBA 33, V, 32—36

166. STATUE B, VI, 21ff; CYL. A., XVI, 15ff

167. GENOUILLAC, H. DE, *Fouilles de Telloh* (Paris I, 1934, 44; II, 1936, 88)

168. LEGRAIN, DP XVI, 31

169. PLENDERLEITH, J., *Metaltechnique* (In: C. L. Woolley, Ur Excavations, London, 1934, II, 284)
170. *Bab. Misz.* XII. 4
171. SCHEIL, V., *A propos des métaux d'Umma* (RAss XII, 1915, 60)
172. LEGRAIN, L., UET III, *Business Documents of the Third Dynasty of Ur* (London, nos. 324, 354, 357)
     LIMET, H., *Le travail du métal au pays de Sumer au temps de la IIIe Dynastie d'Ur* (Paris, 1960)
173. DOSSIN, G., *Le nom du cuivre en sumérien* (Bull. Class. Lett. Acad. R. de Belgique 5e. sér. XXXVIII, 1952, 433—438)
     DOSSIN, G., *Le vocabulaire de Nuzi SMN* 2559 (RAss XLII, 1948, 21—34)
174. BIRGI, S. E., *Notes on the influence of the Erghani copper mine on the development of the metal industry in the Ancient Near East* (Jahrb. f. kleinas. Forschung I, 1951, 3, 337—343)
     LEWY, J., *Some aspects of commercial life in Assyria and Asia Minor in the nineteenth pre-Christian century* (JAOS 78, 1958, 89—101)
     STRONACH, D., *Metal objects from the* 1957 *excavations at Nimrud* (Iraq XX, 1958, 169—181)
175. OPPENHEIM, A. L., *The seafaring merchants of Ur* (JAOS 74, 1954, 6—17)
     FIGULA, H. H. and MARTIN, W. J., *Letters and Documents of the Old Babylonian Period* (London, 1953)
176. UET III, 1511, 1689
177. UET III, 346, 296, 721; *Reisner, Tempelurkunden* no. 134
178. UET, I, no. 181
179. FAUST, D. E., *Contracts from Larsa* (New Haven, 1941, 143)
180. MATSON, FR., *Amer. Ceram. Soc.* Bul., 34, 1955, 33
181. UET III, 294, 291; LIMET, H., RAss 49, 1955, 82; *Lexical list Nabnîtu*, tablet E, 200—211
182. STRASSMAIER, J. N., *Inschr. von Nabonidus*, Leipzig, 1889, 429
183. CROS, G., *Nouvelles fouilles de Tello* (Paris, 1910—1914, 151)
184. LEEMANS, W. F., *Foreign Trade in the Old Babylonian Period* (Leiden, 1960)
     FORBES, R. J., *New evidence on Late Bronze Age metallurgy* (Sibrium III, 1956/57, 113—128)
185. UET V. 678
186. WISEMAN, D. J., *The Alalakh Tablets* (AL) (London, 1953)
187. *Archives Royales de Mari* (edit. A. Parrot and G. Dossin, Paris, 1950) (ARM II. 91; I. 21, 38, 63)
188. NOUGAYROL, J., *Une glacière centrale à Terqa.* (C. R. Acad. Inschr. Belles Lettres 1947, 265—272)
     PARROT, A., Syria XX, 1939, 14—16
189. UET V. 367; TCL X. 17
190. AL 401, 397, 402, 431, 406, 407, 396, 17, 327, 398, 403, 404, 405
191. UNGNAD, A., *Subartu* (Berlin, 1936, 179)
192. CY VI. 25

193. LUCKENBILL, D. D., *Ancient Records of Assyria and Babylonia* (Chicago, 1926, 2 vols.) (ARL)
194. ARL 222, 223
195. ARL 412
196. ARL 443, 447, 454
197. ARL 456, 460, 475, 476
198. ARL 585, 589, 601
199. ARL II. 173
200. CAH I. 566
201. BITTEL, K., *Prähistorische Forschung in Kleinasien* (Istanbul, 1934)
    NICOU J., *Le cuivre en Transcaucasie* (Ann. des Mines 10e sér. VI, 1904, 13—34)
    HANČAR, FR., *Urgeschichte Kaukasiens* (Wien, 1937)
    ROSTOVZEV, M., *L'age du cuivre dans le Caucase septentrional et les civilisations de Soumer et de l'Egypte protodynastique* (R.A. (5) XII, 1920, 14)
    MONGAIT, A. L., *Archaeology in the U.S.S.R.* (Pelican Books, London, 1961, 123, 129)
    Ancient Mining and Metallurgy Committee, Bronze Age Metal Objects from Azerbaijan (Man 1949, 178; 1950, 49)
202. PRZEWORSKI, ST., *Die Metallindustrie Anatoliens zur Zeit von 1500 bis 700 v. Chr.*, (Leiden, 1939)
203. CCT 43
204. HALL, H. R., *The civilisation of Greece in the Bronze Age* (London, 1928)
205. FIMMEN, E., *Die kretisch-mykenische Kultur* (Leipzig, 1926)
206. CHILDE, V. GORDON, *The Dawn of European civilisation* (3rd. edit. London, 1939)
207. WACE, A. J. B. and STUBBINGS F. H., *A Companion to Homer* (London, 1962, 308)
208. MYLONAS, G., *Ancient Mycenae* (Princeton, 1957, 64)
209. SELTMAN, C. T., *Greek coins* (London, 1933, 4—8)
210. BUCHHOLZ, H. G., *Keftiubarren und Erzhandel.* (Präh. Z. 37, 1959, 1—40)
211. KARO, ÅM 55, 1930, 135; WACE, *Mycenae* 1949, 88; PERSSON, *Dendra* I, 1931, 65
212. VENTRIS, M., and CHADWICK, J., *Documents in Mycenaean Greek* (Cambridge, 1956)
213. WEISS, H., *Une hache préhistorique grècque* (Bull. Soc. Chim. France (4) 33, 49)
214. DAVIES, O., *Bronze Age mining round the Aegean* (Nature 130, 1932, 985)
    DAVIES, O., *Prehistoric copper mines near Burgas* (Man 36, 1936, no. 119)
    DAVIES, O., *Ancient Mines in Southern Macedonia* (JRAI LXII, 1932, 145—162)
    GAUL, J. H., *Possibilities of prehistoric metallurgy in the East Balkan peninsula* (AJA, 46, 1942, 400—409)
215. PALLOTTINO, M., *Gli scavi di Karmir-Blur in Armenia e il problema*

delle connessioni tra l'Urartu, la Grecia e l'Etruria (Arch. Class. VII, 1955, 109—123)

216. ILIAD VII. 473
217. GRAY, D. H. F., *Metalworking in Homer* (JHS LXXIV, 1954, 1—15)
218. ILIAD VI, 236
219. ODYSSEY I. 184
220. BLÜMNER, H., *Technologie und Terminologie der Gewerbe und Künste bei Griechen und Römern* (Leipzig, 1887, IV, 38—66)
    MILLER, W., *Daedalus and Thespis* (Columbia (Miss.), 1931 II. 1, 443—485, 561)
    MUTZ, A., *Die Herstellung römischer Kasserollen* (Suisse Primitive XXV, 1961, 13—16)
221. LIVY XLV. 29. 4—14
222. CALEY, E. R., *On the prehistoric use of arsenical copper in the Aegean region* (Hesperia Suppl. VIII (Studies Shear), 1950, 60—63)
    CALEY, E. R., *Chemical investigation of two ancient bronze statuettes found in Greece* (Ohio J. Sci 51, 1951, 6—12)
    CALEY, E. R., *Chemical investigation of a sheet of metal of unique composition* (Ohio J. Sci. 52, 1952, 161—164)
223. HILL, D. KENT, *Ancient Metal Reliefs* (Hesperia XII, 1943, 97—114)
    HILL, D. KENT, *More about ancient metal reliefs* (Hesperia XIII, 1944, 87/9)
    HILL, D. KENT, *The technique of Greek metal vases and its bearing on vase forms in metal and pottery* (AJA 51, 1947, 248—256)
    TERNBACH, J., *The archaic bronze helmet of St. Louis* (Archaeology V, 1952, 40ff)
    YOUNG, W. J., *Technical examination of Greek helmets (Bull. Mus. Fine Arts* 48, no. 274, 1950, 83—86)
    HAYNES, D. E. L., *Some observations on early Greek bronze castings* (Arch. Anzeiger 4, 1962, 803—807)
224. ACHIARDI, G. D., *L'industria mineraria e metallurgica in Toscana al tempo degli Etruschi* (Stud. Etr. I, 1927, 411)
    WITTER, W., *Über Metallgewinnung bei den Etruskern* (32. Ber. röm.-germ. Komm. 1942, 1—19)
225. PLINY, *Nat. Hist.* XXXIV. 20
226. BEAZELY, J. D., *The world of the Etruscan mirror* (JHS 70, 1950, 2)
    GRAZIANO, G., *Contribution to the knowledge of prehistoric bronze alloys of Calabria and Sicily* (Boll. Acad. Sci. Nat. Catania, ser. 4, 2, 1954, 504—514)
    MINGAZZINI, P., *Santuari o Alti-forni* (note su due bronzetti sardi) (Studi Sardi X/XI, 1950/51, 3—17)
    MODONA, A. N., *Etruscan metallurgy* (Scient. Amer. 103, 1955, 5, 90—98)
    PANSERI, C. and LEONI, M., *Esame di specchi bronzei ritrovati in sepolcreti dell'alta Lombardia* (Sibrium III, 1956/7, 179—184)
    PANSERI, C. and LEONI, M., *The manufacturing technique of Etruscan mirrors* (Metallurgia Ital. 12, 1957, 223—241)

REGGIORI, A. and VIANELLO, L., *Esame di alcuni bronzi antichi* (Sibrium III, 1956/57, 161—166)

227. GRAMME, L. and WEIL, A. R., *Examen des clous provenant d'épaves sous-marines de l'époque gréco-romaine* (Revue de Métall. XLIX, 1952, 524—530)

WEIL, A. R., *Analyse de pieces métalliques cuivre et en plomb, provenant de l'épave romaine dite du Grand Conglué* (Rev. de Métall. II, 1954, 459—466)

228. PLINY, *Nat. Hist.* XXXIII. 43; WILLER, H., *Das Kupfer als Rohgeld der Italiker* (Berlin, 1922)

229. REGLING, PW XII. 294

230. PLINY, *Nat. Hist.* XXXIV. 1

231. WHEELER, SIR MORTIMER, *Rome beyond the Imperial frontiers* (London, 1954)

232. CATO, *de Agric.* 135; PLINY, *Nat. Hist.* XXXIV. 95—96

233. EBELING, A. and LOESCHMANN, A., *Kupfernägel der Nemiseeschiffe* (Beitr. Gesch. Techn. Ind. 22, 1933, 40)

234. JUSTIN, XLIV. 3. 4—5; FLORUS II. 33. 60

235. TACITUS, *Ann.* VI. 19. 1

236. VASSEUR, CL., *Une mine de cuivre exploitée à l'age du bronze* (L'Anthrop. XXII, 1911, 413)

BRIARD, J. et GIOT, P. R., *Analyses d'objets métalliques du chalcolitique, etc. de Bretagne* (Anthropologie 60, 1956, 5/6, 495—500)

237. CAESAR, Bell. Gall. V. 12

238. WHITTICK, G. CL. *Roman mining in Great Britain* (Trans. Newcomen Soc. XII, 1933, p. 57—84)

WHITTICK, G. CL. *An examination of roman copper cakes from Wightonshire and North Wales* (Proc. Univ. Durham Phil. Soc. IX, 1933, p. 99—105)

239. TYLECOTE, R. F., *Metallurgy in Archaeology, a prehistory of metallurgy in the British Isles* (London, 1962)

240. COGHLAN, H. H. and CASE, H., *Early metallurgy of copper in Ireland and Britain* (Proc. Preh. Soc. 23, 1957, 91—123)

COGHLAN, H. H., *Studies of British and Irish Celts* (Man 1953, no. 153)

COGHLAN, H. H., *A Note on Irish Copper and Metals*

BUTLER, J. R., *A Report on Elements in Irish Copper Ores*

PARKER, G., *A Metallurgical Report on Four Bronze Age Implements* (Ores and Metals, R. Anthrop. Institute Occas. Paper No. 17, London, 1963)

HAWKES, C. F. C., *On some buckets and cauldrons of the Bronze and Early Iron Ages* (Ant. J. XXXVII, 1957, 131—198)

JOPE, E. M., *Three Late Bronze Age swords from Ballycroghan near Bangor, Co. Down* (Ulster J. Archaeol. 3rd. ser. 16, 1953, 37—40)

MOISSIN, P. H. and VANDAEL, C., *Analyse chimique d'un chaudron gallo-roman provenant de Givry* (Hainaut belgique) (Techniques et Civilisations III, 1954, 152—155)

PROUDFOOT, V. B., *Excavation of a rath at Boho, Co. Fermanagh* (Ulster J. Arch., third ser. XVI, 1953, 41—57)

241. WITTER, W., *Die älteste Erzgewinnung im nordisch-germanischen Lebenskreis* (Leipzig, 1938, 2 vols.)

WITTER, W., *Ueber den Stand der Metallforschung* (Kupfer und Bronze) *im Dienste der Vorgeschichtswissenschaft* (Nova Acta Leopoldina N.F. XII, 1943, no. 82, 197—214)

WITTER, W. & OTTO, H., *Handbuch der ältesten vorgeschichtlichen Metallurgie in Mitteleuropa* (Leipzig, 1952)

242. OLDEBERG, A., *Metallteknik under Förhistorisk Tid* (Lund, 1943)

DRESCHER, H., *Bronzezeitliche Giesser im Östlichen Mitteleuropa* (Giesserei 1962, 49, no. 25, 817—822)

243. OTTO, H., *Typologische und technologische Bronzezeit* (Forschungen und Fortschritte 25, 1949, 73—76)

OTTO, H., *Die chemische Zusammensetzung einiger Hortfunde aus der halleschen Gegend* (Jahresschr. Mitt. Dtsche Vorgesch. 34, 1950, 90—100)

see further valuable data in:

BIBRA, E. VON, *Die Bronzen und Kupferlegierungen der alten und ältesten Völkern* (Erlangen, 1869)

GOWLAND, W., *On the early metallurgy of copper, tin and iron in Europe* (Archaeologia 56, 1899, 267)

GOWLAND, W., *Copper and its alloys in early times* (J. Inst. Metals VII, 1912, 23)

QUIRING, H., *Geschichte des Kupfers* (In: Berg, G. und Friedensburg, F., Kupfer, Stuttgart, 1941)

MARÉCHAL, J. R., *Histoire de la métallurgie*: I. *Les origines* (Ogam IX, 1957, 67—74); II. *La métallurgie du cuivre* (Ogam IX, 1957, 174—186)

244. CHILDE, V. GORDON, *Die Bedeutung der altsumerischen Metalltypen für die Chronologie der europäischen Bronzezeit* (MAGW 63, 1933, 217)

CHILDE, V. GORDON, *Archaeological Ages as Technological Stages* (JRAI LXXIV, 1944)

245. TÄCKHOLM, U., *Studiën über den Bergbau der Römischen Kaiserzeit* (Uppsala, 1937)

DAVIES, O., *Roman mines in Europe* (Oxford, 1935)

246. ZSCHOKKE, K. und PREUSCHEN, E., *Das urzeitliche Bergbaugebiet von Mühlberg, Bischofsofen* (Wien, 1932)

KLOSE, O., *Die zeitliche Stellung des prähistorischen Kupferbergbaus in den Ostalpen* (MAGW 1931, 139)

PITTIONI, R., *Probleme und Aufgaben der urgeschichtlichen Bergbauforschung auf Kupfererz in der Alten Welt* (Anz. Oesterr. Akad. Wiss. 87, 1950, 496—503)

PITTIONI, R., *Recent researches of ancient copper-mining in Austria* (Man 48, 1948, 120)

PITTIONI, R., PESTA, H. und MORTON, FR., *Spektralanalytischen Untersuchungen von Bronze aus Hallstatt. Ein Beitrag zum Problem der Chronologie des urzeitlichen Kupferbergwesens in Österreich* (Wien, 1949)

PITTIONI, R., *Prehistoric copper-mining in Austria, problems and facts* (Seventh Rep. Inst. Archaeology Univ. London, 1951, 16—43)

PITTIONI, R., *Exploitation préhistorique au cuivre en Autriche* (Techniques et Civilisations III, 1954, 104—108)

PITTIONI, R., *Urzeitlicher Bergbau aus Kupfererz und Spurenanalyse Beiträge zur Relation Lagerstätte-Fundort* (Wien, 1958)

EGGER, R., *Die Stadt auf dem Magdalensberg ein Grosshandelsplatz (Die ältesten Aufzeichnungen des Metallwarenhandels auf dem Boden Österreichs)* (Denkschr. Oesterr. Akad. Wiss. Bd. 79, Wien, 1961)

247. FORBES, R. J., *Studies in ancient technology* (Leiden, 1963, vol. VIII, 209)

248. CHILDE, V. GORDON, *The Aryans* (London, 1926)
SCHRADER, O., *Sprachvergleichung und Urgeschichte* (Jena, 1906, II, i)

249. POKORNY, Z., *vergl. Sprachwiss.* 49, 128

250. ANDRÉE, R., *Die Metalle bei den Naturvölkern* (Leipzig, 1884)

251. DEIMEL, Sum. Lex. 132. 1

252. IPSEN, Sumero-akkadische Lehnwörter (IndoGerm. Forsch. 41, 417)

253. BIBRA, E. VON, *Die Bronzen und Kupferlegierungen der alten und ältesten Völkern* (Erlangen, 1869)

254. DUSSAUD, R., *La Lydie et ses voisins* (Paris, 1930)

Chapter Two

TIN AND BRONZE, ANTIMONY AND ARSENIC

Old words *have strong* Emphasis, *others may look upon
them as* Rubbish
or Trifles, *but they are grossly* mistaken *and* Posterity
will pay us in our own Coyne
(Elias Ashmole, *Theatrum Chemicum Britannicum*, 1652)

1. *Introduction*

Though tin, antimony and arsenic were not used separately in Antiquity but mainly in the form of alloys their history belongs to the most important and at the same time the most complicated chapters of ancient metallurgy.

Tin is by far the most important of the three. Agricola in commenting on the general opinion of the usefulness of metallurgy remarks: "Weil die Donnerbüchsen aus einer Mischung von Kupfer und Zinn gemacht worden sind, schelten die Leute Kupfer und Zinn noch mehr als das Eisen", but he quite correctly points out the immense importance of tin and bronze in the history of mankind.

For even to these days steel has never fully displaced bronze in metallurgy, as this alloy is still valued for many specific uses. Thus its important component can be said to have played a major part in metallurgy for more than 4000 years! Still the production of tin was no more than 10.000 Tons a year at the end of last century, but more efficient mining and refining methods brought this figure to 188.000 Tons in 1929.

As the shadows hovering over the prehistory of the Ancient Near East are being dispelled by the spade of the archaeologist we are learning to discern the movements of the tribes descending to the Near East from Central Asia. We have also learnt that they knew gold, silver, lead and copper and perhaps bronze too in the later stages, though fuller analysis of the finds may still reveal more. Still the production of tin and bronze remained small as tin supplies in the Near East are scarce and there is no reason to suppose that they have been much greater in Antiquity. The production of tin developed slowly until larger supplies became available as international trade relations grew.

From the Bronze Age upto the present time tin kept its important place in metallurgy notwithstanding the metal itself does not lend itself for industrial manufacture of tools and weapons. But it still is the undoubted master in the field of transmission of power (bearing metals), the transmission of food energy (tin cans and tinfoil) and the transmission of mental energy (printing). The strangest part of its history, however, is the fact that the pure metal played a secondary role only, it was always the alloy with copper (bronze) or that with lead (pewter) which was used in Antiquity. Finds of pure tin objects date from the Late Bronze Age only. Simple ornaments in the Swiss lake dwellings and in Persian graves, bronze inlaid with strips of pure tin, then in classical times the "tinning" of bronze and copper objects in Gaul, the manufacture of cheap trinkets and its use as a substitute of silver form the few applications known at present. This may be partly due to the fact that tin is not very resistant to corrosion. Thomas of Cantimpré knew already that "tin rusts away when it lays long in water" and indeed, the tin is the first component to corrode in bronze, causing separate layers of tin oxide and copper oxides which again prevent the proper restoration of bronzes if the attack is allowed to proceed too far! It is evident from the archaeological data that bronze was known at least a 1000 years before the metal tin was produced industrially from its ores to be found as worthless a metal to the ancients as lead. The use of tin almost exclusively in alloys has not emphasized the properties of the metal itself and we find therefore that it plays no part in the older magical texts though it was often confused with lead, the magical metal "par excellence". The magical qualities of tin were recognized in the Hellenistic period only. Tinfoil (petala, lipides) is mentioned in magical texts (Dietrich, Abraxas), in alchemy tin is the symbol of Hermes and vice-versa (Olympiodorus, Eustathios), then that of Venus (Celsus) and finally that of Jupiter (Vettius Valens, Stephanos of Alexandria, Syrian and Arabian alchemists and in the Middle Ages). It occurs in the theories of the transmutation of metals as a stage between lead and silver (Hermetic writings), Zosimos considers it to be "solid mercury" and Pseudo-Democritos mentions it with copper, lead and iron as the "Philosophic Egg" from which the precious metals can be prepared. It plays a similar part in the transmutation theories of the Chinese alchemists.

In China tin is considered to be produced by the feminine principle in nature and it is classed between silver and lead. Arsenic generates itself in 200 years and after 200 more years it is converted into tin, which is feminine because of its tender qualities; by applying the masculine principle to it, it can be converted into silver. In the late Lapidary of (pseudo-) Aristotle tin is considered to be unclean silver which has to be purified because of its weakness, its smell and its cry (the typical "tin-cry" emitted by a bent bar of tin and caused by the internal friction of its crystals). Not until the Middle Ages it is used side by side with lead for defixiones (Thomas of Bologna).

The story of these three metals is greatly confused by the loose use of the words "tin", "antimony" and "arsenic" to denote either the metal, the ores or both as though the difficulties raised by the ancient texts were not yet sufficient, for the ancients did not clearly distinguish the same three metals from lead. We shall revert to this point when dealing with the nomenclature of these metals. In unravelling the early history of these metals care should be taken not to enhance our difficulties and to use the proper terms which is the only way of finding our way in this maze of data.

Before discussing the early history of tin (which is partly that of bronze) it will be useful first to turn to the mining and refining of tin.

2. *The ores of tin*

Though small nuggets of native tin are said to occur in Australia and Nigeria, they are very rare and of no importance for the production of tin. The only important ore is *cassiterite* or tin-stone, a tinoxide. It is a heavy ore, usually dark brown or black and except the weight there is nothing to tell us that it is a metallic compound, as Pliny already recorded. This tin-stone or "black tin" is found in two distinct forms. It is found as *vein ore* (Bergzinn) in veins of granite or granitic rocks, consisting mainly of quartz in which the cassiterite is embedded either in fissure veins or dispersed through the rock masses as small crystals. The main impurity causing the dark colour of the cassiterite are iron compounds, in the case of other impurities the colour may vary, these varities are called "ruby tin", "wax tin", "rosin tin", etc. Where these lodes of granite or other acid eruptive rocks bearing cassiterite reach the earth's surface they have often been eroded and disintegrated. In that case the debris including the cassiterite has been carried a way by water and the ore and other heavy minerals deposited on the way in alluvial gravels as well-worn crystals deformed into rolled lumps, grains and sands called *stream tin* (alluvial tin, float tin, Seifenzinn, Waschzinn, shode) heavily contaminated with clay and sand. It is important to remember that not a single tinfield in the world has tinstone in situ except near granite or granitic rocks, alluvial tinstone only if the debris is derived from granitic rocks. This both limits the number of tinfields and gives us a clue as to veins or lodes now exhausted but formerly bearing tinstone. The alluvial stream tin deposits are still the most important source in tin-mining, no less than 5/6 of the present world tin production is derived from such alluvial deposits, at present only in Bolivia and Cornwall is vein ore mined.

In Antiquity too the bulk of the tin stone seems to have been drawn from these alluvial deposits. Though Theophrastus does not mention cassiterite, Pliny is emphatic on the point of stream tin (1); "Next let us consider the properties of lead, of which there are two species, dark and pale. The latter the Greek cassiteros, is the more valuable. The legends say that men seek it in the isles of the Atlantic and that it is transported in boats of osier covered with hides stiched together. We know, however, that it occurs in Lusitania and Gallaecia where the surface strata of the ground are sandy and dark-coloured. The only property which serves for its identification is its weight. Small nuggets appear occasionally, especially when the torrential streams by which they have been deposited have dried up. Metallurgists wash this sandy material and roast the concentrates in a furnace. It is also found in gold-mines which they call alutiae. Water is driven in and washes out the nuggets which are black with a splash of white here and there. Their weight is the same as that of gold and they therefore accumulate with gold in the pans in which the latter is collected. The ore being subsequently separated from gold in the furnace is after fusion resolved into pale lead".

Though Pliny makes a small mistake in the course of his description, for the specific gravity of tinstone is about half that of gold, he has all the essential facts on hand. This description allows us to conclude that the ancients were aware of the association of stream tin and gold, a very important factor in the history of tin.

Though pure cassiterite contains 78.6% of tin, the vein ore is so contaminated with the quartz matrix that it generally contains only 0.2 to 2.0% of tin. In the case of alluvial tin this percentage is considerably higher because the natural washing action during its deposition has removed a large part of the useless debris from the granite. This higher percentage of ore in alluvial deposits together with the association with gold and similar concentration methods to be used formed an important stimulus to work the stream tin as soon as it had been recognized as a metallic compound useful in bronze production. This association also accounts for the fact that so many old deposits have been depleted in the course of time. Agricola favours the use of a divining rod of spruce-wood in the search for cassiterite and he mentions earth of the colour of lead-oxide (yellowish) as a certain indication of stream tin deposits.

A second important factor in the history of tin mining is the association of copper ores with tin ores in certain localities such as Cornwall, Bohemia, Tillek, Syria and China. This means that both tin ores and copper ores are here found in veins close together (but *not* in the same vein), which is rather exceptional as tin ores are genetically different from copper ores. In this case mixed ores may have been produced by the ancient miners, in other, more frequent, cases where copper ores are found in the neighbourhood, that is at some distance of deposits of tinstone, the separate production of these ores could lead only to the combined refining and therefore to the production of bronze from this mixture if the mixing was done deliberately which again could occur only after the time when cassiterite had been known to be a metallic compound or at least an ore beneficial to the production of the "better" type of copper which we call bronze.

But before discussing the early history of tin and bronze we shall deal with the production of cassiterite itself. In the case of alluvial stream tin the operations were simple enough. Remembering the association with gold in alluvial deposits we need only repeat the methods discussed for gold-production from such deposits, viz. 1) panning or pan-washing, 2) placer-mining (ground-sluicing) and 3) hydraulic mining (hushing). In fact it meant only the adaption of gold-mining methods to deposits of tinstone after the recognition of the black unseemly by-product of the gold-mines as a valuable ore for bronze-production. All these methods were undoubtedly applied to tin-mining in Antiquity, the third method of tin production on a large scale was adapted by the Romans in Spain. It gave them the means of totally depleting these tin fields by means of an enormous water-supply for which they built large aquaducts. The application of these mining methods to the tinfields of the Ancient Near East has not been investigated but we know far more about their application to Cornish stream tin. We know that the ancient Britons worked stream tin there, concentrated it by gravitation in sluice-boxes or "tyes" like gold and after sufficient concentration and washing purified the ore further by hand-picking. Such is still the essence of the methods used by the natives of Malaya, Sumatra, and Borneo, and we find many variants

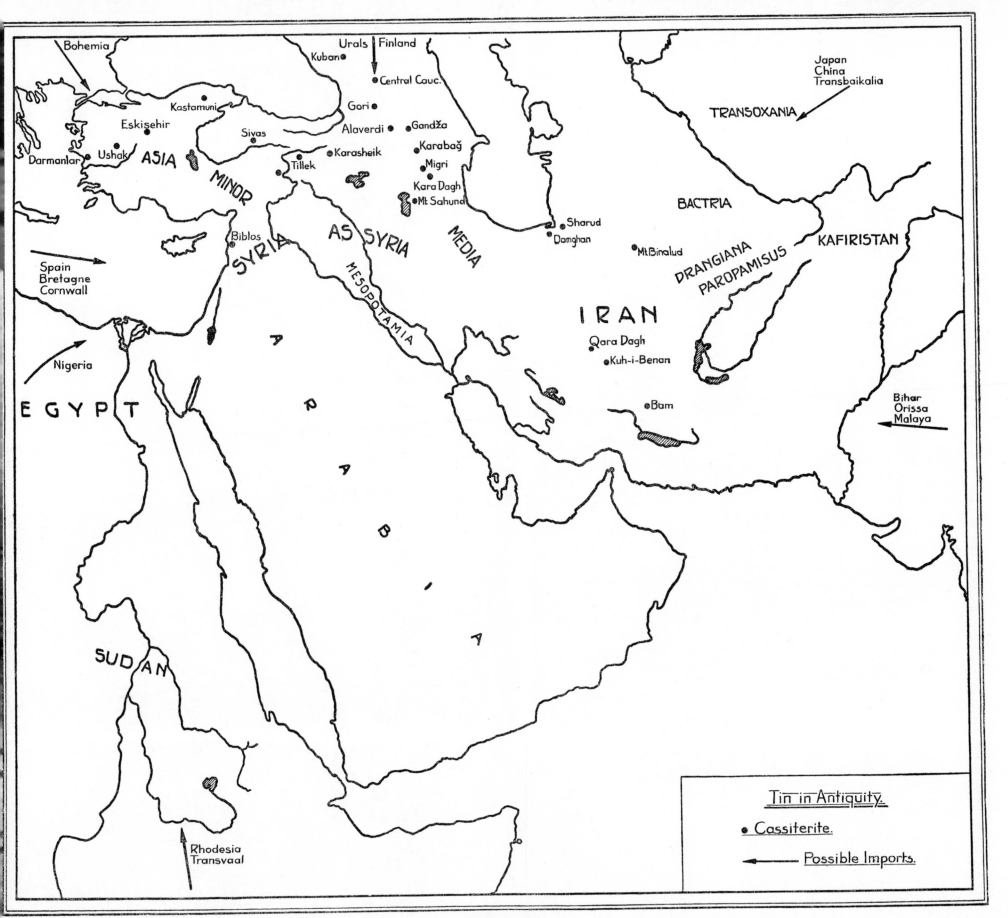

Fig. 22.
Map of tin in Antiquity

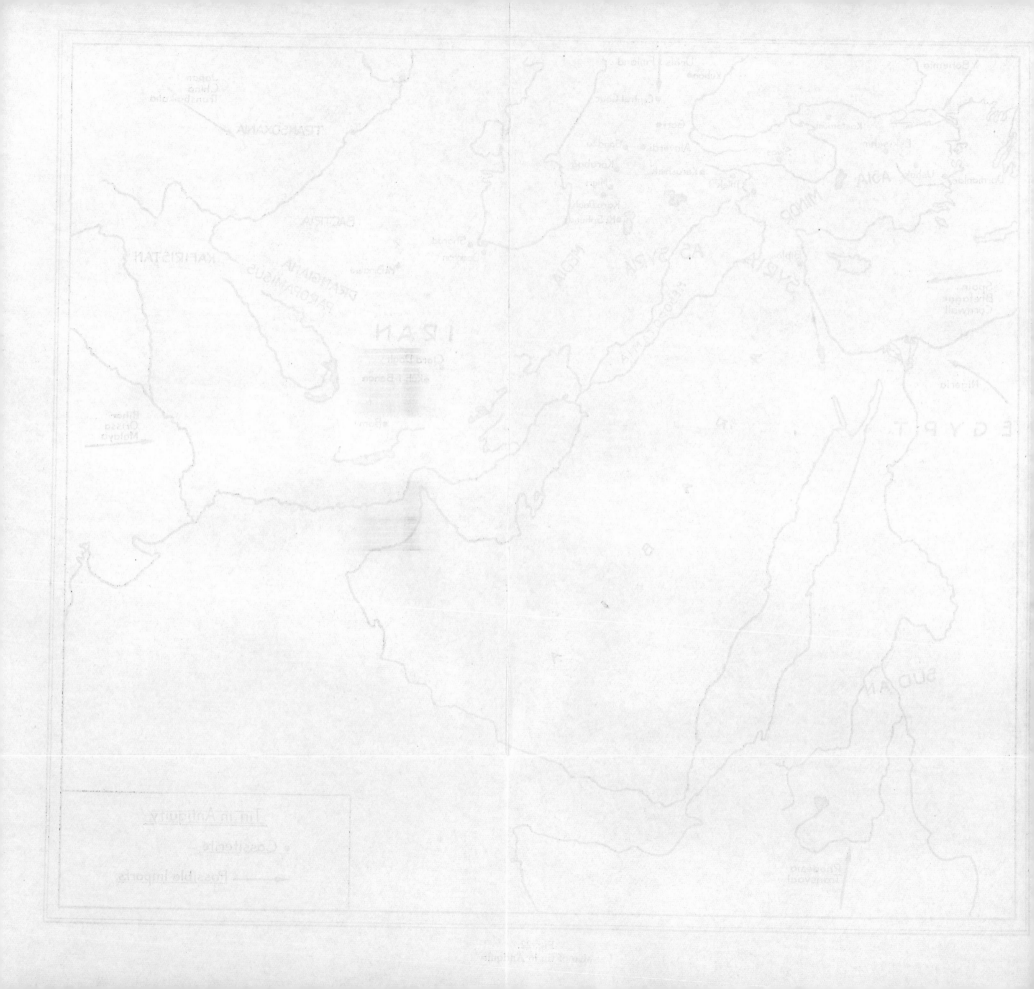

described by Agricola from everyday practice in his times in Saxony and Bohemia (2). Modern tin production is still based on these old methods but the quantities of tin-stone produced have been greatly increased by development of dredging and washing technique in the course of this century.

The mining of decomposed surface outcrops of vein ore proceeds on the same lines. Undoubtedly the ancient miners when the alluvial deposits began to be exhausted searched for further tin-stone, hit on the larger fragments of vein ore (called *shode* in Cornwall) in these decomposed rocks and were thus led to the true source of the cassiterite, the veins below these outcrops. Until the days of the Roman Empire the alluvial stream tin and the weathered outcrops of vein ore (mainly those in Spain) were the most important sources but from then onwards vein ore was mined in increasingly larger quantities especially in Cornwall. The methods were similar to those used in reef-mining of gold. The oldest shafts and corridors of Cornish pits still show practical and efficient application of stoping and hand-laid stones (the debris of tin stone washing) used as props. Agricola describes special fire-setting methods to break up the vein ore underground. The vein ore could not be refined as such, it required elimination of the quartz matrix and to this end the stone is calcined, which facilitated the breaking up and at the same time removed such harmful impurities as sulphur and arsenic compounds. The rock was then crushed and washed; this cycle was repeated until the cassiterite had been sufficiently concentrated to warrant smelting. Apart from the crushing the same methods were applied for concentration as those used for stream tin; Agricola describes a series of these methods which by their primitiveness show how long they must have been in use already. Usually the ore is classified after concentration according to size prior to the actual refining, such groups as lumps (Agricola's glarae majusculae or Graupen (called after the mining town of Graupen where German tin mining was reopened in 1146) to the size of 60 to 15 mm, "sands" and "slimes" are distinguished and sorted to fill the furnace more effeciently and to improve the separation of the slag.

Before discussing different tin deposits in the Ancient Near East and also those that may have been important for this area we must devote a few lines to a tin mineral which is sometimes mentioned in connection with the history of bronze. This mineral is called *stannine* (stannite, "bell-metal ore", "tin pyrites", Zinnkies), a compound of tin, copper, iron and sulphur, containing about 25% of tin. Its appear ance, however, is entirely that of normal copper or iron pyrites, nothing suggests its connection with cassiterite, even if by smelting it would have been possible to obtain a 50% bronze. Its rarity in the Old World and the complicated refining methods necessary to extract bronze from this iron and sulphur bearing ore preclude the possibility of its use in ancient times to any extent, though it is now mined in Bolivia and Cornwall.

3. *The Tinfields of Antiquity*

The present tinfields are not those of Antiquity. Though 5/6 of the world's tin production is obtained from stream tin, most of the important centres are situated far outside the ancient world. In 1936 the total world production was 182.500 Tons, Malaya producing 37.2% of this amount, the Dutch East Indies 17.6%, Bolivia 13.4%, Thailand 7.1%, China 5.9%, Japan, Germany and England being minor producers.

In the eighteenth century tin was produced mainly in Cornwall, Saxony and Bohemia. In the Near East deposits of cassiterite are scarce. Though Cassiodor ascribes the discovery of tin and lead to king Midas of Phrygia (2) no important fields are known in this region. In *Asia Minor* there are: 1) a few veins of tin-stone near Darmanlar, south-east of Smyrna, 2) near Eshkishehir (3) in Central Anatolia and 3) near Ušak in the Murad Dagh. No further details on these fields are available. Stream tin vein ore are found 4) near Kastamuni, 5) in the Ak Dagh near Sivas, 6) near Tillek (Erzincan) in association with copper ores on the south-west slopes of the Dudjik Dagh and the Kubaba Dagh (4), 7) in the mountains between Karasheikh and Erzeroum, 8) near Erganimadeni (vil. Elaziz) where rich copper ores abound too.

In the *Caucasus and Transcaucasia* Jessen and others have described tinfields lately (5), the most important are:

9) The basin of the Belaia river (Kuban) near copper ores.
10) The region between Elbrus and the river Terek in the central Caucasus, the upper Racha and south Ossetia, the Alikhan Dagh containing tin, copper and iron ores.
11) The region of Sharopani, Gori and Phorzom east of Tiflis.
12) The region between Allaverdi and Gandza, which is also rich in copper ores up to the river Terter.
13) The Kara Dagh and Karabakh mountains on the banks of the Araxes near Migri (6).

In *Persia* we find tin ores:

14) On the Kuh-i-Sehend near Tabriz.

15) On the southern slopes of the Elburz near Asterabad and Sharud and stream tin in the goldsands of the Kouh-i-Zar near Damghan (7).

16) In the Kuh-i-Benan and the north-western part, the Qara Dagh, but it is uncertain whether this is stream tin or vein ore, tin ore is also reported from the southern parts of this mountain range near Bam.

17) In the Rabotje Alokband mine 22 miles west of Meshed, 75 miles south of Kutshan near Mion Abot and then on the slopes of Mt. Binalud. Though some consider the tinfields of Chorassan very uncertain, the early reports of von Baer not being very clear, still most authors and especially geologists like de Launay accept them without reserve (8).

18) There are no exact data about the reports on tin ores in Transoxania, the ancient Drangiana (Paraopamisus); Kafiristan and the Tarim basin or the uppercourse of the Hilmend. These are regions mentioned by Strabo (9) and Arabian authors such as Ibn Hauqal, Alisthakri, etc., who report tin mining in these regions around 975 AD. Tin from the Tarim basin is mentioned by the pilgrim Hiuen Tsang. It is therefore not correct to reject Strabo's report without further investigation, but these regions are insufficiently explored geologically. Still the natives of Kafiristan wear small tin ornaments which they fashion themselves.

In *Asia* tin ore occurs near Lake Baikal, in several Japanese provinces and large quantities are mined in China (Kwangsi, Hunan and especially in Yunnan (stream tin). Very important is the "tin belt" ranging from Burma and Thailand, via Malaya to Bangka and Billiton, which now produces the bulk of the world's tin, in the form of stream tin. That this tin would have reached Egypt in 2000 B.C. as Schumann said (10) is ridiculous. Not only has this belt a fairly young history—Bangka was not discovered before 1710—but ancient India got its tin from the West, the Arabs did not find tin in India and they mention the Malayan fields in the ninth century only. Small deposits in India itself were found in the southern part of Bombay Presidency, Bihar and Orissa (near Pihra, Donchurch, Harzibagh district, Chattapund and Nurunga). They were probably unknown in Antiquity.

The southern and western part of the Near East are singularly poor in tin ores, though some have supposed that the Sinai contained tin ores which had been depleted since (11), perhaps because of the report on Midian tin in the Bible (12). But neither in Midian nor in the Sinai there is any trace of tin ore. Ter Braake (13) reports that there was ancient tin-mining on the Red Sea coast of Egypt. These Meuilha Mines (25°N, 34°E) are some fifteen miles from the famous Barramyia gold mines exploited by the ancient Egyptians and about 300 miles from the port of Ezion Geber whence the tin may have sailed!

Some stream tin and vein ore occur near Byblos in Kasrouan between the Near Ibrahim (Adonis) and the Nahr Feidar (Phaedrus) and as there are copper ores in the neighbourhood, this deposit has attracted some attention (14). Some tin ore is also said to occur near Aleppo north west of Beyrouth. As Egypt stood in regular contact with Byblos in very early times there were reasons to suppose that the knowledge of bronze would have penetrated to Egypt at an early date from this region. But archaeological and other data show that this is not the case. We can therefore safely conclude that no extensive tin mining was conducted here at an early date and that no centre of bronze manufacture existed in this region.

In Egypt no tin ore is known to occur except the Mueilha Mines mentioned above and therefore imports from *Africa* were proposed. However, this is very improbable. There are three important tin fields in Africa, first of all Transvaal and Rhodesia, who are mentioned as the sources of supplies for Egypt because of the Zimbabwe culture and its knowledge of bronze. Without discussing this problem fully we may safely conclude after the investigations carried out by Caton Thompson that the Zimbabwe culture is far younger than originally supposed. The tin refining methods in this region have been studied by Gordon, Wagner and Stanley, especially the refineries near Watersberg. There stream tin was refined and as heaps of ore near different sets of furnaces showed tin ores and copper ores were treated separately and the bronze made by smelting tin and copper. This points to a late phase of bronze manufacture. It would seem from the remains that these refineries are hardly older than 300 or 400 years. Again the Zimbabwe bronzes show a very close range of composition which points to their manufacture by mixing tin and copper as metals. It would seem that these South-African tin mines were opened when the Arab traders came down the coast looking for tin, reaching Sofala in the tenth century, when the Zimbabwe culture was at its height. Though there are no Arab records of tin trade in these regions, part of the tin may have been sold directly to Malay or Hindu merchants following in the wake of the Arabs. It is therefore inconceivable that these mines were worked in the Egyptian Bronze Age or that any tin from countries south or south-west of Egypt reached Egypt and passed through it to Mesopotamia and Europe, no evidence of traffic or knowledge of tin and bronze was ever found on this route which can be ascribed to so early a period. A group of tinfields close by in Katanga (Belgian Congo) and Portuguese Nyassaland were discovered only shortly ago.

Fig. 23.
Collecting stream tin (After Agricola)

The placers of the Gold Coast and Nigeria are very important now but fairly recent discoveries. In the Middle Ages the Bauchi of Nigeria possessed tin ornaments according to Dimeshqi, but he added that they loved tin because of its rarity and they valued it more than gold, which shows that these fields were not exploited then. The Kano conquerors of the Bauchi stopped the tin production but started trading the ore along the northern trade-routes. The local smelting was never efficient the Yoruba and Haussa being the only tribes who use the tin-bearing slag in subsequent smelting, which again goes to show that the tin production never developed beyond the local production phase. The tinstone found here is very pure, some records even state that metallic tin was found with the cassiterite in the river sands and gravels.

Disclaiming any importance to the tinfields of the Far East and Africa for the ancients leads us to the discussion of the *European tinfields* which though unimportant now may have been main sources of supply in Antiquity.

Three fields are grouped along the Atlantic seacoast. The first is situated in the north-west corner of the Iberian peninsula, in the Spanish provinces of Orense and Zamorra and the Portuguese districts

Fig. 24.
Sluicing tin ore (After Agricola)

of Beira, Minho, and Tras-o-Montes. The Spanish fields are the most important, lodes and placers occur near Allariz, Monte Balcobo, in the district north-west of Orense between the rivers Avia and Leire, and est of Carballino. Quite close-by copper ores have been found .Rickard has estimated the amount of tin ore produced in Cantabria to be 4.000.000 m³ near Salabe only and a similar amount seems to have taken from Ablaneda south of Sales. In both places the Romans constructed aquaducts for the washing of the ores (15). It is manifest from the passages of Pliny and Strabo that stream tin was exploited here and Pliny mentions that the methods of gold production are used (16), though lodes seem to have been worked too. Some writers have claimed Spain to be the Kù-ki or Tinland of Sargon's annals, but this must be reconsidered in the light of more recent evidence!

Further tin fields are known near Salamanca and in Almeria and southern Spain, but they were of local importance only. Of course they may have been exploited first, but as they were soon exhausted, their prominence must have given way to the fields or northern Spain.

France contains two groups of tinfields. In Central France the districts of Haute Vienne, Creuze and Vaulry contain stream tin which placers were in production from the Late Bronze Age to the Early Iron Age. On the Atlantic coast the south Breton tinfields in the extreme north-west of the province of Loire-Inférieure and the Josselin-Morbihan massif are considered to have been in production from the Middle Bronze Age up to the Early Iron Age. They are certainly pre-Roman, probably shut-down because of the Spanish competition (17), the small islands off the coast may be the Oestrymnides mentioned by Avienus.

The third important field is situated in Cornwall. Though cassiterite is found in Ireland in the gold placers of Wicklow, this can not be considered as a source of primary importance. In Cornwall alluvial ore occurs regularly though most of the references speak of vein ore. Copper ores occur in the same region and indeed side by side with tin ores. In fact Cornwall is the standard example of both ores occuring in the same mines, copper lodes in the surface strata, cassiterite in the deeper strata and some mixed ores in the boundary zone. There are no Cornish remains with which tin is associated before the Late Bronze Age (18). Haverfield considers exploitation before 1500 B.C. extremely improbable. Though Whittick claimed only exploitation of stream tin even in the Roman period, this is now rejected and lodes have certainly been worked from the classical period onwards.

These three fields must be discussed together with the problem of the Cassiterides which Herodotus felt unable to locate. Though these islands were considered to represent the little islands off the Morbihan coast by Besnier, others have included Cornwall and the Scilly islands (where tin ore is extremely rare!). Again the evidence of Diodor who describes the Cassiterides as islands off the Spanish coast and distinct from Cornwall has led others to believe them to be the Spanish tinfield. It is now, however, generally accepted that the "Cassiterides" stand for the "tin localities in Western Europe" in general (Haverfield, Hennig, Cary, Bailey) and later narrowed down in classical tradition (19) to certain islands which took part in the tin trade. Cary has discussed the three tinfields in order to establish the chronology of tin production in these regions (20) and these are his conclusions:

a) The mines of Spain operated from the beginnings of the Bronze Age and they were probably worked continuously up to the Roman period (Pliny, Poseidonius). Tin was mined and exported to France and the Mediterranean region before the beginning of the Iron Age.
b) The deposits of southern Brittany were worked about 500 B.C. and followed Spain, but as no evidence of their production exists from later periods, they must have been abandoned soon because of Spanish competition.
c) Soo long as Brittany worked the Cornish mines were not exploited. Cornish tin production therefore enters international trade about 500 B.C. (though local production may have started earlier) and continues up to Caesars' days (43 B.C.). Their exploitation was partly suspended in the Early Empire but resumed after the failure of the Spanish mines about 250 A.D. when the Romans penetrated the Cornish tin area and constructed good roads for the trade caravans.
d) Tin or tin ore was thus continuously produced from the Bronze Age onwards, Cornwall being an important centre from the fifth or fourth century B.C. until it was overtaken by the efficient exploitation of Spanish tin mines under the Early Roman Empire. In the first and second century A.D. the placers of Lusitania and Gallaecia had almost the monopoly of the Roman market, even in the third century the best "bulla" on the market in Egypt and elsewhere is still Spanish tin (Pap. Holmiensis and Aetius Istricus). In the course of the third century A.D. the Cornish mines regain their old prominence by the failure of the Spanish mines.

Though tin ores occur in *Etruria* there is no proof that the Etruscans exploited the Campagliese tin at Cento Camerello, Monte Valerio, Monte Rombolo, and east of Monte Fumacchio. Vein ore is found there sparsely in iron ore (limonite) with copper minerals. The time of their exploitation is not known, present evidence does not allow us to believe any exploitation before the second century B.C. and the deposits are of secondary importance only.

The tinfields of *Central Germany* (Vogtland, Fichtelgebirge, Erzgebirge, Böhmerwald) play a large part in the development of early bronze industry in these parts as Witter (22) has proved definitely. They are often accompanied by copper ores, mixed ores occur fairly frequently. Undoubtedly these fields play a large part in the tin supply of the Ancient Near East. However, it is embarrasing that no classical writer mentions them (23), there is no evidence of tin or tin ore trade to the head of the Adriatic or to Mediterranean ports along the well-known trade routes carrying amber and other northern products valued by the ancients. Indeed no evidence of their exploitation occurs in literature before the XIIth century A.D. Thomas of Cantimpré is one of the first to mention the new German tin production in 1240 and Albertus Magnus mentions in his de Mineralibus that this German tin is soften than its Cornish competitor. The value of Witter's monograph will be discussed later on.

Less important fields occur in the Urals, Finland and Eastern Europe. Tin ore has been found in the Szemenik mountains in the Banat, between Resita and Karánsebes, but the deposits are small and the time of their working uncertain.

Cassiterite is rumoured to occur near Pangaeum, but Hemhacker's assertions have not been proved; equally uncertain are rumours about tin ore at Volokastro (Thessaly). Finally Davies has found small smelting works at Cirrha near Delphi but the local provenance of the ore is doubtful.

4. *Smelting and refining tin*

Recently the refining of tin has grown more complicated (24). Firstly much tin is now recovered from tin plate or other used materials. Germany for instance produced 2300 Tons of tin from local ores and 4000 Tons from spent materials in 1936! As the different modern uses of tin require a high standard of purity and as pyrites and vein ore are treated too, there is now usually a calcination at 600—700°C to remove as much sulphur and arsenic as possible at the start, followed by "rag-roasting", a part-oxidation of the iron and copper compounds which are then leached out with water. Further "sweet-roasting" to remove the remaining sulphur and electromagnetic separation of wolframite are followed by concentration to marketable "black tin" by water. This pure cassiterite can then be easily reduced with charcoal or with other material in suitable furnaces, the tin being specially refined to remove the last traces of copper, lead and antimony. Of late tin is often produced electrolytically to obtain the purest tin possible, as iron, lead, copper and arsenic even in small quantities spoil the malleability, colour, gloss and toxicity. Of course refinements like these were unknown even to Agricola and were undoubtedly not practised in Antiquity, as tin was then practically always used as an alloy either with copper (bronze) or lead (pewter). In that case the influence of the impurities is felt much less. In modern tin refining the roasting process has now completely been displaced by flotation which yield a much cleaner concentrate for the refiner.

The old simple refining methods of cassiterite are still practised in different parts of the world, and we must use these and also conclusions drawn from the remains of old furnaces, etc. because there are no texts on tin refining even from classical authors, though undoubtedly tin was produced as a separate metal then. Gowland found in Japan (25) that the ore was broken in foot-stamp mills, derived from types used for the decorticiation of rice, and afterwards ground to powder

Fig. 25.
Roasting tin ores (After Agricola)

in hand-mills or querns. In some cases the ore was previously broken with stone hammers or anvils. The powdered ore is then again washed to remove the clay and earth and charged wet into the furnace with alternating layers of charcoal. When reduced the metal is ladled out of the furnace after raking aside the supernatant slag and cast into rods in an open mould. Originally the furnaces have been worked without a blast which caused great loss of tin in the slag and unreduced oxide remaining in the metal. Such is the method formerly used by the natives of Borneo, Sumatra and Malaya in producing tin for their private use. In Borneo the furnace is simply a hole in the ground (20' deep, 14' wide), still when improving the reduction by the use of piston-bellows three men were able to produce 25 lbs of tin in $4\frac{1}{2}$ hours. We know from finds in Cornwall, Central France and Greece (26) that such primitive methods were indeed practised in Antiquity. Simple clay-lined holes or trenches were dug in the ground and wood was piled into it and lighted. If it burned fiercely charges of ore and wood were thrown in alternatingly and the slag tapped from the furnace into a second hole until enough tin had been assembled in the furnace to be ladled out. The trench was really only necessary to hold the embers and keep the metal together. Many of these slag-hearths have been found in Cornwall, retreating the slag was not considered worth while. Still

Fig. 26.
Grinding tin ores (After Agricola)

slags in Gaul contained no less than 21% of tin! It was, however, gradually recognised that cassiterite requires a fairly high reduction temperature so that for instance the gold will melt from mixtures before the tin ore is reduced. This high temperature ensures a good fluidity of the slag but it involves a tendency for the tin to enter the slag. Careful control of the temperature is therefore necessary to ensure a maximum degree of extraction. This is only possible in a well-built furnace and thus we find that as soon as tin ore was no longer considered to be a useful mineral in adding to copper ores to produce bronze but was used as a source for tin production, that is to say shortly before classical times, furnaces were built and worked with blast-air. Circular tuyères were fixed at the hearth bottom to introduce the blast air and a lower flow hole served to tap the metal. Such were the furnaces of Cirrha Maghoula and Volo Kastro, of Trereife (Cornwall), of the old tinsmelters of Transvaal, whose smelting sites were studied by Gordon and Wagner and a similar type was still in use in Zamorra, Spain, in 1856 (27). They were usually lined with clay, even in the time of Agricola, who, however, advises the use of a sandstone block for the bottom of the hearth. He adds rightly that the blast air-opening should not be too wide if the temperature should not rise too far. In his time too

Fig. 27.
Smelting crude tin (After Agricola)

lime was sometimes used as a flux, it was certainly used in earlier times as the old furnaces and slags prove. As in the case of most refining methods in Antiquity a remarkably pure metal was obtained at the cost of a heavy loss of ore in the slag and in the case of tin by volitalization. In later centuries the efficiency of the process in investigated. So we find Agricola insisting on effective temperature control to avoid these losses and he advises to superimpose a small chamber over the furnace to collect the metal-bearing dust that might escape during the process. Agricola was the first to deal with the impurities and to advise liquating (Saigern) the crude tin to free it from iron. The process is similar to that used for the separation of silver and lead, the test for pure tin being its liquidity which changes rapidly if it includes iron. It is, however doubtful whether this refining method was conceived or used in classical times.

Mantell reached the following conclusions from the data available: the many slaghearths found in Cornwall and other places:

"The smelting in the Bronze Age is thought to have been carried out in trenches lined with clay and filled with brushwood. Above this, small logs of wood were piled. The mass was lighted and as soon as the logs were burning fiercely and the trench was full of glowing embers, small quantities of tinstone were thrown upon the fire from time to time. More wood and mineral were added until the required amount of tin had accumulated in the trench. The fire was then allowed to die down or was raked away and the molten metal ladled into a hole in the ground or into a clay mould near the furnace. It is quite likely that later developments led to the use of a deep hole instead of a shallow pit to confine the fire. Primitive blowers or bellows were introduced and the blast no longer admitted over the edge of the cavity, but through an opening just above the base of the furnace, which was excavated near the edge of a bank of earth. Molten tin is allowed to flow out through a tap hole at a point lower than the blast entrance. Later further progress was made by erecting small cylindrical furnaces built of clay, their operation being more convenient. Most native furnaces are developments along this line".

Native tin metal is extremely rare, it is known to occur on a few places in South-eastern Asia, where it was probably formed by the effect of forest-fires on outcrops of lodes of tin ore.

The metal is usually cast into bars of 28 lbs or slabs of 100 lbs today. In Roman times special double-T form slabs called *astragali* were used in Cornwall, it is claimed that two of these slabs were loaded on a pack-animal and that their form is adapted to this means of transport. We know nothing about the forms of the tin bars of earlier periods.

It is very strange indeed, that no metallic tin was found in founder's hoards nor any bars or slabs (though copper and bronze bars abound), except for the bars of the Gelidonya wreck, which we will discuss later on tin ores may have been overlooked because of their earthy appearance, but tin bars would have left behing obvious remains of white tin-oxide powder. This may be taken as a secondary proof that tin was not produced as a separate metal on any large scale before

1500 B.C., but that tin ore was treated together with copper ore or black copper to produce bronze.

5. *The origin of bronze*

When discussing this important problem we should remember two important facts mentioned earlier in this chapter:
a) the association of stream tin and gold in many placers and alluvial deposits;
b) the association of vein ore with copper ores in a few localities such as Cornwall, Tillek, Bohemia and China.

As to the first fact, one of the earliest authors on Cornish tin, Carew, wrote: "Tinners do also find little hopps of gold among their ores which they keep in quills and sell to the goldsmiths" and Siret pointed out the ancient connection between tin- and gold-mining in France where we find place-names like Auray (Auricia, on the Armorican islands) and Ariège (Aurigera, in Central France).

The second fact has been used by many authors to claim that this led to the discovery of bronze. Coffey even went as far as stating: "Only when it has been shown that copper is obtained from ores that are free from tin does it seem allowable to argue that the tin has been added", quite forgetting that this close association of copper and tin ores in the same matrix is very rare though there are of course several places where tin ores occur at some distance of surface lodes of copper ores. Gowland has proved that the smelting of artificial mixes of copper and tin ores always gave bronze and so it was rather plausible to argue that these natural mixtures led to bronze discovery. This is what Siret claims for Spanish bronze; Smith, Lucas, Reid (26) and others have adopted it. The difficulty in this theory remains how to explain that the ancients were led to perceive that the cassiterite in the mixed ore was the compound to cause the "improvement" of the smelted copper, and to identify these cassiterite crystals with the earthy lumps and sands of stream tin. For it remains a fact that in Antiquity the stream tin was used predominantly, if not exclusively, and only in the Later Roman Empire we have any proof of vein ore exploitation. Nor have we any proof that the centres where these mixed ores occur play any important part in the early history of tin and bronze in the Ancient Near East, whatever their part may have been later on. It would, therefore, seem that the origin of tin and bronze was not initially connected with the mixed vein ore.

Witter has elaborated the theory for the Middle European tin and copper regions to explain the development of bronze industry in these parts. By an admirable presentation of the facts and research supplemented with modern scientific analysis of the crude products and bronzes found in ancient mines and excavations he has undoubtedly solved the general line of development in these regions, whatever we might have to say towards the dating of this bronze industry and the priority claimed for this region over the Orient as elaborated by his collaborator in the appendix to his book. There can be no doubt whatever that the metallurgy of gold, copper and lead was known in the Near East in early sites of Mesopotamia and Iran such as Tepe Hissar and Anau at a period far earlier that any chalcolithic site in Europe and before any connection between this region and Middle Europe can be proved. Witter's theory of the development of copper metallurgy will be repeated here in outline only as far as it touches the early history of tin and bronze, for Gordon Childe has already ably dealt with Witter's defective archaeological and typological arguments (27). He claims the following stages:

A—*Natural mixtures treated*: a) Tin-bearing oxydic copper ores heated with wood or charcoal, b) mixtures of oxydic copper ores and tin ores treated with charcoal and wood, c) later mixtures of sulphidic tin and copper ores smelted. In the course of these phases the true value of the tin ore was discovered and from then onwards a further quick development took place along the following lines:

B—*Artificial mixtures treated*: a) naturally mixed copper and tin ores selected and smelted, b) mixes of cassiterite and copper ores treated and finally c) cassiterite and charcoal smelted together with crude copper previously smelted.

This theory suits the Middle European facts admirably but it can not be upheld in all details in the Ancient Near East. Lucas who first propagated a similar theory later adopted a slightly different one which we would like to elaborate on a few points which remain unexplained. It would seem from the present evidence that the early history of tin and bronze proceeded along the following lines:
1. Cassiterite in the form of stream tin was discovered in working goldplacers.
2. This cassiterite was reduced by metallurgists already in possession of the fundamental knowledge necessary for the production of gold, copper and lead. The tin produced was held to be lead, for as we shall

see the ancients at least in the earliest periods did not distinguish lead, tin and antimony properly.

3. The tin was added to copper to form bronze or more probably at an early date stream tin was mixed with copper ores before smelting (Witter's stage B.b) to produce the "improved" copper. Early bronzes are often found to contain lead or antimony, but as the tin ore was found to give better bronzes the addition of lead and antimony ores was discontinued, for the supply of stream tin was still sufficient.

4. At a later stage stream tin is reduced with charcoal together with the crude copper already obtained by separate smelting (Witter's stage B.c), probably about 2500 B.C.

5. In the meantime certain mixed ores were worked unintentionally for copper and thus "natural" bronze was produced, generally with a small tin content which varied greatly according to the ore used, sometimes with a higher tin content. In the latter case a true bronze was produced (all bronzes containing over 2% of tin are most probably artificial products, only very few mixed ores from selected localities would give such true bronzes on smelting!) and recognized to be similar to the product obtained by smelting cassiterite and copper ore (our stage 3). It is highly improbable that the cassiterite from the mixed ore was ever isolated and proved to be a tin compound. At the same time this new fact was remembered and used when the stream tin supply began to fail or used in such localities (Bohemia) where the type of the deposits is better suited to the working of mixed vein ore.

It may even be true that the production of this "natural bronze" sometimes preceded that of the "artificial bronze" in certain regions but it was probably not recognized as a special ore until the production of tin and bronze from cassiterite and copper ore (our stage 3) was well established and the properties of bronze well known. This "artificial bronze" can be found in the earlier bronzes which show not only a higher tin content than would be expected from mixed ores but also less variation in the tin content. A still better bronze and a more stable composition could be obtained by reducing the stream tin with charcoal in molten crude copper (our stage 5) and as the composition of bronze stands in rather narrow connection with its efficiency for certain purposes this was an important advance of bronze technique.

It should be stressed that the 2% limit between "natural" and "artificial" bronzes is not a hard and fast rule. The composition of the oldest Mesopotamian bronzes suggests that their tin content, which in odd cases runs up to 4%, is not intentional but simply an impurity along with the arsenic, lead and iron they contain. "Bronzes" turn up in this region about 3200—3100 B.C., but one can hardly say that the manufacturing of bronzes with a tin content suited to the use of the final bronze object was properly understood before 2500 B.C. By the end of the third millennium, however, a well-calculated tin content of 6—10% was effectively achieved by the Sumerian bronze-smiths. By this time the bronzes from Troy and Crete are also more properly compounded, from an earlier average of 5—6% the tin content begins to rise to 8—11% in Troy III, the average in later settlements at Troy (after the gap in Troy IV, which has no bronze!) being 10%. Hence true bronzes are produced in Cyprus about 2000 B.C. at the same time as the Aegean. However, except for the tin bangle found at Thermi (Lesbos) and dating back to about 2600 B.C., the metal tin is a most exceptional commodity.

6. Gradually the stream tin deposits in the Near East began to give out or could no longer cope with the growing demand, but many a small surface lode was depleted in early times. Thus we find in the Sargonid era inferior hammered axes of unalloyed copper replacing the earlier mould-cast bronze ones (28) after the splendid bronzes of Ur. Childe has ascribed this dearth of tin to the reaction of the supply countries towards the imperial agression of the rulers from Agade, but the length of this "low tin content" period in Mesopotamia is better explained by the depletion of the known deposits and the growing demand for tin. Prospectors, metallurgists and traders struck out West to look for further supplies. Without claiming direct contact this explains the gradual introduction of Sumerian metal types in the Danube regions and finally in Middle Europe where the tin supplies were found in Bohemia and Saxony. No Sumerians came here, it means only that when Caucasian, Iranian, and Anatolian supplies became insufficient, the tin trade (in the form of tin, bronze or cassiterite, this is still a point which needs serious research!) with Bohemia overland via Troy to the Near East was gradually established.

7. Around 1800—1500 B.C., as far as present evidence goes, a further technical improvement was achieved. The cassiterite was reduced separately and tin-metal produced industrially to be mixed with copper to form bronze. This not only allows a better dosing of the tin content but gradually led in centuries to come to the production of different alloys each specially adapted to certain purposes, special bronzes for weapons, mirrors, statues, bells, etc.

In the same period the earliest tin objects begin to appear in mass in the excavations. Also Aegean traders now bring tin from the West to the East. This tin is passed on by many links in the chain of trade stations as is the case with Middle European tin. Cross-dating and relative dating of Near Eastern excavations have now excluded definitely the formerly maintained powerful and stimulating influence which reached the East from the West. Quite contrary to this early opinion the West is now widely believed to have been influenced, if only slightly, by the East. Early tin imports from Spain or Gaul can not have been of much importance in view of the striking poverty of the early Iberian Bronze Age when compared with the anneolithic period. This trade developed in the Late Bronze Age and gradually ousted Bohemian tin from its front rank. Recent evidence also points to tin imports from the East. From Hittite sources we hear that bronze was imported from Cyprus where no tinores occur, so Aegean or Persian tin must have been added there to the local copper and the bronze sold as a valuable trade object. Still some curious compositions of bronzes from this later period remain to be explained. We agree with Prezworski that bronze must have been remelted often because of the expensiveness of tin. This process, however, holds many dangers such as part-oxidation of the tin and lowering of the tin content. From collections of letters of this period such as the Amarna letters we must conclude that "tin trade "was mainly trade in crude bronze.

Here we should remember that in Antiquity every metal was a expensive commodity, even copper was relatively expensive, and therefore recast and reworked when no longer of use. Smelting the tin ore separately to produce the metal tin required a temperature chose to the melting point of gold, its addition to copper produced an alloy, a "kind of copper" which melted at a lower temperature than pure copper and in molten condition it had a lower fluidity, this meant casting to closer dimensions an less hammering of the cast object. Bronze was harder than copper only if the tin content was about 10—12%, more tin would increase the hardness but little but on the other hand the high tin bronzes are too brittle for use as implements. On the other hand they can be highly polished and therefore they are quite suitable for mirrors.

All such points should be taken into account when judging ancient bronze objects (29). As soon as the alloy was made by melting together weighed portions of the two metals the smith could achieve a much better adjusted alloy within close margins of the bronze he strove to make. In the earlier stages of bronzemaking his tools and implements may have had a tin content wavering between 8 and 14% of tin, by mixing the two metals he could well produce an alloy falling within the limits of 10—12% of tin, seeing that he did not yet dispose of the analytical tools which assist the modern refiner in compounding his alloys. We should therefore study more closely what alloy he was aiming at for what kind of object and try to find out how much closer he got in later periods than in earlier ones to establish at what date stage 7 can be set, always remembering that the composition of a bronze may reflect a good metallurgical knowledge as well as a defective production method!

We must also remember, that in the earlier phases bronze was never produced in large quantities at a time, even when compounded of the two metals this took place in crucible. Often used or scrap bronze was remelted and brought up to standard by adding tin (or tin ore plus charcoal). Hence the trade in the metal tin can not have amounted to much in the earlier periods, it seems probable that tin was still imported in Cyprus in the form of a standard bronze rather than as metal by 1500 B.C. In the early texts we hear little of the base materials used in the temple workshops, more about the methods of making the commissioned metal objects. When making a particular UD.KA.BAR (zabar), a "hard copper" or bronze the later texts speak of a "zabar-x-lal", that is to say they indicate the ratio copper and tin, and this seems to point to an alloying of the two refined metals. The x in this formula is usually 7 or 8, the "10-fold" bronze being called a light metal and the "6-fold" bronze (with 17% of tin) a strong one. This way of expressing the composition of the bronze to be made is very similar to the Egyptian term "ḥmt m sm3 nt 6" (bronze in the 6-fold alloy) which we find in late New Kingdom texts. Such indications are found in texts of the first millennium B.C. or slightly earlier. In the Alalakh tablets the ratio 900/70 is given (30), the later smiths often aimed at 5/1 (31) or "six of alloy" (32). Some of these texts mention the addition of charcoal to the melting crucible to prevent the expensive tin and copper from oxidizing.

The excellent casting qualities of bronze furthered the development of such processes as the lost-wax (cire-perdue) process and the construction of intricate moulds. Cast Roman coins go back to 450 B.C. but better techniques were used from the second century B.C. onwards. Generally speaking the development of casting techniques meant a partial eclipse of hammering techniques for bronze will not allow hot forging. For tools and implements bronze held its place for

many centuries until at last proper steel tools could be fashioned.
8. Again in the classical period as the alluvial tin of the West got
exhausted too vein ore was worked, especially in Cornwall in Later
Roman times.

Tin now becomes more and more a separate object of trade, it is
still much traded as bronze (or pewter), but finds of astragali in England,
etc. seem to show that at least near the mining centres tin was made up
into blocks or slabs and tin objects become more frequent in the Near
East in classical times. Still the bulk of the tin was worked up to alloys
and as bronze metallurgy was first practised in certain centres only to
spread out gradually over the Near East we will have to look to the
bronze trade in further unravelling the mysteries of the history of tin.

First, however, we must deal with the strange *quenching of bronze*, the
"chalkos baphos" first mentioned by Aeschylus (33) which keeps
cropping up in classical texts (34). Thus Pausanias (35) tells us about
the waters of the Peirene Fountain at Corinth: "They say that the
Corinthian bronze, when red-hot, is tempered by this water, since
bronze... the Corinthians have not", and Plutarch has the following
passage (36): "Was there, then, some process of alloying or treating
used by the artisans of early times for bronze, something like what is
called the tempering of swords, on the disappearance of which bronze
came to have a respite from the employment in war?". Pliny seems to
have some notion of what was behind all this when he says (37):

"The chief difference, however, arises from the nature of the water in
which the glowing metal is plunged from time to time. This, in some
places better for the purpose than in others, has quite ennobled some
localities famous for their iron such as Bilbilis and Turiasso in Spain,
and Comum in Italy, even though there are no iron mines at these
localities".

Of course bronze does not derive its hardness from quenching. In
the case of steel this rapid cooling consolidates a structure of the metal
achieved at the high temperature to which it was heated, its "steel"
structure would get partly, if not wholly, lost if the metal were cooled
very slowly and a structure more stable at low temperatures would
be allowed to emerge during this cooling period. Hence Caley rightly
says:

"Probably a bronze worker at Corinth discovered accidentally that
high-tin bronze could be forged in the cold state after a certain empirical
treatment which included the quenching of such bronze in the water of
Peirene after the metal had been heated to a given high temperature for

a given time, the success of the process as a whole being wrongly ascribed to the nature of the water instead of to the method of treatment. It was the discovery of a method for the working of high-tin bronze in the cold state which made Corinth a famous bronze manufacturing centre, the rest is either a misguided belief or a means of covering up their trade secrets!"

This quenching of bronze is also practised in Negro Africa (38), where Smets watched a native smith in Urundi make a bronze bracelet. which after heating in the fire was quenched in a calabash full of water. He claimed that this treatment made the bronze less brittle from over-heating and ready to be properly forged. Smets points to the "baphein" (which sometimes included dyeing) in which ancient smiths believed as strongly as the Urundi smith, and to the practise of adding a "phar-makon" to the water used for quenching. It would seem that this misguided belief or practice of the ancient smiths arose only in the Iron Age and that it was taken from the true quenching (Greek sto-mosis) of steel, where this operation really had a meaning and trans-ferred to the alloy bronze where quenching would not have any effect at all.

6. *The coming of tin*

In *Egypt* the situation is perfectly clear. There is no doubt that the earliest tin objects date from the XVIIIth dynasty, a ring of pure tin, one made of a gold-tin alloy and a pilgrim bottle from Abydos. Tin occurs in Egyptian glass of this period. No tin ore is known to occur *in* the Egyptian gold placers, no traces of it were found either in the Sinai copper ore or the slags near these mines. Bronze does appear in the Old Kingdom, probably introduced from abroad, but not until the XVIIIth dynasty do we find undoubted bronze objects in sufficient quantities in Egypt to justify the assertion that tin bronze was then in common use. In dealing with the nomenclature of tin it will be seen that any possible Egyptian name for tin is of a late date. The old statement of W. M. Müller that Keftiu brought tin to Egypt in the Old Kingdom remains unproved. These "Keftiu" probably do not hail from Crete but from Northern Syria or Southern Asia Minor and they bring ḏḥty that is lead which was certainly imported at such an early date from the North. Nor is the thesis of Wainwright correct who pointed to the copper-tin ore of Kesrwan near Byblos and asserted that the Egyptians had learnt the manufacture of bronze in these regions. This can hardly be true seeing the old connections of Egypt and Byblos and the late appearance of bronze in Egypt. If there ever existed a centre of local bronze manufacture in Kesrwan it was probably of late date and local importance only. The oldest bar of tin was found on an Egyptian mummy (39), it is free of lead and silver and must have been manufactured from a pure cassiterite, its date is not later than 600 B.C. No Egyptian texts state any source for tin, it was probably imported in the form of bronze as we suggested above. More finds of tin objects belong to the later part of the New Kingdom and classical

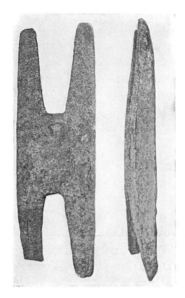

Fig. 28.
Block of tin found at St. Mawes, Falmouth (After Gowland)

times, such as two finger rings from Karanog, tinned bronze bowls and a bowl of pewter. It occurs also in late classical Egyptian coins.

The bronzes from the fifth century B.C. onwards, such as dies, show by their higher tin content that the tin supply became more abundant. Later Hellenistic papyri mention "tinworkers" and quote receipts for solder consisting of 4 parts of lead and one part of tin, but the tin mentioned is always used either as bronze or as a tin/lead alloy. The most important source for Egypt is now England; Stephanos of Alexandria calls tin *è brettanikè métallos* and we know from the Periplus Mar. Erythr. (cap. 28) that it was reexported again to Somaliland and

India. The source of early Egyptian tin seems to be the North, but this can only be considered in the light of evidence from other regions.

As regards *Crete* which after 1500 B.C. certainly served as a link between Western European tin and the East, there is no doubt that this tin trade can hardly be proved to have existed earlier. Though both bronze objects and small tin buttons of types found in Celtic and Iberian graves have been found in EMIII remains (2000 B.C.) this must have meant the opening of a source of local importance to Crete only, which very slowly grew to be the object of an important trade to the East. Fimmen has supposed this early Cretan tin to come from Spain and Sayce, Albright and Casson have connected it with a "Ku-ki" mentioned in a Sargonid tablet which would go to prove that a connection between Spain and the East existed at so early a date. This is, however, extremely doubtful and Cretan early tin may still have come partly from Anatolia and Caucasia as the new supply slowly won later. In *Asia Minor* Troy was an important site for the history of tin as it lies on the overland trade route from Bohemia to the East. In Troy II bronzes are well known but they still show large variations in their tin content; those of Troy V however are well propoitioned. A pure tin ring was found at Thermi IV (40). The early bronzes of Anatolia date from at least 3000 B.C. but copper forms are still used for a long period and as tin seems scarce the tin content is hardly ever outside the 2—10% range. Only from the Middle Bronze Age onwards, say from 2200 B.C., true bronze forms are used and higher percentages of tin appear more regularly and not only for intricate forms as in the earlier period. Before the Iron Age tin is still more or less a precious metal, it is often used for inlay-work in bronze, foi instance at Tel Halaf, while the Iliad mentions it three times (as a substitute of silver) in decorative work (the shields of Agamemnon and Achilles and the war chariot of Diomedes). It is not mentioned a tall in the Odessey! However, before dealing with Homeric and classical Greece we should first discuss the evidence recently available from Mesopotamian sources.

In *Mesopotamia* true bronzes were found fairly frequently in Djemdet Nasr and Early Dynastic sites (c. 2800 B.C.). The finds in the Royal Cemetry of Ur (2500 B.C.) show that the Ur smiths of that period understood the metallurgy of bronze and copper perfectly. Where the tin ore they used came from is still a mystery. The twenty-second tablet of the famous HARRA-ḫubullu series (41) mentions a "KUR Zaršur (-ḫa)" as a mountain which is the source of AN-NA, tin. The Lipšur litanies mention another mountain "KUR (Za)-ar-ḫa-a" as the mining region (42). A cuneiform text (SH. 868) from Tell Shemshâra in Iraqi Kurdistan (43) dating back to the eighteenth century B.C. states that the author requires from the country of Kusanarim a large consignement of wooden objects and a good supply of the mineral "annakum" (tin ore), which was probably to be alloyed with copper. As lead bronzes were still rare at this date there is no doubt that this refers to tin supplies available in Southern Kurdistan. Moulds and spearheads of bronze of the same date have been discovered at Shemshâra (the ancient Šušarrâ).

Leemans (44) mentions several texts of Old Babylonian (1800—1500 B.C.) and later date which refer to the tin trade. One (45) mentions the payment of a quantity of tin as a penalty for the late delivery of a shipment of silver. Another (46) contract for quantities of $8\frac{1}{2}$ minae of tin to be delivered mentions a penalty of $\frac{1}{3}$ of a shekel tin per ten shekels as a monthly interest in case of late delivery! The strange thing that emerges from texts from Sippar and Babylon is that there was a considerable export of tin from Babylon to Western Syria after the days of Hammurabi, tin which in its turn must have been imported into Babylonia as a continuation of earlier trade, possibly from the East (Drangiana or Tilmun?). The archives of Mari show that important quantities of tin came to that town from the East (47). Large quantities of tin went westwards from the town of Assur to the trading depots in Kaneš in Asia Minor, during the second period of that settlement, where the Assyrians bought their silver and lead. Assur itself obtained the tin from Kurdistan and Caucasia or from the Kara Dagh district in North-western Iran or may be Chorassan.

In other texts of Assyrian date the kings take "white bronze" as a tribute from the Northern and Eastern border regions, mainly from Muṣaṣir (on the Upper Zab) and Ellipi (between Behistun and Hamadan).

The trade of tin from the East to the North-west through the North Syrian towns seems to have continued even after the collapse of the Assyrian settlements in Anatolia. The Larsa texts mention relatively small quantities of tin, which is still very expensive, the silver/tin ratio being 1/10 (48), the quantities 2 minae on the average (49). The Mari texts, however, mention quantities such as "3 talents, 21 minae 3 shekels" (about 100 Kg.) which is bought at a rate of 1/14 and later at 1/30 whereas the rate in Asia Minor seems to have dropped slowly from 1/6 to 1/17, which shows that though Przeworski rightly pointed out that a few tin deposits were available in Asia Minor, these were not sufficient to cope with the greatly swollen demand for bronze in the second millennium B.C. An Alalakh letter of the fifteenth century mentions a lot of 900 shekels of copper and 70 shekels of tin (AN-NA), probably for the manufacture of an 8% bronze (50).

Finally we have a letter from Išḥi-Addu, king of Qatna to Išme-Dagan, king of Ekallatim, reproaching him for not properly having rewarded his gift of two horses (51): "One cannot really say this thing and still I insist in saying it to relieve my conscience! Thou art a high king! Thou hast asked me for two horses which thou desirest, I have had them brought to you. And now, thou hast sent only twenty minae (10 kgr) of tin! Is it not without discussion and completely that I have fulfilled thy desire. And thou darest send me this little tin". He mentions that the two horses have cost 600 silver shekels and that the small quantity of tin is hardly a compensation for so princely a gift. "Whosoever hears of this will not place us on the same footing!... If you had sent me no tin, my heart would not have had the slightest reason for being angry. You are no high king. Why have you done this? And still this house remains your house!"

From these new documents we see that in these early days tin came to Mesopotamia from the North and the East after the slump in tin imports during the late third millennium. This continues until the end of the second millennium as Mari texts go to prove (52) and by way of Aleppo, Carcemish, Qatna and Haṣôr to Anatolia to supplement the production of the few tin deposits which Przeworski mentions (53). In later periods tin comes from the West, thus Assurnasirpal gets his tin from the Phoenicians. In Neo-Babylonian times the price of tin was still eight times that of copper and in early bilingual texts it is mentioned after silver but before bronze and iron.

The texts also allow us the conclusion that during the second millennium bronzes were being made by alloying the two metals tin and copper (54).

In the *Indus civilisation* bronzes occur containing $4\frac{1}{2}$—13% of tin though copper is still generally used for tools and weapons in this latter half of the third millenium. The source of this tin must be sought in the western mountain boundary as the tin from Bihar and Orissa is unknown even in classical times in India.

In the *Caucasian region* bronze came into use around 3000 B.C. according to Jessen. Its use spread widely in Transcaucasia and the central Caucasus towards the end of the second millenium and reached its height around 1000 B.C. Local tin was used upto that date but gradually and increasingly tin from Western Europe was imported in the classical period and the local sources ceased to be worked. Jessen's dates are now generally considered to be on the low side.

Up to the end of the second Millennium Anatolia, Mesopotamia and the North-Syrian plain seem to have used up all the tin they could somehow import. There is little chance that Egypt could obtain supplies from these regions for direct trade contacts between Egypt and Mesopotamia were still very rare before 1500 B.C. (55). Egypt had to be supplied by Aegean and Cretan traders, who by this time began to ship tin from Spain eastwards in larger quantities, probably in the form of ingots of bronze and later in the form of ingots of tin only. However, surprises may be in store for us. Recently the wreck of a freighter was discovered off the south-west coast of Anatolia near Cape Gelidonya, dating back to 1200 B.C. On this wreck (56) several dozen "ox-hide" copper ingots were found, presumably from Cyprus. With theses ingots were found a number of piles of white, powdery tin-oxide, apparently the remains of tin ingots (the shape of which now escapes our observation), the earliest industrial tin consignment yet found. Evidently this tin sailed from east to west into the Aegean along the important south-coast trade route. We have no idea whether the small Anatolian tin deposits played any part in supplying the Aegean area as von Bissing claimed (57), but seeing the high prices of tin in Anatolia itself this seems hardly plausible. However, supplies from Spain shipped by Minoan and Phoenician traders became increasingly important to the Aegean area, though one can hardly see this Mediterranean tin trade as the object of commercial and colonial rivalries as Mireaux did (58).

In Mycenaean *Greece* tin evidently still plays the part of a rare and expensive metal. It is mentioned several times in the Iliad (59) but usually as a metal used for decorative purposes, for the Minoans and Mycenaeans loved metal work and especially metal-inlay in which variously coloured native metals and alloys rivalled with precious and semi-precious stones to form colourful panels and decorations. In this they rivalled with the metal-workers of Syria and Mesopotamia where similar work was also greatly appreciated. But the "greaves of new-wrought tin which rang terribly" (60) are probably an example of poetic licence in describing bronze greaves, for the metal tin would hardly be suitable for the purpose. In the same way when Hephaestus "put on the fire stubborn copper and tin and precious gold and silver" (61) the poet probably meant to say that the divine smith alloyed copper and tin, for he would hardly have contaminated his precious metals with the base ones, nor would he have mixed gold and silver unless he wanted to make coloured alloys for decorative purposes. Gray (62) made it clear that the corselet of Asteropaeus, the tin bosses on the shield of Agamemnon and the tin fittings on the chariot of Diomedes were probably tin coatings of a bronze substratum, which is technically quite possible as tin has a low melting point, and such a surface coating of a bronze base could be polished to give the object a silvery appearance. Still we have no evidence that this was practised in the Aegean, though tinned bronze plates were used on an iron helmet in the much later Sutton-Hoo ship-burial.

In classical Greece tin supplies came from Spain and beyond, and it was used for many purposes, but it always remained fairly expensive and hence there was a tendency to replace it, at least partly, by lead if possible. This is what happend in bronze coins (63). In Rome Cornish and Spanish tin, over 99.9% pure, was imported in the form of astragali or rings. Roman pewter generally consists of 2 parts of lead and 5 parts or tin. For the tinning of the inside of copper vessels tin alloys were used such as argentarium (50% of tin) and tertiarium (33% of tin) (64).

When the tinfields of Bohemia and Saxony were discovered and how and when tin supplies by the overland route through the Danube valley reached Troy and Anatolia is still a mystery. By 1500 B.C. bronze was being made on a large scale in Central Europe and Oldeberg argued convincingly that the tin supplies for Scandinavia came from Vogtland and the tin content of Scandinavian bronzes was somehow related to the methods of casting used there. Tin ingots in the shape of rings are common in the north of Europe by the Late Bronze Age and they probably hail from Cornwall, which became increasingly important during the Imperial period as the tin mines of Spain were giving out. In Italy tin-ore was exploited by the Etruscans near Cento Camerelle where fairly large quantities are found in the local "Brauneisenstein", but it seems that exploitation of these deposits ceased in Roman times.

7. *Nomenclature of the three metals*

Some interesting facts can be gleaned from a discussion of the ancient nomenclature of tin. We must then first draw the attention to the great resemblance which lead, tin, antimony and arsenic bear to each other for an observer who has no knowledge of chemistry and has to judge from external characteristics only as had the ancient metallurgist. It is almost certain that arsenic was not known in Antiquity or at least not known as a separate metal but the confusion in ancient (and alas in modern literature too!) of the first three metals and their ores already presents sufficient difficulties. The following table gives some essential data:

	Lead	Tin	Antimony	Arsenic
Colour	Blueish white	Silver-white	Lustrous white	Silvergrey
Specific gravity	11.3	7.3	6.7	5.7
Melting Point °C	327	232	630	814
Boiling Point	1613	2270	1380	615 (sublimates)
Hardness (Moh's scale) .	1.5	1.5-1.8	3.0-3.3	3.5
Hardness Brinell.	4.2	5.0	30	147
Crystals	cubic	tetragonal	hexagonal	hexagonal
Tensile Strength Kg/mm²	2.0	3-4	10	-

The first three metals differ slightly in colour and no wonder that Pliny considers them to be lead and speaks of plumbum nigrum (lead) and plumbum album (tin) and even Agricola has terms like plumbum nigrum (lead), plumbum candidum (tin) and plumbum cinereum (antimony). We find that throughout Antiquity these metals are confused held to be three rather similar types of lead. Taking the figures of the above table we see that there is little difference in colour but a greater one in melting point and mechanical properties. Arranged in decreasing order of brittleness we get the order lead, tin and antimony; for the malleability the order is lead, tin, antimony; for the ductility antimony, tin, lead.

The ancient Egyptians had a definite term for lead :dḥty (Coptic taḥt) but a similar term :dḥ(y) (HWB V. 605.6) occurs thrice in the Papyrus Harris, twice in a list of metals (quantities of 95 lbs and 2130 lbs) immediately after lead. It seems fairly certain that this late word denotes tin. Another instance of its use in the stela of Tanutamon (Period of Tarhaka, AR IV, 929) mentions double doors of electrum with two bolts (krty) of dḥy, which suits tin. This suggestion also fits in with the third occurence of the word in the Papyrus Harris (Pl. 41.14) in a list of statues of the Nile God made of different materials and metals. The old theory of Dufrené that keshpet meant tin and that this word was connected with Kasbek or kaspa still haunts technical literature, but this is wrong since the word keshpet, more correctly written ḥsbd, means lapis lazuli. It can not be decided from the context whether the "dḥty ḥd" or "white lead" mentioned in the London Medical Papyrus means tin or lead carbonate, both being used in drugs, etc. In later Coptic documents we find a new term for tin ⲟⲣⲁⲛ, tran (in the Bohairic dialect only) sometimes written ⲁⲟⲉⲟⲉ : trn. Sethe pointed out that this term, also written ⲡⲓⲧⲣⲁⲛ, was derived from Britannia. In the Sahidic dialect the word for tin seems to be ⲃⲁⲥⲛⲉⲥ, which Sethe derives from bi3.n.pt (ⲃⲉⲛⲓⲡⲉ) the old term for iron and especially meteoric iron.

It is clear from the classical texts that both kassiteros and stagnum may mean alloys with or without tin and also tin itself. The stagnum of Pliny is crude lead (Werkblei) but in the fourth century the term "*stagnum, stannum*" appears (65) to denote tin solely. Price did already record this fact and he was the first to connect the word with the Celtic *stean, sten* (Welsh *ystaen*) from which terms like *stagno, estano*, etc. were derived. The earliest rendering of *kassiteros* by *stannum* occurs in the IV—Vth century translation of the Periegesis of Dionysios. Pliny identi-fies the *plumbum album* with the Greek *kassiteros* (66). This *kassiteros* has been the subject of a prolonged dispute between different school of philologists. Reinach believes it to be derived from the Cassiterides, which he holds to be a Celtic word, Pisani (67) wants to connect it with a Celtic root *kas*-meaning "grey-white", but this would mean early connections between Gaul and Greece and Celtic tin coming to Greece in pre-Homeric days! Others look eastwards for the origin of this word. Lenormant tried to prove that it was a Caucasian word and he compared it with the Georgian *gala*, Ossetic *kala*, Turkish *kalai*, Armenian *klajek*, which was the opinion of Sayce too. One of his school even tried to connect the word with the name of the town of Qalah (Malaya)! It was believed to have been derived from the town of Kas-patyros on the frontier of Bactria and Persia in the country of Herodo-tus' golddigging ants. Pokorny and Hüsing (68) have derived it from an Elamite *kassi-ti-ra*, "the land of the Kassites", but even if it were true it does not help us very much as we do not know exactly where the Kassites lived in the third millennium and whether their home was a tin-producing country. Others have tried to connect it with the "Caspian" without proof (Hrozny). As both the Babylonian and Sanskrit related words are late it is probably an original Greek word and Siret may be right to connect it with *taxéros* (fusible). If not, we will probably have to look to Anatolia for the original term.

The related Neo-Babylonian term is *kastira* (69), which must be derived from the Greek as there is no Assyrian *kâsaṣatira* or an Accadian *id-kasduru* as Bapst and some others have claimed. The same late date must be assigned to the Sanskrit word *kastīra*, which does not occur in the classical literature. It is probably a loan-word from the Hellenistic traders exporting tin from Egypt to India. The same trade connections are probably responsible for the Arabian word *kasdir* and the Central African *kasdir*, which latter term proves that tin was an object of Arabian trade. The classical Sanskrit word for tin is *trapu*, a later synonym is *piccaṭa*. The terms *sasaka* and *niga* which some translate tin really mean lead. The word *trapu* is fairly common in the older classical literature but better distinction between lead and tin is made by later writers such as Kautilya, Sushrata, Charaka, etc. The Sumerian *nagga* (AN-NA) (Accadian anâku) generally denotes tin, but in the Cappadocian letters and some other texts there is no doubt that tin ore is meant by annakum (70). Probably the ancient meaning was both tin and lead which were not yet distinguished while gradually separate terms grew up. Thus lead is usually denoted by the Sumerian a-bâr or agar$_5$ (A.GÚG) (Accadian abâru) but this term may also mean antimony in some cases. Abâru is directly connected with the Hebrew ophérêth and there is no doubt that this word means lead in the different texts though translated kassiteros and stannum in the Vulgate. The passage (Num. 31.22) also contains the word bedil which also occurs in Ezech. 17.22 and Isaiah 1.25 and which is rendered kassiteros in the Septuaginta but molybdos, plumbum in the Vulgate (71). If Gesenius is right to connect it with the root *bdl* meaning "to separate, eliminate", it would seem that "lead" would be a better translation or perhaps the original meaning, as the metal tin is not separated from any other metal during its production, while lead is of course the by-product of silver. On the other hand it may be connected with the Arabian bedal, "substitute" which would suit tin, often used as a substitute for silver in inlay-work as we have mentioned. It is clear that the meaning of the two Hebrew words is still vague because there was no proper distinction between lead and tin in those days outside the metallurgical craft. Even in later documents like the Syriac version of the writings of Zosimos "soft metal" or "easily fusible metal" may denote both lead and/or tin. Pisani's suggestion connecting the Irish crèd and the Basque cirraida, urraida for tin with the Sumerian URUDU (bronze or copper!) must be rejected.

It is claimed that the word "aonya" in the Vendidad meant tin, but this word really means "heating device" and the passage where it occurs gives no food for the assertation stated above. The term "arjiz" for tin is a late one occuring in such writings as the Dâmdâd Nask, etc. Unfortunately, therefore, there are no philological proofs of an early knowledge of tin in Persia. Probably here too the early confusion between tin and lead reigned, even in modern Arabic raṣâṣ still denotes both tin and lead!

8. *Some applications of tin*

The tin produced by the Romans (we can not judge the earlier tin for the lack of tin bars or slabs!) was very pure, all Cornish ingots analysed contained more than 99.9% of tin, but this efficiency went hand in hand with considerable loss of tin in the slag during refining. A test for its purity mentioned by Pliny (72): "The papyrus test is used for pale lead; the molten metal should seem to burst the leaf by its weight rather than by its heat", in reality a melting point test, and this is what he says about its qualities (73) "Silver which is abundant in dark lead is absent from pale lead. Dark lead can not be welded together without pale lead, nor pale lead soldered to dark without oil and even two pieces of pale lead can not be united without dark lead... Pale lead is naturally dry, while dark lead is pre-eminently moist, and so pale lead if unalloyed is useful for nothing, and silver cannot be soldered with it, since the silver liquifies first (sic!)." The types of solder mentioned here are still the common solders of the present plumber, we now usually recognize three types differing in ratio tin/lead. This ratio is 2/1 for fine solder, 1/1 for common solder and 1/2 for plumber's solder. The Romans never used pure tin for household uses but they used a lead/tin alloy for pewter! This is of course no longer done to avoid lead-poisoning, but the Roman pewter, containing 2.5 parts of tin and 1 part of lead, still has its modern equivalent in our 4 to 1 alloy for art objects and in the Middle Ages pewter, always contained from 5 to 15% of tin. Household objects are now usually made of pure tin hardened by the addition of antimony and small percentages of copper and bismuth.

The tinning of metal objects especially of bronze and copper seems to have been invented in Gaul, for Pliny says (74): "The method of plating copper articles with pale lead (*incoctilia*) was devised in Gaul" and this statement is confirmed by Dioscorides (75). The tinned copper objects found in Egypt were probably imported. Originally this plating was done with *stagnum* (crude lead) and Pliny gives several recipes for counterfeit stagnum (76) consisting of 2 parts of brass and 1 part of tin, another called *argentarium* (1 tin/1 lead) and also one called *tertarium* (2 lead/1 tin). It is probable that these alloys were made by simple practical considerations and that their composition was found by trial and error only.

9. *Antimony and antimony bronzes*

A few pages must needs be devoted to antimony and arsenic here, because these metals (or at least metal-like substances, for chemically speaking they are metalloids!) are so much like tin and lead to the early metallurgist devoid of chemical knowledge, that their use instead of these two metals and the constant confusion between the four of them need not astonish us. In the case of antimony and arsenic the confusion is aggravated by the extra difficulties introduced by practically all modern authors without a chemical training who insist in calling both metals and ores from which they are prepared by the same name, thus often stating scientific impossibilities! For in the case of both antimony and arsenic it seems extremely doubtful whether their intentional preparation was carried out on a large scale in Antiquity though the ores were known and used.

In the case of antimony we must distinguish the metal (antimony) and the sulphidic ore, stibnite, the ancient stimmi or stibi, which many authors insist in calling antimony too.

The metallic antimony does occur naturally in granular masses with silver, but this is very rare. Still it is one of the most common elements, though not produced in large quantities, for it has only few important applications such as hard-lead, bearing metals and Britannia-metal. It is mostly produced from compound ores, upwards of fifty minerals contain antimony, but only a few are worked commercially. These are mainly ores containing compounds of antimony and/or sulphur with copper, iron, lead and other metals.

Some of these minerals are auriferous or argentiferous and in that case they are refined to obtain the precious metals, antimony being a by-product. Such an ore is the silver-bearing pyrargyrite or ruby silver. Other compound ores containing large quantities of antimony are tetrahedrite (Antimonfahlerz, Schwarzerz, a copper ore), chalkostib-nite, zinckenite, hypargite, etc.

A very common pure antimony-sulphur compound is stibnite (anti-mony glance, Grauspiessglanzerz), a brittle mineral with a metallic gloss like galena.

Its decomposition product (Weisspiessglanzerz), the oxyde, occurs in surface lodes .At present China produces the bulk of the stibnite used (about 87%), minor producers being Mexico, France and Algeria. As the metal was produced in a few localities only and the stibnite seems to have had a few cosmetical and pharmaceutical applications only, the mining of stibnite can hardly have been important. Thus there is no evidence of any important stibnite mining in Roman times in Europe, though a high antimony content in the coins of the Ileuici and Sequani suggests stibnite mining at Markirch or Giromagny. Furthermore the Romans understood the extraction of gold from such arsenic ores as mispickel and realgar (77) and from stibnite as is shown by the high percentage of antimony and arsenic in slags from Malbocs, Porna and Pangaeum and from numerous workings of quartz veins carrying mispickel in Creuze and other provinces in France. Again stibnite was used in desilvering natural gold.

It is described by Pliny (78): "In the same silver-mines is found what we might best describe as petrified foam, white and shining, but not transparent. It is variously called stimmi, stibi, alabastrum and larbasis. There are two varieties: male and female, of which the female is con-sidered the better. The male is coarser, rougher and less dense. Its surface is not shining and it contains more grit. The female, on the other hand, glistens and is easily broken, showing a lengthways cleavage instead of crumbling into small lumps". Dioscorides (79) makes the same distinction, which is, in fact, much older as the Papyrus Ebers which mentions stimi speaks of "true and male" stibnite no less than 36 times. Though Parly and von Nies have thought the male and female stibnite to represent the quartz-containing, impure, light and the pure, brittle form, it is more likely that the male represents the granular type of stibnite, the female the acicular form, though there is little difference in density between the two forms. On the other hand Bailey (80) de-clares that the male stimi is stibnite and the female native antimony, but the latter is very rare and if the identification be correct it can only be cast antimony prepared from stibnite, which ressembles the ore in many respects and may have been confused with it by the ancients.

When mapping the antimony ores in the Near East we have limited ourselves to the most important deposits only. In Asia Minor we have to record deposits on Mytilene and Chios. On the mainland there are the deposits of Kordilio, Cinlikaia and Avdin near Smyrna, at Bilecik, Trebzon, Karahissar and Keban Ma'den. The lead ores of the Kura valley in Transcaucasia contain large percentages of stibnite. The deposits in the mountains near Buršahanda which are mentioned in the Epic of the King of Battle, Sargon, must be somewhere over the Cilician mountains, but cannot be located exactly. In Persia the present Taht-i-Suleiman in the province of Afshar represents the "mountains of Gizilbunda near the town of Kunika" which was the source of stibnite for the Sumerians and Assyrians (81). Other deposits occur near Teheran, Mt. Demawend, Rey, Asterabad, Isfahan and the Kuh-i-Benan. Those near Isfahan Rey and Mt. Demawend are mentioned by Avicenna, Abulfeda, and Alqazwini. Several deposits are known to exist in Afghanistan and British India (North-West provinces, Punjab, Baluchistan, Madras, Mysore, Bihar, and Orissa) and in the Far East in Burma, British North Borneo, Indochina, China (Hunan, Hupeh, Yunnan, Kweichou, Kwangsi) and Japan. In Africa antimony ores are found in Damaraland, Transvaal, South Rhodesia and Algeria. None have been found in Egypt, traces occuring in the well-known copper and lead deposits. The ores from Midian have not been confirmed. Stibnite also occurs in Northern Syria near Alexandretta and Antioch. Many European countries such as Great Britain, France, Portugal, Spain, Switzerland, Bohemia, Yoguslavia, Greece, Germany and Sweden contain deposits.

It would have been easy to produce the metal on a large scale even in early days by oxidizing the sulphidic ore to the oxyde and reducing the latter with charcoal at a fairly low temperature to avoid volitalization of the metal. This process was actually known in Antiquity, for we have a long description of it in Pliny's Natural History (82): "It is roasted (the stimmi) in an oven, after smearing with lumps of cow-dung, then quenched with mother's milk and ground in a montar after addition of rain water. Next the turbid liquid is transferred to a copper vessel and purified with soda. The precipitate which sinks to the bottom of the mortar is considered to be very rich in lead, and it is rejected. Then the vessel into which the turbid liquid has been transferred is covered with a cloth and left overnight. The supernatant liquid is poured off next day, or removed with a sponge. The solid that subsides is considered to be the best and is dried in the sun with a cloth over it, but not so as to remove all moisture. It is then ground again in a mortar and made up in little tablets. It is a matter of prime importance that the roasting should not be too vigorous, lest the product turn into lead. Some workers use fat instead of cow-dung in the roasting; others strain through a triple cloth the product which has been ground up with water and reject the residue. The filtrate is transferred to another vessel and the deposit collected and used for mixing with plasters and eye-salves".

Dioscorides (83) has a similar description of the roasting of stibnite to obtain the pharmaceuticaly important white oxide of antimony. It is important that both authors warn not to carry the reaction too far lest the product "turn into lead" and Dioscorides calls the heavy praecipitate "faex plumbosissima". This means that the antimony-metal obtained during the process by part-reduction of the oxide by the cow-dung was held to be lead and therefore rejected. This goes to show that the classical metallurgists did not go further than the preparation of the oxide, as they had no special use for the metallic antimony. That this preparation would have been easy is shown by their description, indeed, stibnite melts in the flame of a candle!

The metal is lead-like, silverwhite but less susceptible to oxidation by the air so it retains its lustre far longer than lead. It is, however, brittle and easily pulverised. It mixes readily with metals such as copper, iron, lead, silver, gold and tin and usually decreases the malleability and increases the hardness, if the percentage is not too high.

We find many antimony-bronzes among the oldest copper alloys, but these need not always have been intentional. Indeed in most cases the percentage of antimony is so low that we can safely ascribe it to the natural impurities of the copper ore used and not to any addition of antimony ore during the smelting of the copper. Thus some of the oldest Mesopotamian bronzes contain up to 3% of antimony, it was found in Anau I copper, in old Abyssinian alloys, in Japanese, Indian, Chinese and Gallic bronzes.

There are, however, a few centres in Antiquity where the addition of antimony to copper was standard practice, in this case the percentage may be as high as 15—20% and objects of pure antimony are found there too. Such a centre is Velem St. Vid in Hungary. Von Miske thinks that the ore used does only contain lead and arsenic as impurities and that the antimony was added intentionally because tin was lacking in the region. Others believe that the mixed copper-antimony ore was so rich in antimony that the alloy was obtained unintentionally. It was a success, for we find objects from this centre in Silezia,

West Prussia and Bavaria. Some of the lake dwelling bronzes containing upto 15% of antimony may have come from Velem St. Vid. For weapons, however, this alloy was too brittle and tin ore was imported from Bohemia for their manufacture (84). Though Petrie proposed at a time to ascribe some Egyptian bronzes containing antimony to import from Hungary, there is no proof for any trade-connection at so early a date. The antimony may well have been derived from local copper ores and some of the "antimony" of earlier analyses was later found to be bismuth!

In La Tène times another centre of antimony-bronzes grew up in the Vosges mountains. In the Near East the Caucasus region was another centre of the manufacture of antimony and antimony-alloys. Many antimony objects were found in the graves of Redkinlager on the Aksatfa, a tributary of the Kura river, near Tiflis, including footrings, bracelets, etc. These objects are said to date from the ninth or tenth century B.C. Others have been found at Koban. Gradually these objects disappear and tin objects take their place. It can be proved that they were made by roasting and reducing stibnite for some of them still contain an appreciable sulphur percentage due to insufficient roasting. Other antimony objects have been found near the copper mines of Khedabek. Most of them are cast, but their use must have been restricted, as they are very brittle. Other objects were beads, amulets, buttons, etc. The Caucasus may have been the source of some of the antimony objects found in Mesopotamia. There is a bowl of the Gudea period and the vase found at Tello and analysed by Berthelot. The metal was also used from time to time in the Assyrian period for Sargon II mentions it among other metal tablets of the foundation deposit of his new bît-hilani at Chorsabad.

Antimony occurs in some Sumerian bronzes, but simply as an impurity of the ore used for the preparation of the copper. Stibnite ("guḫlu") is known in Mesopotamia since the days of Gudea and earlier as an eye-paint, it was probably not produced in Assyria itself but imported. Tiglath Pileser gets a tribute of 1 homer from Malatia and the annals of Tukulti Ninip and Shamši Adad mention that guḫlu is obtained from the mountains of Gizilbunda near the town of Kinaki in Afshar. The oxide seems to have been used for tinting glass yellow.

In Egypt there are no proofs that the metal antimony was known and used. Garland suggested it but he confused antimony and stibnite! The sensational discovery of Fink and Kopp that the ancient Egyptians understood the art of plating copper objects with antimony was disproved by Lucas, who quite correctly points out that this "antimony-plating" is due to the electrolytic reduction of the copper object, the antimony is simply an impurity of the copper and the so-called plating due to the method of restoration and not a process applied to the original object. The only instance of antimony in Egypt is the find of a few beads in a grave at Lahun of the XXIIth dynasty. Petrie quite correctly infers that these are imports as antimony ores are not known to occur in Egypt. Several older bronzes contain antimony. The eye-paint used from immemorial times in Egypt is usually held to be stibnite. It is pictured on the Deir el Bahri reliefs (85) as one of the products obtained from Punt and, indeed, the Periplus mentions many centuries later the existence of a stibnite trade from the coast of East Africa to India (Ist cy. A.D.), while the Pap. Kenyon mentions stibnite from Coptos, Italy, Calchedon and "Occidental". Still modern analysis has proved that the ancient Egyptians did not distinguish well galena and stibnite and the term *mśdm(t)* usually translated stibnite applies to both. Out of 34 eye-paints analysed no less than 21 were pure galena, the rest mainly mixtures and a few consisted of pure stibnite, being of New Kingdom or later date! In the same period antimony begins to appear in Egyptian glazes and somewhat later in enamels too.

Stibnite is also mentioned in the Bible. The Vulgate renders both the kahâl of Ezech 23:40 and the pûkh of II. Ki. 9:30 and Jerem. 4:30 as stibium. Early finds of ḳoḥl pencils at Tell el Hesy and Gezer open a long row of finds of later date. In these cases no analyses are available but probably both galena and stibnite were used indiscriminately.

Stimmi or stibi was used not only as a "plathyophtalmon" but also in ancient medicine according to the testimony of the Papyrus Ebers, Celsus, Pliny, Dioscorides and many others. The *stibi tetragonon* of Hippocrates (86) were probably small cubes of ground stibnite mixed with fat or talcum.

In the Middle Ages and in Iatrochemistry stibnite was used in pharmaceutical recipes and as an emetic.

The nomenclature has mainly suffered from the modern confusion of antimony and stibnite, for it is quite clear that we have only one word which probably denotes the metal antimony, the others all describe the sulphide stibnite!

Campbell Thompson has identified LIŠ-A-BÁR (abaru) with antimony. Though *abaru* generally means lead, it may in several cases, such as the foundation tablet of Sargon II at Chorsabad, mean antimony as lead is then mentioned separately. The old translation *abaru*: magnesite is now of course untenable, it does not fit the many passages where this word occurs. Thureau Dangin has identified the NE-KÙ of an alloy with antimony but this means "wastage". Haupt has suggested the *dagassu* of the mountain of Buršhahanda to be antimony, (87) but he probably means to say "stibnite"! The usual word for stibnite is SIM-BI-ZI-DA (*guḫlu*), an equivalent of the Hebrew *kaḥâl* and the Arabic *koḥl* (from ḳḥl, to stain), another synonym is *ṣadidu*, the Syriac *sadidâ*, a more general term for eye-paint which is also and more frequently used for chrysocolla.

Though formerly translated "antimony" the Egyptian *mśd . t* is most certainly not stibnite or antimony, for the correct term is 𓅓𓈖𓂝 𓍑 , or 𓅓𓈖 𓍑 mśdm(t) (88), the Coptic stem, Greek stimmi, Latin stibium. It is usually translated antimony, but this should be stibnite, though we have seen that this ore was confused with galena and so the term may denote both and should be more correctly translated "eye-paint". The metal antimony could of course not be used as such for it is far too gritty and the sulphide is clearly meant. Crum gives a Coptic term ⲃⲁⲥⲟⲩⲣ (89).

The classical authors have added to the confusion by using stimmi indiscriminately to denote both the metal and the ore. This is clear when we read that Democritos calls stimmi "our lead", that Olympiodorus makes "lead" from galena, lead oxide and stimmi. No proper distinction is made by the early alchemists between lead and antimony; the source of the "Great Work" is said to be "lead" obtained from stimmi, galena or cadmeia! But Maria calls it molybdos emeteros as distinct from molybdos melas, the true lead.

Our present "antimony" is of course not derived from "anti-moine", a story still appearing in our textbooks like that of the fake discoverer Basilius Valentinus. The "Lapidary of Aristotle" calls stimmi or galena "ithmid, itmad, azmat" and Ruska thinks that "antimony" is derived from "al-ithmid". More probably Diergart is right in deriving it from "anthémonion", a term occuring already in the writings of Constantinus Africanus and Vincent of Beauvais, while a treatise of jewelry of the XVth century mentions "antémonium".

10. *Arsenic and arsenical copper*

It is exceedingly doubtful whether the metal arsenic was ever produced intentionally in Antiquity. Though Burton Brown maintains the alloying of arsenic and copper at an early date (90), the ancients possessed neither the apparatus nor the technical and chemical knowledge to produce this very volatile and toxic metal, many arsenic compounds sublimate easily and can be handled only in special apparatus which they did not posses, certainly not earlier than the Alexandrian alchemists who did not know arsenic as a metal at all!

The earliest author using arsenic compounds who devines that they might contain a metal is Albertus Magnus. It has no specific uses and even at the present time the only important application is 0.3% of arsenic in lead-hot. Arsenic (Scherbenkobalt, gediegener Fliegenstein) occurs in the native state as a dull-grey, brittle mass with a tin-white fracture often associated with native antimony or silver. This fairly rare mineral may be the IM-ŠIM-TÁK-SAHAR, ᵃAŠ-GE₄-GE₄ (aš-giku) of Mesopotamian texts. Though some arsenic ores occur in a fairly pure state, they are usually found as admixtures or mixed ores with sulphides of copper iron and lead, such as cobaltite, arsenopyrite, proustite, enargite, mispickel, etc. Therefore the metals refined from such ores tend to have a small percentage of arsenic if the refining is not carried out in a special way to avoid this unwanted impurity.

One of the most common purer arsenic ores is *realgar*, which got its name only in late Arabian literature. It was formerly called *sandaraché* or *sandyx* (Festus) which name is probably connected with the root sand- or sard- meaning red, which we also find in the name of the Hittite god of agriculture Sandan, Santas. In ancient times this beautiful orange red or deep red mineral was found in Lycia (91), in Paphlagonia (92) and Carmania (93). Mines on Topazus island in the Red Sea are mentioned by Pliny and Isidore (94) also occurs in Kurdistan near the Taht-i-Suleiman and it was known to Aristotle and Theophrastus. Campbell Thompson identifies it with ŠIM-GUŠKIN (*leru*, *šipu*).

A second pure arsenic ore was orpiment, another sulphur compound of a bright yellow colour called *arsenikon* in ancient times. This term is probably due to metathesis of the Persian *az-zarnikh*, Old Persian *zaranya*, Armenian *zarik*, Syriac *Zarnîkî* and Hebrew *zarniq* meaning "golden". The ancients found it in Carmania, Mysia, Pontus, Cappadocia, Shiraz, on the Taht-i-Suleiman in Kurdistan and near the river Hypanis (Bug) in the Ukraïne (95). This is probably the ŠIM-BI-SIG₇-SIG₇ (*lêru*, *sipu damatu*) of ancient Mesopotamian texts. Its relation to arsenic was already known to Theophrastus (96).

These two minerals reached a certain fame as pigments though their poisonous properties were well recognized (97). Sandarache was often mistaken for red lead (98) while arsenikon was also sometimes called *arrhenikon* (99).

This is what Pliny has to say about these arsenic compounds (100): "There is moreover, a recipe to make gold from orpiment which occurs near the surface of the earth in Syria, and is dug up by painters, its hue is similar to that of gold, but it is brittle like the "mirror stone". (101) "Sandarache occurs both in gold and silver mines and its excellence is proportional to the depth of its red colour, its sulphurous smell and its brittleness. Arrhenicum is another derivative of the same substance. The best kind is coloured a fine shade of gold, specimens which are paler or which ressemble sandarache are thought inferior. It ressembles sandarache in its properties but its actions are less severe. To make it more active it is roasted in a new earthenware vessel until it changes colour". Similar reports on the roasting of orpiment are told by Dioscorides and Olympiodorus, the white product obtained being "white arsenic", the oxide, which is very poisonous. It occurs in nature as the decomposition product of the two former minerals (Arsenolith, Arsenikblüte), probably the ancient MUH-AŠ-GE$_4$-GE$_4$.

These minerals are also found in the Caucasus (Topprakaleh, Tushpa) and in Persia (Mt. Demawend) but their application in Antiquity was mainly pharmaceutical and medicinal, though they have been used as poisons and pigments too.

The metal could have been made by roasting and reduction of the three last-mentioned minerals taking great care to avoid volitalisation of the metal. It was done by the first-century Coptic alchemists, but we have no proof of any earlier preparation. Of course the occurence of arsenic ores as admixtures to copper and iron ores was the cause of small percentages of arsenic in ancient copper and bronze. Its influence on the properties of copper have been greatly overrated and several authors have concluded that artificial arsenic-copper alloys were made in Antiquity on purpose. Though upto 0.5% of arsenic increases the thoughness of copper, the brittleness increases rapidly as soon as this percentage reaches 1%. As it increases the casting properties of copper only in quantities of more than 1.5% the ancient metallurgists would have overshot the mark by making a copper well suited for casting but very brittle and hard too.

In the early Bronze Age (3000—2000 B.C.) copper-arsenic alloys containing upto 10% are made in the Caucasus region, which upto the present has not yielded a Copper Age. The alloys were presumably

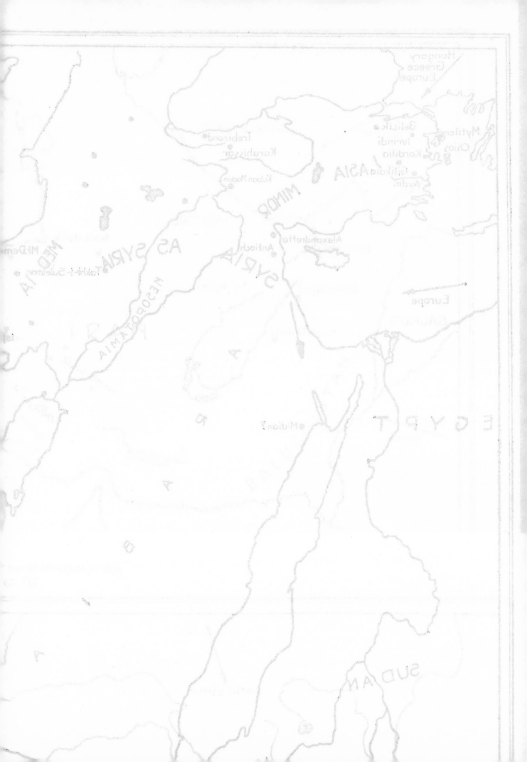

obtained by smelting the copper and arsenic ores (abundant in this region) together, not by real alloying of the two metals (102). Two small objects, a ring and a needle of pure arsenic are reported from Kumbulte, in this case the native metal was probably mistaken for lead. In Hungary early copper and antimony bronzes contain upto 4% of arsenic due to the ore worked. Some Indus bronzes have $3—4\frac{1}{2}\%$, while even the copper of Anau sometimes contains some arsenic. In early Mesopotamian bronzes the percentages seldom rise above 0.6%, as we might expect from impurities of normal ores.

Intentional arsenic-copper alloys have been claimed for Egypt, but the early copper which may contain upto 4% of arsenic was never found to be annealed and it was probably a natural alloy too. As we have already stated the hardening properties of arsenic are of a low order and it is also found in objects where softness is essential. There is no arsenic in either ore or slag from the Sinai but some copper ores of the Western desert contain it.

Witter has proved that the natural copper-arsenic alloys have been recognised and used as a kind of "better copper" very early in Central Europe. In most cases the copper was further hardened by hammering at low temperatures.

Arsenic played a large part in alchemical theories from the first centuries A.D. onwards. Democritos calls orpiment "yellow sand" and realgar "red sand", and Maria and Kleopatra mention them. Zosimos obtained arsenic metal and called it a second mercury which burns up to the "soul of the colour", the white oxide.

There are still many dark points in the history of these three metals and especially the confusion of tin, lead and antimony in the few ancient texts that deal directly with them makes it difficult to present more than an outline of their history. Much will probably be gained by a closer study of the history of bronze from this point of view:

> "But if thou wilt enter this Campe of Philosophy
> with thee take Tyme to guide thee in thy Way"

BIBLIOGRAPHY

(For further details consult my Bibliographia Antiqua, Philosophia Naturalis (Leiden, 1947) and Suppl. I (1950) and II (1963))

1. PLINY, *Nat. Hist.* XXXIV. 156—157
2. CASSIODORUS, *Variae* III. cap. 31
3. BISSING, F. W. VON, *On the occurence of tin in Asia Minor and in the neighbourhood of Egypt* (JHS 52, 1932, 119)
   BITTEL, K., *Prähistorische Forschungen in Kleinasien* (Istanbul, 1934)
4. CRAWFORD, O. G. S., *The discovery of bronze* (Antiquity X, 1936, 87—88)
   CRAWFORD, O. G. S., *Tin-deposits in the Near East* (Antiquity XII, 1938, 79—81)
   KARAJIAN, H. A., *Mineral resources of Armenia and Anatolia* (London, 1920)
5. FIELD, H. and PROSTOV, E., *The tin deposits in the Caucasus* (Antiquity XII, 1938, 341—345)
   HANČAR, FR., *Urgeschichte Kaukasiens* (Wien, 1937)
6. KARAJIAN, H. A., *Mineral resources of Armenia and Anatolia* (London, 1920)
7. CRAWFORD, O. G. S., *Tin deposits in the Near East* (Antiquity XII, 1938, 79)
8. BAER, K. VON, *Von wo mag das Zinn zu den alten Bronzen gekommen sein?* (Archiv f. Anthr. IX, 1877, 263—267)
   JONES, W. R., *Tinfields of the world* (London, 1925)
   FAWNS, S., *The tin deposits of the world* (London, 1907)
9. STRABO, 15. 2. 10
10. SCHUMANN, C., *Untersuchungen über die Zimtländer* (Erg. Bd. no. 73, Peterm. Mitt. 1883, 9)
    LOEHR, M., *Chinese bronze weapons* (Ann Arbor, 1956)
11. BISSING, F. W. von, JHS 52, 1932, 119
12. *Num.* 31 : 22
13. BRAAKE, A. L. TER, *De uitdaging van St. Aniol* (Erts VII, 1955, 11, 209—210)
14. WAINWRIGHT, W. A., *The occurence of tin and copper near Byblos* (JEA 20, 1934, 29—32)
    WAINWRIGHT, W. A., *Egyptian bronze-making* (Antiquity 17, 1943, 96—98)
    WAINWRIGHT, W. A., *Early Tin in the Aegean* (Antiquity 18, 1944, 57—64)
15. DAVIES, O., *Roman Mines in Europe* (Oxford, 1936)
    GOWLAND, W., *The metals in Antiquity* (JRAI 42, 1912)

JOLEAUD, G., *L'ancienneté de l'exploitation de l'étain dans le nord-ouest de l'Espagne* (Anthrop. 1929, 134—136)

DITTMANN, A., *Kurze Mitteilungen über Zinnerz-Lagerstätten in Spanien und Portugal* (Metall und Erz XXX, 1933, 1, 6—10)

MARÉCHAL, J. R., *Nouvelles considérations sur l'origine et l'évolution de la métallurgie du bronze* (Ogam XIV, 1962, 389—392)

16. PLINY, *Nat. Hist.* XXXIV. 158

17. DAVIES, O., *Roman mines in Europe* (Oxford, 1936)

18. GOWLAND, W., *On the early metallurgy of copper, tin and iron in Europe* (Archaeologia 56, 1900, 2)

19. HESIOD 258; ARISTOTLE, *de Mirab. Ausc.* 81; STRABO 3. 2. 9; 5. 11; 5. 15; 5. 30; CAESAR, *de Bello Gall.* 5. 12; POMPONIUS MELA 3. 6. 2; DIODOR 5. 38. 4; 5. 22. 5; HERODOTUS III. 115

20. GOWLAND, W., *The metals in Antiquity* (JRAI 42, 1912)

PHILLIPS, J. A., *Thoughts on ancient metallurgy* (Arch. J. 16, 1859, 12)

21. CARY, M., *The Greek and the ancient trade with the Atlantic* (JHS 43, 1923, 166)

22. WITTER, W., *Woher kam das Zinn in der frühen Bronzezeit* (Mannus vol. 27, 1936, pp. 446—456)

WITTER, W., *Eine in Vergessenheit geratene 4000 Jahre alte Legierung von Kupfer und Arsen* (FUF vol. 13, 1937, pp. 39—40)

WITTER, W., *Die Kenntnisse von Bronze und Kupfer in der alten Welt* (Leipzig, 1938, Mannus Bibl. vol. 63)

23. HILLER, J. E., *Minerale der Antike* (Arch. Gesch. Math. Naturw. Techn. 13, 1930, 358)

24. MANTELL, C. L., *Tin, its mining, production, technology and applications* (New York, 1949)

GIBBS, F. W., *The rise of the tinplate industry* (Annals of Science VI, 1950, 390—404; VII, 1951, 25—62)

KAMP, A. F., *De standvastige soldaat* (geschiedenis van de N.V. Billiton Maatschappij, 1860—1960) (The Hague 1960)

25. GOWLAND, W., *Metals and metal-working in Japan* (Trans. Japan Soc. (London, 13, 1915, 20—85)

26. LUCAS, A., *Notes on the early history of tin and bronze* (JEA 14, 1928, 97—108)

LUCAS, A., *Ancient Egyptian Materials and Industries* (London, 1962)

REID, CL., *Bronze and tin in Cornwall* (Man 18, 1918, 9)

27. CHILDE, V. GORDON, *The Orient and Europe* (AJA XLIV, 1939, 10—26

CHILDE, V. GORDON, *The Final Bronze Age in the Near East and in Temperate Europe* (J. Preh. Soc., 1948, 177—195)

28. CHILDE, V. GORDON, *New Light on the Most Ancient East* (London, 1954)

29. CHILDE, V. GORDON, *The technique of Prehistoric Metal Work* (Antiquity XXII, 1948, 29—32)

GOOREICKX, D., *Composition et structure de quelques cuivres et bronzes anciens de Chypre* (Bull. Inst. R. Patrimoine Artist., Bruxelles, II, 1959, 132—138)

30. WISEMAN, D. J., *The Alalakh Tablets* (London, 1953, 105, no. 399)
31. STRASSMAIER, *Nabonidus*, 924
32. LUCKENBILL, *Sennacherib* (Chicago 1924, 133)
    WINCKLER, H., *De Inscriptione Sargonis* (Berlin, 1886, 1. 205)
33. AESCHYLUS, *Agamemnon* 621
34. CALEY, E. R., *Corroded Bronze of Corinth* (Proc. Amer. Phil. Soc. 84, 1941, 748—761)
35. PAUSANIAS II. 3. 3
36. PLUTARCH, *Moralia* V. 262—263
37. PLINY, *Nat. Hist.* XXXIV. 144
38. SMETS, G., *La trempe du bronze, Eschyle et les Barundi* (Bull. Acad. R. Belg. Classe Lett. XXXV, 1949, 141—158)
39. CHURCH, A. H., *An ancient specimen of tin* (Chem. News 23, 1877, 168)
40. LAMB, W., *Excavations at Thermi*, 165, 171—173, 215
    LAMB, W., JHS 59, 1939, 291
41. LANDSBERGER, B. JNES XV, 1956, 146—147
42. REINER, E., JNES 129, line 23
43. LAESSØE, J., *Akkadian annakum, tin or lead* (Acta Orient. 24, 1959, 83—94)
44. LEEMANS, W. F., *Foreign Trade in the Old Babylonian Period* (Leiden, 1960)
45. TCL X. 125 (AO 8480)
46. CT VIII. 37b
47. ARM VII. 87, 115, 117
48. TCL X 17
49. YBT V. 207
50. AL 399
51. ARM V. 20
52. ARM VII. 294
53. PRZEWORSKI, ST. *Die Metallindustrie Anatoliens in der Zeit von 1500—700 v. Chr.* (Leiden, 1939)
54. LEVEY, M., *Chemistry and Chemical Technology in Ancient Mesopotamia* (Amsterdam, 1959, 196—211)
    LEVEY, M. and BURKE, J. E., *A study of ancient Mesopotamian bronze* (Chymia V, 1959, 37—50)
55. LEEMANS, W. F., *The Trade relations of Babylonia and the question of relations with Egypt in the Old Babylonian Period* (J. Econ. Soc. Hist. Orient. III, 1960, 1, 21—37)
56. BASS, G. F., *The Cape Gelidonya wreck, a preliminary report* (AJA 65, 1961, 267—276)
57. BISSING, F. W. VON, SBAW 1911, 6, 6; JHS LII, 1932, 119
58. MIREAUX, J., *Les Poèmes homériques et l'histoire grecque* (Paris, 1948/49: I. *Homère de Chios et les routes de l'étain*; II. *L'Iliade, l'Odyssée et les rivalités coloniales*

59. ILIAD, XI. 25, 34; XVIII. 474, 565, 574, 613; XX. 271; XXI. 592; XXIII. 503, 592
60. ILIAD, XXI. 592
61. ILIAD, XVIII. 474
62. GRAY, D. H. F., *Metal-working in Homer* (JHS LXXIV, 1954, 1—15)
    SANDARS, N. K., *The antiquity of the one-edged bronze knife in the Aegean* (Proc. Preh. Soc., 21, 1956, 174—197)
63. CALEY, E. R., *The composition of ancient Greek bronze coins* (Philadelphia 1939)
    CALEY, E. R. and DEEBEL, W. H., *Chemical dating of bronze coin blanks from the Athenian agora* (Ohio J. Sci. LV, 1955, 44—46)
    BIBRA, E. VON, *Die Bronze- und Kupferlegierungen der alten und ältesten Völker* (Erlangen, 1869)
    BAPST, G., *Etudes sur l'étain dans l'Antiquité et au Moyen Age* (Paris, 1884)
    BAPST, G., *L'orfèvrerie d'étain dans L'Antiquité* (Rev. Archéol. (2) vol. 43, 1882, p. 226; (3) vol. 1, 1883, 100)
    WILSON, J. B., *Lead and tin in ancient times* (Princeton Theol. Rev. vol. 15, 1937, pp. 443—450)
64. SMYTHE, J. A., *Notes on ancient and Roman tin and its alloys with lead* (Trans. Newcomen Soc. 18, 1937/38, 255)
65. FLASDIECK, H. M., *Zinn und Zink, Studiën zur abendländischen Wortgeschichte* (Tübingen, 1952)
    PLINY, *Nat. Hist.* 34. 156
66. PISANI, V., *Kassiteros* (REA 37, 1935, 152)
67. HÜSING, A., *Der Zagros und seine Völker* (AO 9, 1908, 3/4, 24)
68. SCHRADER, RL 995
69. LAESSØE, J., *Akkadian annakum: "tin" or "lead"* (Acta Orient. 24,
70. 1959, 83—94)
71. ABRAMSKI, S., *"Slag" and "Tin" in the first chapter of Isaiah* (Eretz-Israel V, 958, 89)
72. PLINY, *Nat.1 Hist.* XXXIV. 163
73. PLINY, *Nat. Hist.* XXXIV. 158, 161
74. PLINY, *Nat. Hist.* XXXIV. 162
75. DIOSCORIDES I. 38
76. PLINY, *Nat. Hist.* XXXIV. 160
77. PLINY, *Nat. Hist.* XXXIII. 79; XXXIV. 177
78. PLINY, *Nat. Hist.* XXXIII. 101
79. DIOSCORIDES, V. 99
80. BAILEY, K. C., *The Elder Pliny's Chapters of Chemical Subjects* (London, 1929/1933, 2 vols.)
81. MEISSNER, BR., *Das Antimongebirge* (OLZ 17, 1914, 52)
82. PLINY, *Nat. Hist.* XXXIII. 103—104
83. DIOSCORIDES, V. 99
84. DAVIES, O., *Antimony bronze in Central Europe* (Man 35, 1935, 91)
85. LIEBLEIN, A., *Handel und Schiffahrt auf dem Rothen Meere* (Christiania, 1886, 20, 64, 70)

86. HIPPOCRATES, 209. 14; 211. 2
87. HAUPT, OLZ XVI. 492
88. HWB II. 153. 8; also written śdm (HWB IV. 370. 9)
89. CRUM, *Coptic Dictionary* 44.b
90. BROWN, T. BURTON, *Excavations in Azabaijan* 1948 (London, 1951, 188)
91. STRABO, 11. 14. 9. cap. 529; PHILOSTRATUS *Apoll.* 3. 14
92. STRABO, 12. 3. 40. cap. 562
93. STRABO, 15. 2. 14. cap. 726
94. PLINY, *Nat. Hist.* XXXV. 39; ISIDORE, 19. 17. 11
95. VITRUV, 7. 7
96. THEOPHRASTUS, *On Stones* cap. 89
97. STRABO, 12. 3. 40; ARISTOTLE, *Hist. Anim.* 8. 24; AETIUS ISTRICUS, 4. 45
98. VITRUV, 7. 7; ISIDORE, 7. 9. 11
99. VITRUV, 7. 7; CELSUS, 5. 5; DIOSCORIDES, V. 121
100. PLINY, *Nat. Hist.* XXXIII. 79
101. PLINY, *Nat. Hist.* XXXIV. 177—178
102. SELIMKHANOV, I. R., *Spectral analysis of metal articles from archaeological monuments of the Caucasus* (Proc. Preh. Soc. XXVIII, 1962, 68—79)

CHAPTER THREE

THE EARLY STORY OF IRON

"Our next subject must be the ores of iron, a metal which is at once the best and the worst servant of humanity, for to bring death more speedly to our fellow-man, we have given wings to iron and taught it to fly"

(Pliny, *Natural History*, XXXIV, 138)

1. *Introduction*

To this passage of Pliny we could add the words of the Prophet: "Dire evil resideth in iron as well as advantage to mankind" (1), but Pliny adds: "Let the blame for such death be brought home to man, and not to nature!" and he continues: "Several attempts have been made to enable iron to be guiltless. In the treaty which Porsenna granted to the Roman people after the expulsion of the kings, we find a specific clause forbidding the use of iron except for agriculture. According to the most ancient authors the ordinance that a bone stilum should be used for writing dates from the same period. An edict is extant promulgated by Magnus Pompeius in his third consulship at the time of the tumult occasioned by the death of Clodius forbidding the possession of any weapon in the city of Rome" (2).

The myths and magical practices of many peoples show clearly that iron was a comparatively late metal. By many peoples iron seems to have been received with much suspicion. Celtic folklore has many references to this. Some of the African tribes have objections against iron hoes which they say keep away the rain. Among the Caribou Eskimos iron, a new material, was not worked during the season of the musk-ox hunting.

It would be easy to multiply these examples (3). In Pliny's writings iron figures in magical recipes (4), in some cases he forbids the use of iron implements in cutting herbs (5) or in killing animals (6).

There are many quaint recipes for the correct solutions in which to temper or quench iron. Thus the *Mappae Clavicula* states that urin of a he-goat or a red-headed boy should be used and Bandini's *Fons memorabilium* says that a sword tempered in the juice of a radish mixed with the juice of earthworms cut up and strained through a cloth will cut all iron as if it were lead.

Many other legends centre in the magnet and its properties. Plutarch states that iron rubbed with garlic does not respond to the magnet and the *Causa Causarum* of the eleventh century says that onions are similar damaging substances. The legend of the magnetic mountain in the Indian Ocean, well known from the Arabian Nights, figures in earlier writers such as Constantinus Africanus, who also holds that the magnet comforts those who are afflicted with melancholy.

Iron transfers its magical potencies to other substances. Thus the water or milk in which iron was quenched was said to be a good cure for diarrhoea. Iron will also protect against the baneful influences of evil spirits and such beliefs had a very long life. Socinus of Siena (1450 A.D.) states that one should put a key, sword, or any other object of iron between one's teeth when the bells are first heard on the Saturday of Passion though he himself considers this to be a superstition.

Celsus calls iron the metal of Hermes "because it is busy, loving labour and bearing all fatigues like him", but Hermetic tradition gives the series Mars-haematite-red-iron and the alchemists' symbol for iron seems to have been that of the god Ares (Salmasius). Astrological writings of the third and fourth century A.D. say that Mars is the planet of red-headed men, people busying themselves with iron and fire or giving wounds by iron and fire or receiving them, and this finds its sequel in the medieval tradition that Saint Barbara is the patron of "all those who work with fire or iron". From the fourth century onwards iron is no longer the metal of Hermes but that of Mars (Pibêchios).

Iron plays a part on the colouring experiments of Democritos, who is said to have written "a book on iron", and it belongs to the Tetrasomy of base metals which the early alchemists sought to transform into gold. It can only be worked "by the assistence of the gods" (Zosimos) and it forms part of the "bones of copper" or "Persian bones" (iron, copper, lead and tin burnt) which figure largely in the alchemical writings of Zosimos and Agathodaimon.

In the technological treatises of the eighth century and later we find many semi-magical recipes of the hardening of iron by tempering and quenching it in oil or certain "waters" and of "colouring iron to Indian steel".

These few examples will go to show the important part which iron played in early magic and chemistry.

We must postpone the story of its discovery until we have discussed its production but first we must review the ores of iron and the most important deposits.

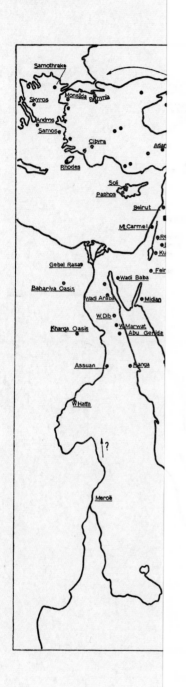

Samothrake

Skyros

Monsida Bithynia

Andros

Samos

Cibyra

Adan

Rhodes

Soli

Paphos

Beirut

Mt.Carmel

Re

Ku

Gebel Rasas

Fein

Bahariya Oasis

Wadi Baba

Wadi Araba

Midian

W.Dib

Kharga Oasis

W.Marwat
Abu Genida

Assuan

Ranga

W.Hafta

↑?

Meroë

Fig. 30.

Some of the most important iron deposits of the Ancient M[...]

2. *The iron ores*

The *ores of iron* are probably the most widespread ores on earth. No less than 4.2% of our earth is formed by iron or its compounds! Though not the most important source of modern iron production the small quantities of meteoric and terrestial iron are prominent in the history of iron.

Meteoric (celestial) *iron* is fairly widespread. It is interesting to note that the density of the recorded meteorites can be correlated with the density of the population of the regions mentioned and therefore many arid and unpeopled regions may hold far more meteorites than we know. Again in the Ancient Near East the natural stock of meteorites will have largely disappeared in the course of history. The celestial origin of meteoric iron was noted early though it was often disregarded. The possibility of collecting or detaching pieces from larger lumps is abundantly proved by the records about Eskimos and other primitive tribes. This meteoric iron contains 5—26% of nickel (with a rough average of 7.5%) and 0.3—5.0% of cobalt.

Iron occuring as a metal of non-celestial origin is called *telluric iron*. It occurs in basalt and other rocks as grains and nodules, generally too small for practical use and mostly hidden in the rock. It often contains upto 65—75% of nickel and generally it is unworkable. In far north-western Greenland there is one of the few large deposits of telluric iron. This native metal, with a lower nickel content was also used by the Eskimo of that district and fashioned into knives and points. But we can state that in general telluric iron must be ruled out as a possible source of the ancient metallurgist.

There are some natural nickel-iron compounds of rare occurence in New Zealand, the Ural mountains and the Piedmontese Alps, in Oregon, British Columbia and California, but in general iron ores and the iron produced from them will not contain nickel or only to the possible maximum of 2.5%. Nickel has not to our knowledge been recorded in specimens from the Near East save in case of meteorites and objects fashioned from them.

Apart from the nickel content there are other sure proofs of the meteoric origin of certain ancient iron objects.

Not all iron compounds are *iron ores*, for we know that the criterion is economical production of iron from the compound. Generally speaking we now consider iron compounds with at least 20—30% of iron to be iron ores. The most important of these ores are:

	Theoretical iron content (in %)	Practical iron content (in %)
Magnetite (Magneteisenstein)	72.4	60—68
Haematite (Roteisenerz)	70.0	40—66
Limonite (Brown iron ore, Brauneisenerz)	59.9	25—58
Oolithic iron ore (Minette)		24—46
Bog ore (Limonite, Raseneisenerz)		35—55
Spathic iron (Siderite, Spateisenstein)	48.3	30—44
Sphaerosiderite (Sphärosiderit)		25—40
Blackband (Kohleneisenstein)		36—40

All these ores are oxides of iron except the types of siderite which are carbonates and therefore contain carbon dioxide and water which should be removed by pre-roasting before the proper reduction can take place.

All these ores occur in many forms; compact, crystalline or amorphous and earthy forms, too many to be described in this short space. It is certain that they were worked in Antiquity too, though the limit of economical production may have been higher than at present and the ores will have been specially selected pure ores or perhaps handpicked. We have already mentioned the considerable knowledge which the Sumerians had of the different iron compounds and ores and Theophrastus gives quite a good description of the most important iron ores (Lapid.): "A dense stone is the haematites which is dry and ressembles its name "bloodstone", it looks like condensed blood. Excellent minerals some of which have an earthy nature, like ochra and miltos are very common in many mines. The workability of some large ores is very different, some can be sawn, others can be chiselled and even turned, like the magnes which has a peculiar appearence and which looks like silver as some say, though there is no affinity. Miltos and ochra occur in silver-, gold- and copper-mines, mostly forming veins or even heavier strata as in the case of ochra. They are often mined, for instance in Cappadocia and in large quantities. The best kind is that of Ceos. One type comes from mines, as miltos occurs in iron mines too, there is also the Lemnian kind and the so-called Sinopian, which is none but the Cappadocian kind which is brought to Sinope! It occurs in three qualities, red, white (chalk?) and one in between. A further quality is made by burning ochra. This is an invention of Kydios who is said to have observed during the fire of an inn, that ochra was coloured red when half-burnt".

Pliny has many scattered remarks on iron ores "which occur in greater quantity than those of any other metal. Where the ocean washes the coast of maritime Cantabria there rises a lofty mountain which is entirely composed of iron ore" (7). The following passage refers to bog ore: "In Cappadocia only the question is raised, whether iron is to be placed to the credit of the water or the earth, for the earth yields iron to the smelter only where the water of a certain river has flooded it" (8). And on the magnetite he says "The common folk call the lodestone "quick iron" and wounds made with magnetic iron are worse than ordinary wounds, this mineral occurs in Cantabria also, not as a massive rock but in scattered pebbles called bullae, but its influence on iron is the same" (9), but his further description of magnetite is rather confused: "Passing to other stones with striking properties, who would hesitate to deal first with the magnet? For iron, the tamer of all substances is drawn by the magnet. So the magnet is given another name, sideritis, while some call it Heraclion. Nicander is our authority that it was called magnes from the man who first discovered it on Mount Ida and he is said to have found it when the nails of his shoes and the ferrule of his staff adhered to it, as he was pasturing his herds.

Sotacus classifies magnets into five varieties, the first found in Aethiopia, the second from the Magnesia which has a common boundary with Macedonia, the third found at Hyettus in Boeotia, the fourth in the neighbourhood of Alexandria in the Troad and the fifth from Magnesia which is in Asia. The first point of distinction is whether the stone is male or female, the second depends on its colour. Magnets found in Magnesia near Macedonia are a reddish-black colour, while the Boeotian magnets are more red than black. The magnets found in the Troad are black and of the female sex and therefore without magnetic power, but the worst of all come from Magnesia in Asia. These are white and have no attraction whatever for iron. It is an ascertained fact that the more blue they are the better magnets are likely to be. Those from Aethiopia bear off the palm and sell for their weight in silver. They are found in Zmiris, for so they call the sandcovered district of Aethiopia. In the same district is found the haematite magnet which is the colour of blood and which gives, when powdered, a material of a saffron hue. Haematites has not the same power of attracting iron as the magnet, though the Aethiopean variety attracts other magnets" (10). It would seem from this passage, that Pliny's *magnes lithos* does not imply magnetism and his account is rather muddled when he contrasts *haematites* and *magnes* and even speaks of *haematites magnes*! Other classical writers also mention the *magnes lithos* but refer to the magnetic properties only and not to this ore as a source of iron production, for though it was probably little worked in Egypt and Macedonia, it was certainly treated in Noricum. Just as *magnetites* or *magnes lithos* does not always cover our magnetite, the *haematites* of the ancients had a wider meaning though it refers to our haematite in the case of Elba and Cantabria. But in the case of *haematites* too, its working for iron is not mentioned. The *schistos* mentioned by Pliny (11) is probably a form of limonite, and the *schistos* of Theophrast is clay ironstone. The *hepatites* of the ancients is certainly limonite, which "when burnt yields miltites". Pliny's *schistos* is probably a fibry variety of limonite. The *aetites* or "eagle stone" (12) is probably a type of concretionsof clay iron stone. The ochre varieties (also called *sil*) hail from Laurion, Cappadocia, Cyprus, Lydia, and the neighbourhood of Rome. The ore of Noricum is the spathic iron ore (Bohnerz) still worked in Styria and Carinthia. It is doubtful whether the ancients ever worked iron pyrites which they can not have failed to observe as they are very similar to the copper pyrites both in colour and form, possibly the word *chalcitis* is sometimes used to denote iron pyrites instead of copper pyrites, but the descriptions of the chalcitis are not very clear (13). Pliny also knew the celestial origin of meteoric iron (14) and he mentions that the quality and composition of the ore is important in smelting (15). He also mentions that iron ores "are recognised without difficulty by the striking colour of the soil" (16) a remark repeated centuries later by Agricola who says that "iron rust is an indication of good iron ores" (Book II). It seems that oxydic ores of an earthy or of a loose structure were preferred by the ancients and their disciples for even Biringuccio says that good iron ore is brown and that the black ores or those of the colour of pyrites should be avoided. The earthy iron ores of the ochre class were used as pigments from times immemorial, limonite, goethite and haematite are all found in a soft form, rich in iron, and well adapted to rudimentary smelting operations. Magnetite though a compact crystalline ore and rather difficult to work, may have been among the earliest iron ores to be worked when gathered as a byproduct of gold-washing and treated in a crucible process. Still, with early metallurgical methods only the more reducible ores were utilizable and the first-comers must have gathered unique harvests of native meteoric metal and ores accumulated during previous ages near the earth's surface and in streambeds, "the sluice-boxes of nature".

It seems certain that the washing and roasting of certain iron ores was an old standard practice in the Near East. In some cases as that of the working of spathic iron and other carbonates it was imperative to drive off the carbon dioxide by roasting, but many other ores profited from pre-roasting by losing water and slight amounts of sulphur from admixtures or by obtaining a more loose structure. Roasting was for instance standard practice in the iron mines of Elba (17). The washing and crushing of iron ores did not differ from that of other ores.

Some iron ores were used in ancient medicine (18).

3. *The deposits of iron ore*

It would be impossible to enumerate all the *deposits of iron ores* in the Ancient Near East, we shall confine ourselves to a rapid survey of the most important ones, which have been marked on our map (Fig. 30).

In *Egypt* there are haematite, pyrolusite and psilomelane in Wadi Baba and other valleys of the Sinai peninsula, but it is doubtful whether these deposits were ever worked. As they contain iron ores holding titanium and manganese they would have yielded an excellent iron.

In the eastern desert Wadi Araba contains ferrugineous limestone and red ochre is found to the north. In Wadi Dib there is haematite, in Wadi Marwat limonite and on the road to Qosier near Abu Gerida there is haematite just as near Ranga (near Ras Benas) where the haematite is titaniferous. Near Wadi Halfa there are banks of oolithic ironstone and between Assuan and Shellal there is magnetite. The alluvial Nilesand contains much magnetite, often worth washing, and the oases of the western desert have strata and concretions of ochres and limonite. There is a good quality of brown ochre in Dâkhle Oasis and red ochre near Aswan. The Egyptian red ochre is mentioned by Vitruv (19). In Gebel Rassa, north of the Fayyum there is psilomelane and west of Cairo there is yellow ochre. Though Burton reported exhausted iron-mines in Wadi Hammamat, no inscriptions were found and no iron mine of Egypt can be ascribed with certainty to Antiquity. It is doubtful whether the iron mines of Meroë mentioned by Strabo (20) were exploited as early as some writers contend.

Palestine and Syria have a few deposits of rich iron ores, though poor ores are very common, for it was a country "whose stones were iron" (21). The deposits of the southern Lebanon are poor and can hardly have been worked by the Phoenicians and Hebrews as some claim.

Still there are a few deposits of limonite and weathered haematite near Nahr el Kelb and Beyrout which may have been worked in Antiquity, and there are a few deposits worth exploiting near the sources of the river Jordan. There are traces of old mines near Merdjiba (Nahr el Kelb) but their date is uncertain. Other old mines are situated near Ikzim on Mount Carmel.

East of the Jordan there are deposits near Ain Tab, Resheya (north of the Hermon mountains), Birma and Mogharet el Warda south of Adjlun, where red and yellow ochre and marcasite abound. These are probably the deposits mentioned in the Letter of Aristeas as situated "in the neighbouring mountains of Arabia". They were probably exploited in Roman times like some ores near Jericho. There are several other deposits in the mountains bordering Moab and in north Edom. Josephus mentions an "iron mountain and mines" in Transjordania (22). Other deposits occur near El Kura and in the neighbourhood of Pheinan. Midian is very rich in deposits of heamatite and magnetite, and in Yemen there are deposits in the neighbourhood of Usala and Sana.

In Syria there are richer deposits near Alexandria and mines were exploited near Germanicia north of the famous town of Doliche, "where the iron was born".

In *Cyprus* there are deposits near Soli, Paphos, and Tamassos, mainly haematite and limonite, and there are many traces of ancient mines.

The deposits of *Crete* are poor and few; they were probably never worked or produced for local consumption and all the Greek legends about iron working daemons or heroes in Crete are probably untrue. The foundation of these myths is probably the confusion of the Cretan and the Phrygian Mount Ida and it seems that these myths were originally told about the Phrygian mountains and other sites in Asia Minor where there was indeed a very old iron industry.

There are many deposits on the islands in the *Aegean*, for instance on Syros, Cythnos, Ceos, Seriphos, Siphnos, Gyaros where there is chromite, an excellent iron ore, though it is not known whether it was used in Antiquity. Other deposits are found on Andros and Skyros. Iron ore is found on Samothrakè, Samos, Rhodes and Cos.

On the mainland of *Asia Minor* there was the magnetite of Mons Ida near Andeira (23), which is probably Strabo's "stone which when burnt becomes iron". Apollonius of Rhodes mentions "the iron-bearing land of the Mariandynians" in Bythinia (24). To the south there is magnetite near Magnesia (25) and further south there are several deposits in Caria near Latmus and the famous Cibyra "where the easy embossing of iron is a peculiar thing" (26), which are probably the haematite deposits near the present Corancež. The legends of the Telchines (27) and the Dactyloi (28) mentioned by Strabo and many other classical authors probably belong to these ancient mining centres in Phrygia and Lycia. In the centre, in Phrygia Maior, there are several deposits of high-grade haematite.

The Taurus range is very rich in iron. Near Alaya and Silinti (Adana) there is much haematite and iron pyrites. The iron mines of Amaxia in Upper Cilicia were given to Cleopatra by Antonius and the last Armenian king Archelaus had scores of "mettaleuti" (miners) working in iron and other mines of Galatia. Near Jünik Tepessi in the Taurus range there are mighty strata of iron ores which contain upto 53% of iron.

Very important deposits are centred in the north, in Pontus and the neighbouring districts. Near Amasia, Tokat and Sivas there is magnetite and iron pyrites. Hamilton saw many traces of ancient mines west of Trapezus. The Cappadocian iron and the iron-working Chalybes were famous in Antiquity (29). There are many deposits in Pontus up to Kighi near Erzerum. There are bog-ore deposits in the valleys of the Thermodon and Iris. Other deposits are scattered on the lower slopes and foothills of the ranges between the modern Yešil Yarmak upto Batum.

In *Caucasia, Transcaucasia and Armenia* the iron deposits are particularly rich. In Kuban on the banks of the Kotscharka river there are 30 M. thick magnetite strata (62—68% of iron) which were worked from the Persian period onwards. There is haematite near Damyrtash on the river Bolnis and near Tamblut and Tshatash, near Sizimadani and along the Dyblaki pass near Miskan. Very pure haematite is found in the valley of the Bojan and near Elisavetpol. Magnetite and ilmenite occur in the eastern Karabagh district. Iron pyrites and other iron ores are found near Talori and Karadagh. Other iron ore outcrops are found near Lake Urmia and north of Tabriz, smaller outcrops occur in the Tiyari mountains and near Chorsabad.

In *Persia* there were mines and smelting sites near Tabriz, which Robertson saw and which he ascribes to very early periods. The Elburz mountains have old mines near Resht and Massula, where the inhabitants are still mainly blacksmiths. West of Teheran and near Kazwin there is much haematite, to the east near Firuzkuh and on the foothills of Mount Demawend there is haematite and limonite.

The mountains near Damghan, Semnan, and Sharud have rich strata of haematite, and deposits of limonite and yellow ochre. Near Kashan and Kohrud there is magnetite and haematite, and in the Kuh-i Benan region and in Carmania there is yellow and brown ochre and limonite. Remains of early iron workings have been found in the plain of Persepolis and between Kerman and Shiraz and the islands of the Persian Gulf have red ochre and other iron ores. Carmania was long time famous for its iron and steel, though the mines were not worked after the Arabian period. In Chorassan there are several deposits near Semendeh and Ilak and in Afghanistan near Juwain, Herat and Bamian. The old mines of Alexandria and Caucasum in Kohistan are now abandoned.

Several other ancient mines will be mentioned in the course of our story and it would be impossible to include in this survey all the deposits of Europe which were known to the ancients. The principal iron deposits exploited by the Romans were those of Noricum (Tyrol, Styria and Carinthia), Bosnia (30) (Sana valley) and the deposits of Gallia had great importance in the Celtic wars of Caesar, though their importance dwindled in later periods (31). Britain had several deposits which were worked in Roman times and perhaps earlier (32), but the importance of the iron mines of Spain is rather exaggerated by the ancients.

The most important sources of Italy were the mines of Etruria and above all those of Elba (34).

All these mines belong to the classical period except the Celtic (Illyrian) mines of Noricum and Gallia and the local industry of Central Europe which though exploited in prehistoric periods had little influence of the development of iron metallurgy in the Ancient Near East. Their slight connection with this evolution will be discussed in the following lines, it is very probable that the impulse to exploit them came from the East.

4. *Methods, tools and furnaces of the iron-smith*

However, before tracing the story of the discovery of iron and the rise of the manufacture of iron, it is imperative to discuss some of the processes used in its production and to define some of the terms denoting these processes and the apparatus used as they will recur in our arguments, because the production processes are intimately linked up with the story of iron.

A   B

C

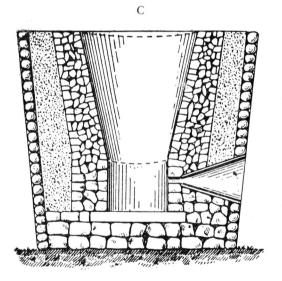

Fig. 31.
The Catalan (A), the Corsican (B), and the Osmund (C) furnace
(After Newton Friend)

We shall have opportunity to prove that the ancients always produced iron in the form of a *bloom* and that they could not make cast iron. A *bloom* is a rough ingot of iron or steel as produced directly from iron ores in a bloomery. This word bloma (Bloom) occurs in English texts before 1000 A.D.

In this most primitive form of direct extraction of iron from its ores a mixture of the ore was treated either in a "hole-in-the-ground" furnace or a hearth-fire with charcoal. The impurities formed a scoria or slag which was fluid and ran out of the fire or collected outside the furnace and the remainder of the ore was reduced to a tough, pasty, spongy mass of iron. This mass was withdrawn in the form of porous blocks after cooling, and these blooms were put into another furnace and strongly heated. The iron was then taken out and hammered into a compact mass so as to drive out any scoriaceous matter.

The earliest bloomery furnaces had a natural draught and they seem to have been generally erected on high grounds in order that the wind might assist combustion. This was not only the common method of building furnaces in prehistoric Europe, etc. but many Negro tribes still build them thus. But as soon as bellows became known, blast air was used to supplement or to replace natural draught. Thus the Roman smelting furnaces of Populonia and those reconstructed from the remains at Wilderspool (Warrington) which both belong to the best examined remains, consisted essentially of a cavity with a wall and covering of clay with holes at the base for admitting a draught and for withdrawing the metal. They were usually built on sloping ground and the remains show that both coal and charcoal were used for smelting. There is no proof that bellows were used, nor is there any proof that cast iron was produced in one furnace and converted into malleable iron or steel in another. The entire plant of a bloomery consisted of a kiln for roasting the ores, a smelting furnace, as described above, and a smith's forge. Minute samples of metal collected on the furnace bottom in a fluid state, but the smelting furnace yielded blooms of spongy iron. The fusion of the iron in the furnace must occasionally have occured when the temperature was higher than usual, especially in those cases where bellows were used, as can be proved in the case of other ancient bloomery furnaces.

The definite adaption of blast air in the manufacture of iron led to the invention of more suitable furnaces. One of the oldest of this type is the *Catalan process* of extracting iron which was formerly practised in Catalonia and also around Ariège (France). The furnace was still used in the seventeenth century in Spain in the provinces of Navarra and Guizpuzcoa. It consisted of a shallow, oval cavity or hearth forming a kind of inverted truncated cone. A *tuyère* or pipe, through which the blast air is forced into the furnace, projected downwards and inwards over the middle of the long sides of the oval. The blast is supplied by two bellows working alternately. Later a continuous blast was obtained by a *trompe* (a mechanical device to supply blast air by means of falling water) where a fall of water was available. A Catalan forge consisted of a furnace, a blowing-machine and a heavy hammer.

Fig. 32.
Stückofen (After Newton Friend)

The so-called *Corsican furnace* is hardly more than a smith's forge.

The *Osmund furnace* was a primitive bloomery smelting furnace formerly much in use in Sweden, Finland, and Norway, called *osmund* after the bloom (*afsumd*). The furnace was an oblong, rectangular cavity to receive the lump of reduced iron; there was a large opening at the side through which the lump of iron or bloom was extracted and which during the working of the furnace was temporarily built up with stones. The inner lining of the furnace was a refractory rock and the space between this and the timber casing on the outside was filled up with earth. The calcined ore was smelted with charcoal and the resulting bloom was forged as required. The blast was obtained by two bellows worked by a treadle.

Biringuccio stated that this was the pre-Roman smelting furnace of the time of Hesiod, and indeed remains of fairly similar furnaces were found by Quiquirez in the Jura, though their date is by no means as sure as this author claims. This type of furnace was usually built anew after each smelting and fired with wood. Many older furnaces must therefore have disappeared as links in the chain of evidence.

The so-called *Stückofen* was a bloomery furnace consisting of two Osmund furnaces, one inverted above the other. They were at a time worked in Carniola, Carinthia, Styria, Hungary, etc. The larger furnaces were 10′ to 16′ in height and the blast was operated by bellows worked by a water-wheel. The product was a lump of unfused malleable iron upto about 6 cwts. This was cut into pieces or "Stücke", which were then hammered in the usual manner. This bloomery furnace must be considered to be the forerunner of the modern blastfurnace. The conditions in the Stückofen were far more favourable to the formation of that highly carburised ("containing carbon"), relatively fusible product known as cast iron, that when obtained had to be decarburised before it could be worked under the hammer. Indeed, the carburised metal was virtually a new metal, which could readily be cast into any desired shape and size.

Up to that moment the production of iron had been a *direct process* which yielded the malleable wrought iron, now the trend became to produce a crude cast iron and to work this up to steel, wrought iron or whatever form of iron was required, thus iron came to be produced by the *indirect process* that is to say no longer in one operation directly from the ore.

The size of the furnace for making iron was gradually increased to save fuel and reduce the cost of manufacture; at the same time it was noticed that the accidental production of cast iron became increasingly frequent because the iron remained a longer time in contact with the fuel or charcoal and it thus became more highly carburised. For a time the Stückofen was used for the production of both malleable iron blooms and molten cast iron. The furnaces gradually replacing it were called Bauerofen, Blaseofen, Blauofen, etc. but the furnace at first remained exactly as it was in the Stückofen and the name referred to the product only not to the construction. Eventually cast iron was the only direct product; and, as is the case at the present time, it was obtained in the *blast furnace* (Hochofen, haut fourneau) which originated in the Rhine province in the beginning of the fourteenth century or perhaps somewhat earlier.

Just as the crude metal was extracted from the ore by fire, so it was found that by another application of the purifying agent the crude metal could be converted into malleable iron. In the modern method of extracting iron from its ores, cast iron is therefore first produced and this crude product is subsequently employed for the manufacture of iron and steel. What was formerly an accidental and abnormal defect in the bloomery furnace is now the regular and normal product of the blast furnace. As the ore came to remain longer in the furnace it could reach a higher temperature and it was also in contact with more

Fig. 33.
Models of a primitive blast furnace (Science Museum)

fuel. There are several zônes in the blast-furnace, in which specific processes take place. First of all the ore is preheated by the rising gases from the burning fuel, then the oxide is reduced by the charcoal or coke, in a lower and hotter zône carbon particles can penetrate the iron formed and carburize it to form cast iron, which melts in a still lower zône and can be drawn off together with the molten slag.

The process in the bloomery furnace was much simpler. The earlier furnaces could contain but a few Kgrs. in contrast to even the earlier blast-furnaces of the Middle Ages which "Stücköfen" working intermediately produced about 100 to 150 Kgrs per charge. In general only rich ore, poor in sulphur, with a siliceous gangue could be worked when only charcoal and no flux was used. The yield would not be more than 30—50% of the iron present in the ore, the rest would be lost in the slag. In the furnace the slag had a decarburizing influence on the drops of molten iron formed from the ore and thereby their melting point was raised and the drops solidified. As the furnaces developed the blast was intensified and higher temperatures were necessary to reduce the growing masses of ores. This led the development of the furnaces towards higher types such as the Stückofen and the later blast furnace. Longer lasting reduction at higher temperatures gave a total reduction of the ore and iron which had time to absorb carbon at high temperatures and to become cast iron. When smelting this again with charcoal wrought iron could be produced at pleasure. Once the blast furnace was evolved its advantages were so obvious that this type spread very quickly. The earliest blast furnace in the Rhine-country dates back to about 1311 but it reached Sweden as early as 1360 (35)!

But elementary as the early furnaces were, they would produce

Fig. 34.
Biringuccio's blast furnace

blooms of quite sufficient size to be handled by the primitive smiths. Furnaces of the types found near Tarxdorf were capable of producing a semi-fused bloom of about 50 lbs in eight to ten hours with some 200 lbs of charcoal and another 25 lbs of charcoal were necessary for the subsequent heating and forging. However simple this operation may appear, it presupposes quite a lot of skill developed by long experience. Both excess carburization and incomplete reduction imperil the process. Neither is handling the bloom a simple task with primitive tongs, anvil and hammer.

All in all starting with a charge of about 300 lbs of ore the metallurgist would obtain something like 25 lbs of fairly good iron. Furnace reactions were not understood neither was the chemistry underlying these processes and this was the reason why primitive forms of furnaces survived until well into the eighteenth century. The necessity of oxygen and the effect of the presence of carbon which determine the furnace reactions were unknown. Medieval furnaces were merely better because they were larger and the bellows were more effecient, but now they are better controlled. From the remains of the Roman furnaces of Noricum it is clear that they did not produce more than 100 lbs per unit. The quality of their iron improved when they smelted the manganiferous spathic iron of Noricum with bellows, and they could now produce steel at will. If "hard iron" or steel was desired more and thicker charcoal was added and the process continued longer with reduction of the draught until the carburisation had proceeded to the desired amount. Reversing the process would give the "soft iron" or malleable, wrought iron as produced of old. With iron as in

Fig. 35.
Simple Swedish blast furnace (After Svedenborg, de Ferro, 1734)

other activities mere quantitative superiority seems to have been the goal of the Romans and few new inventions in the field of iron metallurgy can be put to their credit. Greater masses were simply produced in small bits and welded together. Still the Romans had different smelting furnaces, each being suited to special phases of iron metallurgy, such as carburising, welding, etc. They very skilfully adapted types that had been developed by the Celtic smiths or those of the Ancient Near East.

The main product was the bloom or "spongae" as the Latin texts have it, but they had already noticed the occurence of the "massa" or *flatum ferri* on the bottom of the furnace and retreating this regulus would yield a fairly pure piece of wrought iron, which could be broken up and sold to the smith.

When by the tenth to thirteenth century water-driven bellows allowed the development of the blast furnace the cast iron "pig" became more common and soon a standard product. Thus we read in Borbonius' *Ferraria* (XVIth cy.) that the miners dig a reddish-yellow ore and crush and wash it. It was then reduced by the *fusor* in a square blast-furnace, the slag drawn off with an iron hook and the remaining iron molten and tapped into the fore-hearth. The "pig" is then smelted in a second furnace by the *fabri* to a bloom which is forged by water-driven hammers.

The production of cast-iron was still a very difficult one, and the production of wrought iron from the pig-iron was still more intricate.

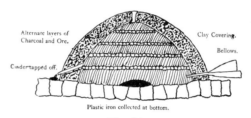

Fig. 36.
Diagram of a bloomery hearth (Straker, Wealden Iron)

Often the iron remained too brittle, for Paracelsus says: "The illness breaks the body as snow-water breaks iron!"

It seems from the texts that the Romans some skill in producing iron and steel by the direct process. For Pliny mentions the effect of the quality of the ore and the metallurgical process on the quality of the iron produced: "There are many different kinds of iron, the chief factors being the nature of the deposits and the climate. Some deposits furnish only an iron which is nearly as soft as lead, others a brittle and coppery kind, quite unsuitable for making wheels and nails, for which the first kind is excellent. The permanency of one variety brings it in favour for shoes and nails for military boots, another has a greater liability to rust. All kinds are called stricturae, a term not used in case of other metals and derived from "stringere aciem". (*Strictura* would mean a lump of metal from which instruments with sharp edges can be made). There are considerable differences in furnace practice too. What we may call the "nucleus of iron" is smelted here into the hardness of steel, there into the compactness of anvils and hammer-heads. The greatest difference, however, is due to the nature of the water into which the glowing steel is plunged from time to time. Widely-divided localities, such as Bilbilis and Turassio in Spain and Comum in Italy, renowned for their iron, owe their glory to the excellence of the local waters, although they themselves possess no iron mines.

Among the varieties of iron, that of the Seres carries off the palm and it is exported by them together with garments and pelts, while the second best comes from Parthia. No other kind is made of sheer steel, for the rest contain an admixture of iron of a softer character. Within our empire, excellence such as this is occasioned in one place by a first-class ore, as in the Noric country, in others by processes of manufacture, as at Sulmo, and in the localities mentioned above by the water.

Strange to say, when ore is smelted, the iron flows like water and breaks up on solidification into spongy masses." (36)

Whatever difficulties this rather garbled text written by a layman presents, it is certain that he recognised that the facility with which, a metallurgical process is carried out depends almost entirely on the character of the ore employed.

Many authors forget that the production of iron was rather difficult for primitive smelters who did not possess good tongs to handle the heavy bloom at red-heat, while the reduction process required much trained intelligence. One of the main difficulties is the gangue of iron ore. This gangue is mainly siliceous and the silica of this component of the ore undergoes separation in the furnace with the ferrous oxide of the ore to form a fusible silicate or slag. The mass of iron becomes pasty and the slag drips onby, leaving a spongy bloom, which after removal is hammered to cause the unreduced slag or ore to fall apart and the bloom thereby becoming compact mass of iron. This is a tedious process which requires frequent heating of the bloom and much of the ore is wasted in the slag. At present fluxes like lime are added to bind the silica to a far more fusible slag, which separates readily and thus a far greater percentage of the iron from the ore is saved.

Now the primitive smelter did not use *fluxes* in smelting the easier type of ore. Still in Populonia the very siliceous Elban ore was mixed with lime as was also the more clayey Monte Valerio ore. In Erzberg the slags show signs of greater liquidity in several cases and as a rule the more iron-rich slags of a particular smelting site can be said to be the oldest. Perhaps older slags were reworked in Roman times, but this should be confirmed by further analyses. Theophrast mentions the "fire-fighting stone" which was used in Pontus as a flux. Persson quite correctly identifies this *pyromachos lithos*, which Liddell Scott translates by "resisting fire, fire-proof stone", with limestone. The furnace used in those regions probably was a rectangular stone furnace with low walls covered with slabs of limestone. In close contact with fire this limestone liberates carbon dioxide and the stone appears "to be fighting fire" but the disintegrated limestone acts as a flux which is useful as the limonite type of ore is generally phosphoric. If the temperature is kept low enough the phosphorus combines with the lime and is slagged away. Aristotle (37) days of the same stone that "it melts and solidifies again", which could be taken as an unscientific interpretation of the disintegration of the limestone. Another flux which was added in Antiquity to form *a scoria* or slag was the *melias lithos* which is probably lava. But lime seems to have been the most

Fig. 37.
Working drawing of a hammer forge (Straker, Wealden Iron)

generally applied flux of Antiquity. However, few analyses of ancient slags are available though Straker has shown what important results can be obtained from the direct process, which does not subject the ore to a very high temperature (600—700°C is sufficient to reduce the iron ore!) and does not bring it in contact with charcoal for a very long period, produced a very pure iron, which is malleable and which we call *wrought iron*. But if kept at higher temperatures and when in contact with charcoal for a longer time the iron is formed by reduction of the ore but it subsequently absorbs carbon upto over 86 lbs/Ton (2.5—4.0%) and the melting point is lowered from that of wrought iron (1530°C) to a minimum of 1170°C as the amount of carbon augments. This carburised iron liquifies more readily and flows out of the furnace as *cast iron*. The carbon which is absorbed by the iron, combines with part of it to form iron-carbide or cementite, a hard but brittle compound, crystals of which form part of the structure of the solidified iron. This cementite imbues the brittleness to the iron, wrought iron which is free from carbon and therefore from cementite is tough and malleable. The cementite, however, is unstable and if the iron is very slowly cooled, a texture of iron with graphite (carbon) particles is formed; if cooled more quickly or even rapidly (quenched) the cementite structure remains with all its inherent properties.

Steel is an iron with much less carbon than cast iron. It is now made by decarburizing cast iron, but formerly when wrought iron was made by the direct process, this method was impossible and steel had to be

Fig. 38.
Smithy with bellows, hammer, and quenching pit (Agricola)

made by carburizing wrought iron, that is by imparting carbon to it. This *carburizing* was probably not achieved intentionally but simply by the repeated heating of the iron bar in charcoal between the hammerings, for as Pliny says (39) "iron which has been heated deteriorates, unless it is hardened by hammering; iron can not be forged when red-hot, nor indeed until it reaches incipient white-heat" at which temperature it more readily absorbs the necessary carbon (0.3—2.0%) to form steel. In steel again the cementite stable at high temperatures forms the component that imbues it with the hardness proper to steel. If slowly cooled this steel would either loose its cementite straight away or fairly quickly after cooling and the iron-graphite structure stable at normal temperatures would be formed. But by *quenching* or rapid cooling for instance by dipping the white-hot steel into water or oil the cementite structure is rapidly carried through the danger-zone of disintegration and more or less stabilized at low temperatures. However, for certain purposes the steel would be too hard and too brittle and it is necessary to find a means to give the steel a certain amount of toughness and take away some of its brittleness. This can be achieved in two ways. By *tempering* (Anlassen) the steel was first hardened to the limit and than "let down" by heating it again until a certain colour is shown on the polished bright steel when it is quickly quenched again. Thereby we impart the steel the exact structure that belongs to the temperature to which it has been heated for the second time. A second method was that of *annealing*, that is reheating the brittle steel and cooling it, regulating both operations very carefully. Hereby the structure is rearranged and any degree of mildness can be imparted and brittleness taken away from the steel. At present this process is carried out in carefully controlled annealing furnaces, but in Antiquity it depended entirely on the skill of the smith, who hampered by the lack of proper means of temperature control, often missed the effect he desired.

Apart from this very simplified explanation of the structural differences of wrought iron, cast iron and steel, many further complications arise in practice because during the smelting of iron ores such impurities as silica, etc. from the gangue may react and form silicium, manganese, phosphorus, copper, arsenic, nickel, etc., which are absorbed with the carbon by the iron and impart the cast iron and steel with different properties. Much depends nowadays on the skill of the smelter who adds fluxes and other compounds to the reaction taking into account the composition of the gangue and thereby regulating the final composition and the amount of impurities of his end-product. The ancient metallurgist must often have been baffled by the result of the smelting operation and only long experience could guide him towards the correct smelting and the kind and amount of fluxes necessary to obtain a good product. Here again it would be very dangerous to judge from the analysis of a few pieces of ancient iron; statistical-chronological series of analyses are the only means that will show us how the ancient smelter overcame his difficulties and when he first mastered them. There is of course the difficulty that terrestial iron rusted away as it is not as resistant as the natural meteoric iron-nickel alloy. As Pliny says (40): "The foe of iron is the customary benevolence of nature which decrees that that which inflicts most loss on short-lived humanity shall be of all materials the most short-lived"; but on the other hand iron-rust is a most stable product and could be easily noticed if archaeologists had paid more attention to it formerly as they do now. Therefore, the abundance of any metal in a particular district now does not stand in a sure relation to its utilization in earlier times. Not is it often clear what ores have been smelted in the earliest periods. The earthy ochres have been used as paints from times immemorial and haematite was early used as a seal-stone. Both limonite and haematite are easily reduced in bloomeries, magnetite is more difficult to attack

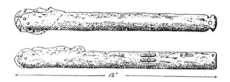

Fig. 39.
Eskimo knives found by Capt. J. Ross at Cape York, West Greenland
(After Rickard, Man and Metals)

because of its compactness, but we have evidence that it was also among the earliest iron ores smelted. Probably in the earliest periods local pockets and lake- and bog-iron ores were worked until a definite iron industry arose with its own technical code and tradition, which gradually mastered the different techniques of smelting the various iron ores.

When iron production became an industry there was already considerable differentiation among the metallurgists, as we have seen; and we need not wonder that at several places the ore was not treated on the deposits but only mined and traded to the smelting centres, as excavations show. It may be that smelting was sometimes a home-industry as it still was in Sweden and Finland in the last century and perhaps in early Caucasia too. But often the crude iron was produced on the mining site, as with many other metals, and traded to special metallurgical centres. Thus iron was produced at Noricum and worked in Aquilea and the surrounding district, at least in the earlier period of Roman domination. But the combination of mining and smelting with the smith's forge was still very common in Antiquity, for instance in Asia Minor, as it is still with such primitive smiths as the Asura of Chota Nagpur. As Apollonius of Rhodes (41) expresses it :

"That folk (Chalybes) drive never the ploughing oxen afield: no

part have they in planting of fruit, that is honey-sweet to the heart;
Neither lead they the pasturing flocks over meadows a-glitter with
dew: But the ribs of the stubborn earth for treasure of iron they hew,
And by merchandise of the same they do live: never dawning broke
Bringing respite of toil unto them, but ever midst of mirk of smoke
And flame of the forge are they toiling and plying the weary stroke".

5. *The origin and rise of iron metallurgy*

Rickard and Zimmer have proved beyond doubt that the earliest
form of iron used by mankind was *meteoric iron* (42). Of course there
were many peoples who remained either ignorant of iron or used
meteoric iron without recognizing its metallic properties and working
it as a kind of stone. For even finding pieces of iron will not teach
its metallurgy! The Andaman islanders when they obtained iron from
wrecks (43) did not employ heat in making it into arrow-heads. They
simply broke off a piece of metal and ground it into shape exactly as
they were accustomed to do with a piece of shell.

As far back as 1889 Hensoldt stated that when Cortez completed
the conquest of Mexico the Spaniards were struck by the fact that the
Aztecs possessed certain implements such as knives, daggers, etc.
made of iron, but it seemed that only the most distinguished possessed
such. Iron was a great rarity prized higher than gold. No smelting site
was ever found and the Aztecs were unacquainted with the smelting
of iron ores, which they did not consider akin to the valuable metal
that they called *tepuztli* or "copper". Their iron was, in fact, of meteoric
origin, like that of the Mayas of Yucatan and the Incas of Peru, of which
many weapons are still preserved in the collections. Nor did later excavators like Joyce succeed in finding any terrestial iron in the New
World.

To primitive man who knew native copper the rough shaping and
polishing of meteoric iron must have been a great succes. He must
have gone on to search dilligently for this stone which enabled him
to fashion tools that were definitely better than the older stone tools,
for the nickel-iron alloy has the properties of steel. Now smaller meteorites rarely fall alone and more likely there are many others to be
found in the same locality (44). The siderites and meteorites have sizes
that range from a few ounces to 50 Tons, but they were undoubtedly
wrought into objects according to their size and shape. Less than 300
Tons of meteoric iron are know at present most of which occurs in

the New World. But we have already pointed out that the amount of meteoric iron observed correlates with the density of population and perhaps primitive man in the Old World used up an equal amount which would explain the preponderance on the American continent. Many types of meteorites can be flaked when slightly weathered and only detachable parts or small masses could of course be used. This is clearly shown by the finds of objects fashioned from meteoric iron such as rings, amulets, images, daggers, etc. It is hardly possible that the lump of iron which Achilles offered as a prize at the funeral games (Iliad XXXIII) was of meteoric origin. Pliny certainly knew the celestial origin of meteorites (45) and the ancients possessed in the natural nickel-iron alloy a type of steel that was not manufactured by mankind before 1890 (46). Nearly all the peoples of Antiquity use such words for iron as "heaven metal" or "something hard (stone) from heaven."

However, even the classical scientists had no idea of the origin of such meteorites which they always held to belong to the "sublunar" spheres, not to the eternal and divine world beyond the moon. The belief in their atmospheric origin and nature stuck until a very large number of stones were seen to fall near l'Aigle (France) on April 26th, 1803 by many people. The investigation carried out on behalf of the Académie des Sciences by Biot finally destroyed the fashion of disbelieving the theory of the astronomers.

The most striking point about meteorites is that they, broadly speaking, consist of one single crystal, even if the meteorite weighs tons! The Widmanstätten structure of lines on the polished surface of such a meteorite is very striking and characteristic. Only recently did Buddhue succeed in synthesizing an octahedrite of iron containing 27.7% of nickel and showing these characteristic Widmanstätten figures though poorly developed.

There is one well-known example of the occurence of *telluric iron* (47). At Ovifak, Disco Island, West Greenland there is a mass of native iron, reduced from sulphide of iron by the action of carbon originally derived from coal measures. This mass contains some 94— 95% of iron with 2.50—2.55% of nickel and a carbon content of 1.6— 3.3%, which is greatly in excess of what is usually found in meteoric iron. Constitutionally this "iron" is a high-carbon nickel-cobalt steel, but the microstructure is entirely different from an alloy of this composition made in the refinery and solidified from the liquid state.

The Eskimos have used it for making knives and other implements without the aid of any suggestion, as far as known, from any sophisti-

cated foreigner. But they also detached pieces from meteorites, treating
the iron as a malleable stone by hammering. On an island in Melville
Bay there are three famous meteorites, one called "the Tent" weighing
36.5 Tons, another "the Woman" of 3 Tons and finally "the Dog"
of 960 lbs only. Pieces were detached by laminating some slight prominence on the surface, pounding repeatedly until a small ridge of
metal was formed which they worried apart in the same manner which
the Indians used to separate fragments from the copper masses of
Lake Superior. In the Turner mounds there are also several pieces of
worked meteoric iron. The Eskimo metallurgy is very different from
that of the Norsemen who lived in Greenland. The latter reduced iron
ores with charcoal in pot-bowl furnaces and forged it. They also knew
the art of tempering in fact, they had brought with them the art as it
was practised in their times in N.W. Europe. There seems to have been
no close enough contact with the Eskimos for passing on this knowledge (48).

It seems pretty certain that as soon as the process of melting native
copper was known the same operation must have been tried with
meteoric iron, but as the furnaces could not yet attain such high temperatures except in crucible smelting, this experiment was doomed to fail.
Even the reduction of iron ore in simple furnaces of the "hole-in-the-
ground" type using blast air will only succeed when using good ores,
but for copper the conditions are far more favourable and therefore
metallurgy proceeded first along the line of the development of copper
metallurgy. The smith was not yet ready for the intricate treatment of
the bloom, in which but few would suspect something that could be
hammered into a piece of metal.

It is still a puzzle what the earliest iron ore was, that mankind tackled.
Probably this is rather a local problem and not open to some general
solution. Several authors have speculated on this problem (49) and
Richardson has presented the case for each type of ore very clearly.
Limonite is rather siliceous and contains a lot of water, its iron content
usually wavers between 30 and 40%, while the limit of efficient treatment is someting like 35% of iron. Spathic iron though an excellent
ore of generally more than 50% of iron has no striking, metallic appearance, it requires pre-roasting and there are but few deposits in
the Ancient Near East. Haematite is a wide-spread ore there, it contains
over 50% of iron, but it is often very manganiferous and its surface
is often weathered to limonite, thus changing its striking appearance.
The only ore that had both a very high iron content (upto 72%) and

a striking metallic appearance that would attract the primitive metal-lurgist would be magnetite, that is quite common in the beds of moun-tain streams and the mountains of Armenia and Egypt. It would appear that though magnetite was probably the earlier iron ore to be worked, it was not treated directly in a bloomery furnace with blast air, as the ore is very compact and requires fairly high temperatures for disinte-gration, but it is suggested by several authors (originally by Quiring) that this direct treatment of the ore began only when the metallurgy of iron was already rather developed in the Near East and that iron was originally produced as a *by-product of the refining of gold.* The Nile sand and especially the gold gravels of Nubia (50) contain grains of magnetite of high specific gravity and an iron content of over 65%. About half the residue of goldwashing is magnetite, the grains gathering with the gold dust and nuggets in the residue of the pan. Now the gold was smelted in Egypt in crucibles in a reducing atmosphere using chaff of clover and straw as the texts teach us. After the smelting a slag rich in iron would collect on the top of the mass in the crucible, a layer of pasty iron would form the middle course directly over the liquid gold. If this pasty iron were extracted, it would be immediately ready for forging. It is clear that the quantities of iron produced in this way were small only. This method of iron manufacture as a by-product of gold would not only account for the peculiar association of small pieces of iron with gold in early jewelry but it would also explain the pygmy character of the early iron objects, such as the small models(?) of tools, amulets, etc. found in the grave of Tut-anch-amun, etc. The Nubian gold production became a regular industry after the incorpo-ration of these lands in Egypt by the dynasties of the Middle Kingdom and the fact that this iron jewelry and the small iron objects begin to appear after 2000 B.C. add to the probability of the early reduction of magnetite as a by-product of gold refining.

Hulme, after a careful study of the crucible processes in use in Anti-quity, concludes that "iron was first discovered in the bath of molten gold. Its identification with meteoric iron quickly followed and its source was traced to the black sands of the rivers and streams. The magnetite was then collected and the preference shown for this ore is maintained throughout the history of the Eastern iron industry".

Of course this early manufacture of small quantities of man-made, nickel-free iron can hardly be called an industry and it would seem that the earliest ores to be worked on a larger scale were the *lake- and bog-iron ores* of Cappadocia, and the process seems to have been a kind of Osmund process. The account of this industry in Pseudo-Aristotle (51) runs as follows: "Iron is obtained in large quantities from the ironstone of Elba and from the mines of the Chalybes near Amisus on the southern shores of the Black Sea. The ore is difficult to smelt on account of the quantity of clay contained in it, and it is softened only by raising it to a great heat. Iron is of great strength and very hard, though it is said that in Cyprus there are mice which are able to gnaw it. The best and hardest of all kinds or iron known is that of the Chalybes, that is chalybs (steel) and it is obtained from iron by melting it repeatedly together with certain stones in a furnace, during which process much slag is formed and a great loss in weight occurs on account of which the process is very costly. The finished steel is hard with a glittering surface and resists rust, but it is not applicable to all purposes for which the less pure iron is used. The quality is judged by the sound given out in working it on the anvil". The earlier part of this text is not as clear in all versions and Hulme after careful study of the available evidence proposes to render it thus": The matrix of the Chalybian and Amisenian iron ore is peculiar to the locality, for it is made up from the silt brought down by the rivers. This they smelt in their furnaces after simple washings, and they superimpose on their furnace the fire-fighting stone which is plentiful in their country. This steel is superior to other forms of iron and closely resembles silver, if not smelted in one furnace (only). It alone is not subject to corrosion but the output is small", an interpretation which is technically more sound. The ore mentioned in this passage reminds us of Pliny's account of the Cappadocian ore (52), "where the earth yields iron to the smelter only where the waters of certain rivers have flooded it". This passage certainly refers to typical lake-iron ore deposits. For limonite and other carbonates of iron are broken down in the presence of carbonic acid and water (53) to hydrated sesquioxide of iron which is soluble in water and deposited by bacteria in the form of silt in the presence of vegetation and still water. Bog-iron requires prolonged roasting, whereas lake-iron needs only washing and drying, but on the other hand the ores are phosphoric and contain greatly varying quantities of manganese. Therefore the smelting requires careful adjustment of the temperature to slag the impurities and to prevent them from alloying with the iron. In Europe where the Germans treated similar ores green wood was used instead of charcoal. The deposits mentioned by these ancient authors seem to be those of the Pyramus river, and this smelting of lake-iron would account for the excuse in the Hattusil letter which mentions that "no iron is available at present", as we shall see, but they may just as well refer to the Iris in Pontus. Further research should be directed towards the distribution of lake-iron deposits, the methods of their deposition and their utilisation in ancient Asia Minor before these questions can be solved.

In Roman times the German tribes worked bog-iron ores but the wrought pure iron obtained at low temperatures was soft and the iron swords were of little use against the superior bronze weapons and stood far behind the iron and steel weapons of the Celts, who had obtained a steel-like iron from the special ore of Noricum and had learned to obtain steel from others. This lake-iron industry does not seem to be a separate phase following the magnetite-phase but merely one aspect of the general *working of iron ores in bloomeries*. The beginnings of the iron industry are still very dark from the technical point of view. All we can say is that the earliest bloomeries must have consisted of very simple clay-lined pot-bowl furnaces or simple bloomery fires (Rennfeuer) both worked with blast air and smelting ores of the limonite and ochre type or weathered haematite. We have seen that these simple furnaces developed into the peculiar shaft furnaces called "Stückofen" by way of the Catalan hearth, and how these Stückofen permitted the smelting of ores of the haematite and magnetite type. But the early iron industry will remain dark as long as the history of the smelting furnace is not known better in detail. It is certain that many types of furnaces were evolved according to local needs and their evolution and spread may prove to be as inextricable as the story of the African smelting plant seems to us now. It seems that by 500 B.C. the normal bloomery was used in most of the then existing iron-smelting sites. The evolution of shaft-furnaces had already begun, as we have several types of prehistoric furnaces from Central Europe which look like the first steps in this direction; but the Stückofen did not succeed until better blast air production was achieved. Here the Celts seem to have led the way and the Romans took over their water-driven bellows and forges, developing them but little. Ancient iron production was always that of a semi-soft iron mass or bloom which by forging was turned into wrought iron, but sometimes by fortitious admixtures or special treatment into steel or harder types of wrought iron. It received little stimulus from the general type of the wandering iron-smith of those days who either worked bar-iron or produced his own iron from the local sources on his way. The iron industries of Noricum and other sites developed their local technique but there was of course no binding research to guide them all and once the most efficient way of working the local ore was found the industry settled down to use these methods and no further progress was achieved. Ancient iron technique differed considerably from that used for other ores in Antiquity, because the iron was not liquified like copper and other metals but the bloom was produced and the heated mass had to be hammered on an anvil until the iron was welded into a solid lump and all the impurities were expelled. If larger pieces were required a number of such blooms were reheated and welded into a single mass by forging as the special re-heating furnaces of Corbridge and Cedworth prove.

Gradually such higher types of shaft-furnaces were evolved, which allowed a better separation between slag and bloom. We often find the bloom wedged half-way in the narrow Roman furnaces or the Silesian "hour-glass" furnaces. On the other hand we have no proof that the earliest pot-bowl furnaces were all equiped with blast air, in many cases no attention has been paid to the clay-nozzles of the bellows, and the furnaces may have been worked with natural draught as some types undoubtedly are. As long as the fundamental reactions were so little understood and so much was left to chance we find the most primitive pot-bowl furnace together with the better Stückofen in a welter of types, the history and spread of which only careful research will be able to disentangle. This medley of methods and apparatus continues to thrive for many centuries (54). Thus Theophilus mentions only the primitive bloomery furnace for the production of iron and does not mention the Stückofen, which was quite well-known in his days (Cap. XC): "Iron is formed in the earth as stones. When it has been mined it is crushed in the same way as copper ore and smelted together into lumps. Then it is brought to higher temperature in the furnace of the black-smith and it is forged to be ready for work. Steel gets its name from the mountain Chalyps where it is found in large quantities and it is prepared in the same way." Even Biringuccio mentions both the bloomery furnace worked with blast air and the shaft-furnace (I. 6), though he also gives a bad description of the blast furnace (III. 3), and Agricola seems quite content with the production of iron in a bloomery fire combined with a smith's forge and hammer, while he approves of the Stückofen for smelting iron pyrites and advocates crucible smelting for the production of good steel. Thus even in the sixteenth century primitive and more sophisticated methods were used side by side and different forms of smelting furnaces adapted to the peculiar characteristics of local ores. No wonder that our picture of Roman and pre-Roman iron smelting is far from clear. Only further research in that very neglected field of smelting furnaces and their products (ores, slags, etc.) will help to clear it. In several furnaces of the Stückofen-type the temperature might rise to a point at which iron is fused and *cast-iron* is produced, this metal was far too brittle and hard to be used for industrial purposes. In order to produce a cast-iron suitable for making castings a much higher temperature is required which only the blast-furnaces of the fourteenth century could reach.

Cast-iron must be considered unknown to Antiquity according to most authors, and there is no certain reference to it in ancient literature. Still there is the possibility that some knowledge of cast-iron reached the Roman Empire from the country, where cast-iron was invented, from China by the way of the desert route. But cast-iron seems to have been known to the Graeco-Roman world as an accidental and useless product formed by raising the temperature, but as its nature was not recognised it was thrown away. Even at Halstatt sites cast-iron pieces were found in the slag-heaps. The frequency with which pieces of cast-iron have been found at Roman bloomery sites has led some writers to suppose that its production was intentional. Thus May claimed that it was produced in coal-fired furnaces as a bloom which then purified with charcoal in crucible, but the best metallurgical opinion is against this. Still the Warrington piece found by May in 1904 seems to be true cast-iron (55) and further analysis of this piece is an urgent matter. But the claim that a "Roman" blast-furnace was found at Colsterworth has been denied by Straker. Some Roman objects like the head from Beauraing are definitely stated to be cast but the final proof is mostly lacking, as frequently such "cast-iron statues" have proved to be figures of pure wrought iron which had been chased. We have the statement by Pausanias (III. 12.10) about "Theodorus the Samian who invented how to cast ("diacheai") iron and to fabricate statues from it", but most authors consider this sixth century invention very doubtful or, like Read, suppose that Pausanias mixed up the casting of bronze and iron. Another passage in Pausanias' account (56) runs: "The working of iron into statues happens to be the most difficult work and a matter of the greatest labour. The work of Tisagoras (whoever he was) is wonderful", but this does not imply the casting of iron and may well refer to chasing or even hammering into a mould (swaging), which Lucan (57) mentions, though this passage is also read to mean welding pieces of iron into a bloom.

Yet there is a passage in Pliny (58) where he discusses the use of pine logs for the melting of iron and copper and in this text he uses the word "fundo" instead of the "excoquo" of other passages, but there is nothing in this text to indicate that the manufacture of cast-iron is meant. A similar case is the passage from Hesiod (59) which may refer to the fusion ("tekethai") of iron, but this does not imply casting. On the other hand the "ponderous mass of iron as a quoit" (60) ("sólos autochónos") is considered by some to be a meteorite but Richardson rightly thinks that it was a bloom described by one who was contemporary with the beginnings of iron-working. A passage in Aristotle (61) refers to "weak, malleable iron".

The direct production of cast-iron in blast-furnaces was impossible, the only other possibility was smelting with a flux in crucibles. Certain prehistoric furnaces like that at Rudic (near Brno) are well adapted to crucible-smelting, which is unusual and uneconomical for the production of a bloom. In Gradišče (Carinthia) many fragments of crucibles impregnated with iron have been found. But these are probably crucibles used for the production of steel by the cementation process, during which iron may have occasionally absorbed excessive carbon and liquified. There are no further indications that cast-iron was manufactured outside the Roman world except in China, to which fact we will revert in due course.

The passage in Daniel (62) which some hold to refer to cast-iron seems to combine clay and iron only as a simile illustrating the impossibility of combining the weak and the strong.

In contrast to this negative result we are sure that *steel* was produced in Antiquity. Steel is called *chalybs* but also *adamas* (untamable) or *kyanos* (the dark-blue). By *acies* or *stomoma* the sharpness or the sharp of a weapon or tool was meant, but these words were never used for steel itself, though they may denote "steeled" portions of an implement.

It is doubtful whether the ancients knew any direct method of producing steel, but they produced it accidentally when they treated suitable ores. If working manganese-bearing iron, ores, free from phosphorus, arsenic or sulphur, there was a possibility of obtaining steel in the bloomery furnace. Care should be taken not to decarburize the bloom fully and thus a good malleable steel would be obtained. This fact was probably discovered by the Celts in Noricum around 500 B.C. though of course not understood. The specific shaft-furnaces, about 1—2 M. high, found in this field would suit the *production of such "natural" steel* excellently. Such a fortitious composition is not limited to spathic iron ore only and the possibility of a direct production of "natural steel" may have existed in several other ancient metallurgical centres, but this point can not yet be settled for the lack of proper analytical data on ores and products.

A second possibility would be a crucible process of preparing steel, a *fusion process*. It is uncertain whether the Romans ever produced steel or iron by the fusion process, but in the light of present evidence it seems very unlikely. They may have occasionally produced amorphous iron carbide if we may believe Richardson's interpretation of Pliny's passage (63), but a sure proof that they did not known the fusion process seems to be the fact that all their best steel was imported from the East. Pliny wrongly believes Seric iron to be Chinese steel, but it was in reality Indian steel from the Hyderabad district, known at present as "wootz". Wootz is produced from black magnetite ore, bamboo-charcoal and the leaves of certain carbonaceous plants sealed in a crucible of native clay. Smelting the contents in a charcoal fire with blast air yields a button or regulus of metal, which is alternately melted and cooled again four or five times until round cakes of 5″ diameter and $\frac{1}{2}$″ thick, weighing about 2 lbs, are obtained.

Such crucible processes for converting iron into steel (64) were the only practicable way of obtaining good steel in antiquity, and Ktesias mentions that it was used for smelting ore too. His account is not incredible; for until the Indians had learnt a way to reduce granular magnetite in the open hearth, crucible smelting, however uneconomic, may have prevailed. Its survival in Shansi (China) is explained by the abundance of anthracite in that province.

The "wootz" steel process differs from all others by two pecularities: carbon was introduced into the crucibles in the form of wood and leaves of specific plants, which were held to be indispensable to success and wootz steel was unique in the production of the "damask" pattern, which was suggested by the crystalline (octohedral) structure of meteoric iron. These Eastern crucible processes were based on the control of a higher range of temperatures and denote a deeper insight into the principles of iron metallurgy than those of contemporary Europe. Such developments took place during Hellenistic and later centuries and we will have occasion to discuss the damascened swords and objects later on. A brief outline will be given here to show what influence taste, skill and the availability of certain materials will achieve.

In Antiquity the "wootz" cakes were exported to Damascus and later to Toledo and other Arabian metallurgical centres for the manufacture of so-called "damascened steel". This was a high quality steel with a certain pattern dictated by taste. Such damascened blades were forged from wootz cakes by causing the metal to flow in two or more directions by blows of the hammer. After prolonged annealing the blades were then quenched and drawn to the desired hardness, polished and etched. The last operation brings the "damask" pattern to the surface. Pattern and colour largely determine the quality of this Oriental steel. There are different methods of preparing this steel, one of which we have described. Another consists in forging and working the steel at dark-red heat without quenching (65) but whatever method of forging is used, the general characteristic of the damascened steel is a structure with small particles of globular cementite, which is easily identified under the microscope (66). The Persian steel seems to have been produced by carburising and melting wrought iron with charcoal in a crucible and this "Parthian steel" was inferior in renown to Seric iron only. The fame of this Oriental steel lasted until present times and we often find references to it in literature, mostly without intimate knowledge of this secret process of which we will have more to say. Thus Thomas of Cantimpré tells of an oriental iron called "andena" or "alidea" which is very good for cutting and which is fusible like copper and silver but is less ductile than iron from other parts of the world. Of course this excellent steel was soon imitated and even in Antiquity similar products were attempted. Thus the Celtic smiths of the first century A.D. have invented a process of welding steel strips or wire into an wrought iron bar and falsely damascening it by cross-forging as proved by the Nydam find. It is very probable that this "damask" pattern was adopted from meteorites. Siderites when passing through the atmosphere to the earth get covered with a thin film of magnetic iron oxide. When forged at low temperatures a crystal pattern, the so-called Widmanstätten figures, show up, a pattern that is destroyed at white-heat. It seems very probable that the "wootz" pattern, a contrast between carbon-rich and carbon-poor particles in the steel is an imitation of this "damask" pattern of meteorites.

Such direct steel by the fusion process depends upon high furnace temperatures, much charcoal and the proper clay and other ingredients for refractory crucibles. At present "cast steel" is still largely prepared in such crucibles by a fusion process, but often crude iron is carburised to "blistersteel" and forged directly into tools (67). Cast steel is of course a modern invention, though Biringuccio hints at the direct production of cast steel from Stückofen-iron. But the true development of the process was the work of the generations of metallurgists between Réaumur (1722) and the early nineteenth century (68).

Richardson maintains that the Chalybes also used a fusion process in crucibles for their famous steel, but there is no direct evidence.

However, most of the ancient steel was made by a third process, by *cementation* or *carburisation* of wrought iron. The ancient wrought iron is not always very pure, it often contains small particles of slag, and above all the carbon content varies throughout the object. In other words the purified bloom is partially and unevenly steeled. Now the gradual conquest of this "steel-making" process was the real impulse of the rise of iron metallurgy in Antiquity. For wrought iron objects

Fig. 40.
Ornamental "steeled" battle axe from Ugarit (Schaeffer)

could of course be used for many a purpose, but it was generally inferior to bronze, the production of which was already well in hand for centuries before iron to the fore. The modern process entails the heating of wrought iron or mild steel in a powdered mass of carbon-rich material. It is generally called *case-hardening* and the surface of the piece is carburised to a depth depending on the length of the treatment. It is commonly effected by cementation with charcoal, powdered horn, dung or similar carbonaceous matter, though by modern processes with potassium cyanide a mere skin of steel can be formed at will. It is probable that this cementation which is very common among the analysed steeled tools was an accidental discovery. When forging the bar of wrought iron, the primitive smith had to reheat it often and if he achieved this heating by embedding his bar in the heart of a charcoal fire and maintained the temperature by using a blast insufficiently strong to penetrate the heart of the hearth, he would have ideal conditions for the process.

We have some inkling of the gradual development of this process in the Near East from the researches of Carpenter (69). When analysing several iron objects from the period between 1200 B.C. and Roman times, all hailing from Egypt, he discovered, that the earliest objects were only carburised, then about 900—700 B.C. the art of quenching is added to the secret operations of the smith and tempering is introduced by the Romans. The latter, probably the most difficult of heat treatments was not yet properly understood and some of the objects were overheated. If therefore Negroes often produce crucible steel nowadays, we must remember that these black smiths are vastly sophisticated compared with the classical smith who seems to have used casehardening as a general rule, however difficult he found it to control the operation without instruments like ours. Carburisation or decarburisation was long the bane of the Roman metallurgists and it remained a difficult problem how to retain or restore the cutting edge of an implement. Very often, therefore, the Romans resorted to other means and annealed part of the tool or carburised only its blade, so that it should not be too brittle. If a combination of strength and toughness was required for a tool, this could be attained by the false method of damascening, by welding together plates or strips of softer and harder iron and steel by forging. The Celtiberians were greatly hampered by the varying properties of their home-produced steel and according to Diodor (V. 33) they buried it for some time and then reforged it. The softer iron rusts more quickly than steel and thus by reforging the iron rust is expelled and the remaining steely parts are welded together. Thus they were able to repair the insufficient mastering of the smelting process in their primitive furnaces.

The heat treatments like quenching and tempering were certainly no Egyptian inventions for the tools analysed by Carpenter fall in a period when iron was still far from common in Egypt, which enters the Iron Age not earlier than 700—600 B.C. They must have been imported objects or perhaps the work of foreign smiths in Egypt. Tempering was a Roman achievement as it seems. A Roman chisel from Chesterholm, for instance, has a steely portion in which the carbon content varies widely. The edge of the tool was heated to 900°C and quenched in water, but only the cutting edge (70). This is but one of the examples of implements hardened by tempering and quenching, which now can no longer be denied as Johannsen did several years ago.

It is, however, a wrong idea, that heating a steel tool to red-heat and quenching it would harden the tool, without forging it with a hammer this operation would only soften it. The tool is heated to be able to hammer it properly but unless keeping it at white-heat any other temperature would only cause the loss of the "steel" structure acquired at higher temperature and formation of the iron-graphite structure, stable at lower temperatures. Copper is softened by the heating not by quenching. Quenching was well known to the ancients. We not only read in the Odyssey (71): "As when the smith an hatchet or large axe, tempering with skill, plunges the hissing blade deep in cold water (hence the strength of the steel)...", but the term *baptein, baphé* occurs in several passages (Sophocles, Aiax, 650, etc.). The Latin expressions are *tinguere* (72), *restinguere* (73), *temperare* (74). Quenching in water or oil was the recognised method in Antiquity, but of course the actual process was not understood. As late as 1370 the Quodlibeta of Oresme put the following problem: "Why does cold water harden ignited iron or steel and why does it soften when put in the fire again?" Cooling in oil was generally advocated to avoid making the steel too brittle (75) and in the case water the contents of the cooling trough or *lacus* was considered of the utmost importance, for certain waters were said to be most effective. We have already cited Pliny on this matter and others (76) also believed in the special properties of the waters of the Jalon at Bilbilis,etc. Later special solutions were manufactured. An encyclo-paedia of the fourteenth century even mentions quenching in honey to get a steel that is readily softened and easily liquified in the fire! These tales are not all myths, as some solutions seem to have an effect indeed. Possibly these stories also served to conceal the essentials of the temper-ing methods at Como, etc. as Richardson suggested. Of course some of these stories may have ascribed the properties of the local steel to the wrong factor, whereas the true reason of its quality lay in the ab-sence of harmful impurities and the presence of manganese or titanium.

The ancients recognised many qualities of steel. The Chinese had only "natural" and "artificial" steel, but the Greeks of the age of Alex-ander had many qualities according to Daimachus. There was the Sinopic steel used for carpenter's tools, the Chalybic kind, Laconian steel for files and borers and Lydian steel for swords. In Roman times we find the Spanish and Noric steel prominent together with the Seric and Parthian steel imported from the Orient.

Technically speaking we must, therefore, distinguish the following phases of iron industry. First a period of the use of meteoric iron, then iron produced as a by-product of gold-refining, followed quickly by the evolution of the reduction of iron ores in bloomery and shaft-furnaces, which rose to prominence when methods of cementation allowed the manufacture of steel. For only steel is definitely better than bronze for tools and weapons and only the invention of steel could herald the Iron Age. This is an important fact which we must keep in mind, if we want to trace the discovery of iron.

Having discussed the technical development of iron manufacture it will now be clear how tremendous a break the advent of the Iron Age was. To some it might be a matter of surprise that the Iron Age did not come earlier, when it is remembered that every ton of the earth's crust contains a cwt. of iron of a varying degree of purity. We saw, however, that the amount of heat required and the temperatures involved are so much greater than those in the case of copper and its alloys, that the accidental appearance of the metal in a crucible or a camp-fire would need to happen many times before the early craftsman would notice it or connect the effect of heat with the occurence of fusibility, and even then the deduction from effect to cause might not be made. The bronze smiths had to unlearn much of their craft and to acquire new knowledge and skill to produce his bloom, a word derived from the Anglo-Saxon "bloma" (lump) from the new furnaces and "bloomeries". He had to learn how to purify this plastic lump by continual hammering and reheating in order to squeeze out the slag and to produce wrought iron. Even this material was still an expensive commodity, though it could only be used in a limited way. Iron pots, spits and frying pans were classed among the Crown Jewels in the reign of Edward III, even in the fourteenth century, though they may have been of special and elaborate fabrication. Even in warfare and workshop the wrought iron had little use. The frequent heatings in the charcoal fire for forging carburised iron occasionally produced weapons such as swords, which, when properly quenched for cooling, became tempered steel. No wonder that we read of swords with miraculous powers possessed by such heroes as King Arthur or Charlemagne. Only with the advent of the blast-furnace and its waterdriven bellows could an strong artificial draught and a much higher temperature be attained and only by the middle of the fourteenth century A.D. can the Iron Age really be said to have begun and produced good iron and steel tools for the masses, thus making iron the "popular metal" which everyone could soon afford, whereas copper and bronze had in their days always been more or less a luxury. In this sense the advent of iron was a social revolution and the study of its history now has adherents from many quarters (77).

6. *Where was iron born?*

From the earlier chapters it will be clear that not the occasional smelting of iron ores but the conquest of the art of converting the wrought iron into a carburized, "steeled" iron, which was superior to bronze, constituted the real advent of the Iron Age.

The production and working of iron spread more widely than that of copper and bronze had as it ousted these as the main materials of the metal workers. In Africa where iron came first copper is used almost entirely for ornamental purposes. Both the agricultural and pastoral peoples of the Old World know iron but in the New World and Oceania it remained largely unknown. Nor could the simple exchange or trade in this new metal start an Iron Age. As we have proved the technique of the Iron Age is built up of an entirely new set of methods and processes, which differ fundamentally on many points from those used in the manufacture of copper and bronze. Therefore even if the Polynesians lost their earlier knowledge of iron metallurgy during their wanderings from Hinter India to their new island empire (78) they could not recover it or learn it from the iron which reached them driftwood, wrecked ships, shipwrecked Europeans or simply by trade. The knowledge of iron metallurgy was carried over the ocean by travellers, it could not be learnt by casual finds .

No Iron Age could start from the knowledge of meteoric iron alone. It is true that Zimmer showed that meteoric iron is practically always malleable, more than 99% of the known meteorites consist of a malleable iron-nickel alloy and only 0.56% is definitely non-malleable. Even the rare natural nickeliferous iron is mostly malleable. But the Iron Age could be initiated only by a people who knew how to reduce iron ore and had acquired the special knowledge of working the bloom obtained from the ore, a most unmetal-like substance for a generation which had all the lore of copper-, lead- and other metalcraft. The ironsmith is the real smith in our sense of the word, the Iron Age is the period in which the first smithies are built, with their characteristic equipment.

Now the craft of the black-smith is fundamentally different from that of the copper metallurgist, iron metallurgy is coupled with its typical furnaces, bellows and apparatus, tongs, crucibles, etc.; the arts of hardening, carburising, quenching, annealing and tempering are new acquisitions of several generations of smiths.

The fact that iron metallurgy spread relatively quicker than copper and bronze has misled many authors to believe that this complex of operations was not diffused from a certain centre and that it could be and was indeed re-discovered in many regions of the earth (von Lippmann, etc.). But this special set of techniques and the knowledge of other techniques of other metals which iron working presumes, do not only dub it a late comer, but are strong arguments for its diffusion from a certain centre.

That iron is a late metal no one can deny in the face of evidence. The history of folklore and religion favours the comparitively late origin of the Iron Age. The superstitions attached to the use of iron some of which persist upto the present day and the taboos often imposed on it by religion, all point to the fact that iron is a newcomer and an importation in older civilisations.

Gowland, Day, Beck and others considered the assumption that meteoric iron was the earliest source of mankind quite unnecessary, because iron ores can be so easily reduced to metallic iron in an ordinary wood-fire or charcoal fire. But there is no reason why iron should be the first from a technical point of view. Many authors like Percy under-estimated the difficulties that would attend the manufacture of iron by primitive smiths. For if the bloom may be easy to obtain from the ore, the transformation of this bloom into good wrought iron or steel remains a difficult operation and one which can not be performed by a people unless it possesses some degree of trained intelligence and is well acquainted with the pitfalls of metal-craft (79).

Secondly, as soon as man learnt how to obtain iron from its ores, of which large deposits are widely distributed, he would begin to use it for industrial purposes if he could produce a "steel-like" quality from his local ore. If he knew how to produce one pound, he would proceed to produce five, ten, fifty pounds. If therefore we find iron rare and costly, if it was valued as highly as silver and gold during a certain period, we are justified in concluding that at that time and place the inhabitants had not yet learnt to extract it from its ores, in short that their iron was celestial and not terrestial. If we find a piece of man-made iron in the pyramids it is more probable that this iron is not contemporaneous with the building of the pyramid than that it is man-made iron. It is improbable that a religious taboo would be operative for so long a period of say 2000 years and that the possession of the secret of its manufacture could be kept by those in power. Not is it probable that these early "accidental" smeltings would have taken so long to be rationalised by peoples who were conversant with the metallurgy of copper, bronze, gold, etc.!

Thirdly, Sir John Evans has pointed out long ago that early iron objects have "bronze" forms and not those for which it is best adapted, as we can see in the case of the earlier Hallstatt swords! (80).

What we see in the Near East is the early appearance of iron in jewelry, amulets and the like or statues, then the use of iron as an ornament of bronze implements, the gradual use of iron for parts of these tools and weapons, until iron ousts bronze from its place and is used for the principal part of the implement, while bronze serves as an ornamental material. Finally the entire tool or weapon is made of iron, which gradually acquires its specific "iron" form.

Long after gold, copper and silver meteoric iron was collected and worked by hammering. Primitive man may have attached magical importance to this meteoric iron when he discovered that it fell from heaven. Many ancient terms for iron are of the type "heaven-metal", etc., Hittite texts speak of "black iron" or "black iron from the sky". It is, however, still a matter of doubt whether this recognition of its celestial origin was as early as many authors suppose, for the observation of the fall of meteorites coupled with the finding of these pieces is not as common as silently implied in their statement. Probably it was first held to be a kind of native copper until the real origin and its specific nature was learnt. Meteoric iron certainly was believed to have magical properties in later times, but whether this was already the case in prehistoric and early historic times remains an attractive hypothesis, but it is still to be proved.

However, as early as the first half of the third millennium B.C. pieces of man-made iron appear in Mesopotamia (Tell Asmar, Tell Chagar Bazar, Mari) and Asia Minor (Alaca Hüyük), and possibly Egypt too. It is still incertain what ores were worked first. Such brilliant, "metallic" ores like magnetite, haematite, iron pyrites and some striking forms of limonite may have attracted the attention of primitive smelters first. The use of haematite for seal-stones was widespread in Sumerian times and fragments of specular ore, a hard metallic variety of haematite, were found on the smelting site near the ziggurat of Ur (81). On the other hand the ochres were used as pigments in prehistoric times, they are found in a soft form, rich in iron and well adapted for rudimentary smelting operations. Probably the natural inquisitiveness of the primitive smith led to the "trial by fire" of these ores and he discovered that he could obtain a lump of malleable metal from them. Lucas thinks that the first production of iron was almost certainly an accident due to the use by mistake of iron ore in the place of copper ore and that there can be no doubt that when iron was first obtained it was treated as copper and bronze to shape it. But hammering iron cold was found useless. This experiment must have been repeated many times before it was realised that complete command over this new metal could only be obtained by hammering it red-hot. By the aid of heat the smith could weld the small pieces of iron together into a larger piece. But the new metal represented no improvement over copper and bronze tools, it was much less easy to work, the forging demanded much expensive fuel and the cutting edge made by hammering blunted quickly. Then he discovered that repeated hammering and heating in a coal-fire followed by plunging in cold water gave the iron a hardness superior to bronze. The delay of the discovery of quenching was due to the fact that copper when heated softens but is not affected by quenching at all. Only if heating the iron to white-heat and hammering it patiently followed by quenching the smith would accept the new metal as something of practical use for tools and weapons. In fact, not before the discovery of steel or case-hardened iron could the metallurgy of iron rise from the status of a tentative experiment. The difficulties of slagging the ore, working the bloom and forging at red-heat combined with quenching delayed the Iron Age. It would seem from the archaeological evidence that the earlier stage of iron-working, the production of wrought iron from the bloom obtained from ores, was an achievement of the mountain-region of Armenia (between Taurus and Caucasus).

From 1900 to 1400 we see the spread of iron ornaments and ceremonial weapons, which remain precious. It is probable that some of the knowledge of iron working also spread from this same centre in different directions. The earlier attempts (before 1900), which probably were also made in this centre are still too isolated, but some finds, such as small smelting sites at different places, for instance at Ur (of Ur III date, that is about 2000 B.C.) show that even then the smelting of iron was known and slowly spread. However, Richardson is right in saying that these rings, beads, amulets, etc. are only the heralds of a coming dawn. Iron was still a costly and precious metal, though probably its identity with meteoric iron had been recognised in the early second millennium B.C., there was no special stimulus to improve its manufacturing methods as the metal was quite useless for the tools and weapons, which determine the career of a metal or alloy.

Weapons and tools of iron appearing and growing more and more frequent, that is the Iron Age. For the objects mentioned in early Hittite and other texts the ore smelted is quite immaterial, meteoric iron would do too and some of these objects could even be made of haematite without difficulty. When, however, the smelting of iron became an industry there was a demand for good and pure ores in large quantities.

It would seem from the available data that the "steeling" of iron was discovered in the same centre around 1400 B.C., thus giving the Hittites a monopoly of the manufacture of "true iron" or steel for another 200 years. Iron objects now appear more frequently as objects of trade, even in northern Europe of the thirteenth century B.C. (Seeland and Bornholm). An early Italian smelting site at Nevigata near Manfredonia, Apulia must be dated before 1200. But whatever progress iron trade made, the new metal was still subordinate to copper and bronze. It is even doubtful whether steel was more frequent in Asia Minor itself than say in Palestine and Syria, where iron begins to penetrate between 1400 and 1200.

The invasion of Thrako-Phrygian and other peoples in Asia Minor around 1200 B.C. and the subsequent destruction of the Hittite Empire had an enormous influence on the spread of iron-working and the knowledge of case-hardening processes. Between 1200 and 1000 there is a quick growth of the iron industry in Iran, Transcaucasia, and Syria and Palestine, while Cyprus, Mesopotamia, Caucasia, and Crete follow closely. In all these countries some knowledge of iron-smelting had penetrated in earlier periods. Now the new processes which made steel an equal (or better) material to bronze found their way prepared and local industries could prosper quickly as the foundations of the craft had already been laid. This is probably the reason why iron-working spread so much quicker than copper-working, but the latter did not find its way prepared and had to be introduced as an entirely new craft.

Now the centre of origin of these iron-working processes was long hotly debated. Richardson (82) made out a good case for an European origin and his arguments were these. China and India are too far removed from the stream of civilisation in these early days, the latter country has an iron industry which was but a few centuries old in the days of Alexander. To Palestine iron was brought by the Philistines from the West. It is certain that there was an iron industry in the Armenian mountain region and in Central Europe (Styria) around 1000 B.C. Precedence of the West can be claimed as this region fulfills

more nearly the combined premised conditions of available ore, metallurgical knowledge and economic necessity. Both bronze and iron
Hallstatt forms, though the same, are well-advanced shapes.

In the fifteenth and fourteenth century B.C. the stream of European
imigrants begins to move southwards and it is no coincidence that
the earliest references to iron-working in Asianic-Egyptian texts corres-
pond so nearly with the invasion from Europe! That the use of iron
was forced upon Asia by conquering races is implied by the widespread
taboo of this metal. This is quite natural for peoples at a disadvantage
of securing raw materials or working them, for from the Upper Nile
to the Caucasus there are no deposits comparable in quantity and
quality to the spathic iron of Europe, the best ore adapted to the
groping technique of iron-working. Again Hallstatt forms have a long
history behind them, as the metallurgical progress of Central Europe
was quickened between 2000 and 1500 by the trade with the East.
The claim of the "Caucasian" region is nothing but an epic tradition
without tangible proof. The earliest hoard of iron work mentioning
is that of Sargon II, even among the Hittites iron was only common
after 1200, their ores being only low grade haematite and some magnetite. The "ancient times of the Chalybes" fall between Homer (ninth
century) and Aeschylos (fifth century), by which time the Chalybes
were the producers of famous steel. The Celts of the La Tène period
have spread the iron weapons over the main part of Europe.

Richardson was violently attacked by Hertz, Wright, Harland and
others, who held that the Chalybes were the discoverers of iron-working (83). Now Prezworski is quite correct in stating that some of the
protagonists in this battle, like Quiring, Persson, Richardson and
Wainwright, have given little attention to archaeological proof. Thus
Wainwright held that the Hittites used iron freely as early as the twentieth century B.C. Neither can we believe Hertz who claims that the
Sumerians were the inventors of iron metallurgy though she quite
correctly refutes several of the claims of Richardson. Nor is it possible
that iron was a Cretan invention as Montelius believed mainly on
account of the Parian Marble, for to take one argument, Crete has no
iron ores worth while working.

However, Richardson's hypothesis is still very much in the realm
of speculation as there was certainly iron in Palestine and well developed
and specialised furnaces at Gerar at least a century earlier than the earliest possible date for the Hallstatt cemetry. Also the Indo-European
peoples in Greece and the Balkans used bronze at least upto the Aegean

wanderings if not later, and iron spread back on the way of the invaders. The famous Thracian swords were probably obtained elsewhere, just as the Damascene blades came from India or Parthia. In the Mycenean Age iron was used for ornaments only and the Homeric Age was a Bronze Age though of course the passages on iron can not be explained away. But Homer makes iron common only among the Trojans (84): "For ample stores I (Tydides) have of gold and brass and well-wrought iron" or among the Achaeans after they had plundered Asiatic towns. Whether we believe the Chalybes to have been already a famous tribe of metallurgists of Pontus or whether they were late-comers in this region from the Armenian highlands; whether iron-working was first discovered by the Khaldi of Lake Urmia and Lake Van and then went westward or whether it was a development of the Chalybic-Pontic-Chaldic peoples under the stress of their Hittite masters as Heichelheim believes, it is certain that iron-working as we have learnt to understand it, the "steeling" of man-made iron, which alone made it superior to bronze, origi- nated somewhere in the Hittite realm of Asia Minor, probably in the Armenian mountain region and not in Europe. The possibili- ty of the transmission of the knowledge through the Balkans to Noricim must not be overlooked and should be thoroughly investi- gated. On the other hand the sea way is quite possible too. We have mentioned early smelting sites in Southern Italy, whence it was brought to the Umbrians round Bologna quickly, may be by Greek or Illyrian traders and thence northwards to Noricum, to be stimulated by the Etruscans. It is difficult to support Witter who claims that the Philistines were Illyrians, who brought the secret of iron from Noricum! Even an authority like Kossinna, who is not apt to post-date Central European events, admits that the invention is due to Asia Minor in the fourteenth century B.C. even if he dates the earliest iron finds at Seeland and Bornholm in Northern Europe as early as 1400. He also believes that it spread quickly to Noricum and finally reached the German tribes of Central Europe by 750—700 B.C.

We must leave the problem of the exact location of the earliest "steel manufacture" to future research, it might turn out to be the region of Doliche "ubi ferrum nascitur" or it may even be true that the Chaly- bes were the aborigines and did for iron what they did for other metals.

At any rate from 1200—1000 B.C. iron-working spread from the Armenian mountain region. Now not only weapons but more and more agricultural implements were manufactured though "bronze"

forms were usually adapted. The same can be observed in Central
Europe where since 1000 iron is first used for ornamental purposes
then quickly for weapons and tools, but long iron and bronze objects
co-exist and even in the later phases of Hallstatt civilisation combinations of bronze and iron are frequent in weapons and tools. Then
from 800 onwards iron is supreme here and the centre of gravity of
iron manufacture wanders from Asia Minor to Carinthia and later in
La Tène times to the Celtic dominions and to Spain. This extensive
Noric industry led to important conquests and tribal migrations which
moved European politics.

Thus after a long evolution and series of experiments parallel in
the Near East and the Eastern Mediterranean countries the original
centre Armenia again found the solution the "case-hardening" of iron,
and passed it on quickly to the other countries where the foundations
for a quick rise of the iron industry were already layed. But still for
many centuries when intricate objects had to be made, bronze was
used, as casting was immensely superior to the hammering technique
which dominated iron metallurgy long after the eighth century when
in Muṣaṣir (near Lake Van) lamps, vases and kettles were still swaged
(hammered in moulds) and even in other fields such as welding, etc.
the methods used for bronze were long in use for iron too, before
more specific methods were discovered.

7. *The early days of iron in East and West*

We must now discuss the evolution of iron metallurgy in the different countries in further detail, and we shall deal with *Africa* first.
Here we find an ideal field of study of ancient metallurgical methods,
for there is a great variety of smelting methods, furnaces ranging from
pot-bowl types up to well-built shaft-furnaces using clay, termite
cones, etc. as building materials, working with or without blast air.
Generally a bloom is produced, but occasionally the product has a
steely character. Large masses are easily obtained but many Negro
tribes do not know how to make steel and rely on chance production
of this valuable form of iron. They are as helpless as the Vikings who
knew how to make iron anchors but who could not make steel swords
with good cutting edges. The bloom is generally produced by smelters
who break it up and sell the pieces to the smiths in the neighbourhood.

We can obtain an idea of Negro technique from Bellamy's description of iron smelting in Lagos. (85). The siliceous haematite is roasted,

pulverised in a wooden mortar and washed in a water-filled hole in the ground. Then it is conveyed to the furnace in the smelting shed. This furnace is a 7' circular space built of clay and about 3' 9" high. A depression in the floor gives acces to the bottom of the furnace, the dome of which is bound by ropes of twisted vine. In the centre of the bottom there is an aperture 3" in diameter, which communicates with the tunnel entered from a pit in the shed. There is also a small kiln used for firing the tuyères. The smelting lasts 36 hours and blast air is given by nine pairs of earthenware pipes. The selected slag from each suc-

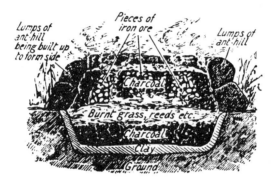

Fig. 41.
Primitive Uganda iron furnace

cesive smelting is used as a flux. The slag is run off by opening the orifice in the bottom of the furnace. For removing the bloom six clay-sealed apertures are opened, the earthenware tuyères are removed and the doorway of the furnace is opened. The contents of live charcoal is raked out and the 70 lbs bloom is removed red-hot with a loop of green creeper. It is then broken up with stone, pounders to convenient sizes and sold to the smiths. This natural steel is brought down by the smith to tool steel with about 1% of carbon. This one example must suffice, we must refer the reader for further details to Cline's monograph (86).

Iron was certainly the first metal to reach the Negroes, thus Kaffir tribes use *tsipi* (iron) as a basic word for metal and call gold "yellow iron", silver "white iron" and copper "red iron". Many tribes reckon values in terms of bars of iron. Von Luschan (87) and after him Balfour have claimed the invention of iron metallurgy for the African continent on the following grounds:

1. The high antiquity of iron-working among the Negro and Bantu tribes is evidenced by the wide-spread dispersal and high degree of skill of the native smiths.

2. Iron ores are very abundant in Africa, and can be collected with ease on or near the surface.

3. Some of these ores are easily reduced even by an open fire.

3. The full evolution of pot-bowl furnace to kiln and shaft-furnace can still be seen observed in the different African regions. If they had been introduced by advanced metallurgists, these crude methods would not have been adopted. There is evidence for the early stages in the progression from simple to complex.

But such early dates for African iron-working as 1500 B.C. as von Luschan claimed remain without any proof! There is plenty evidence that Negroes did not know iron until historic times. Agatarchides states that copper or bronze chisels were used in the Nubian gold mines because "iron was then still unknown" and the Periplus states that iron for spear-heads and weapons was exported in the first century A.D. from Alexandria to Aethiopia. Procopius even says that the Romans forbade the sale of iron to the Aethiopians who had none, but this may refer to steel. If "Meroë" used iron fairly early, this is because the Aethiopians had to import both iron and copper from the Graeco-Roman world. Not is it likely that the Negroes learnt iron-working from the Egyptians early as Roeder claimed, for the Egyptians themselves did not enter the Iron Age before the seventh century A.D. at the earliest.

Indeed, Cline, who has carefully sifted the available evidence, reached the following conclusions. The beginning of iron-working in East Africa between the sixth and twelfth century A.D. can be ascribed to the stimulus of trade with India, Arabia and Aethiopia. This would allow a century or more for the growth of the metallurgy at Zimbabwe. From folk-tradition in the Northern Congo and Central and Western Sudan these regions form together with parts of Northern Rhodesia a relatively old iron-working centre, that probably received its stimulus and traditions from Aethiopia. Still it is more probable in the face of present evidence that the Negroes of the Western Sudan learnt to smelt iron from the first waves of camel-riding Berbers who put them in touch with northern civilisation about 400 A.D. At first only the bare elements of northern technique came in and the Negroes developed some crude methods of their own.

The art of smelting did not reach the forested coast-lands of Guinea until late and then only in certain districts, but it spread quickly through central Sudan into the Congo basin carrying with it a simple technique (though very effective) of forging with drum-bellows, nail-shaped iron anvils and a straight unshafted hammer, that could be used as an anvil as well. This technique diffused further through the Congo to Rhodesia and Nyassaland, eastwards to the Upper Nile and the Lakes and even at a few points to the Indian Ocean. It spread in divergent and interlacing streams which left a few Neolithic islands. Over most Negro areas the smelting technique is roughly the same and remained so. Fine wrought iron is produced under a hand-forced draugh in a simple pit or hearth. Sometimes the smelters increased their yield by building over the pit a small clay furnace two or three feet high charged with alternate layers of ore and charcoal, but still they had to work the bellows through out the smelting and produced only small quantities of wrought iron. In two widely separated areas, the interior of West Africa (west of the middle course of the Niger) and the interior of South-east Africa (from the Congo-Zambesi water-shed to Lake Nyassa and the Kafuo river) iron smelting became a big industry, the furnaces grew taller and free ventilating tubes were substituted for bellows.

Natives of the Southeast coast first learned of iron from Arab or Indian traders about 600 A.D. and passed the knowledge on to the south and west to inland groups who had not yet received knowledge of ironworking from the north-west. It filtered into East Africa from the North-east as well but more slowly for the Aethiopians and their neighbours lacked the adventurous proclivities of the Arabs.

The Yoruba resmelting of selected iron clincker imitated Northern Nigerian tin working and in the South-east the use of crucible smelting and fluxes were taken over from copper working by iron metallurgy! Knaff analysed African iron blooms under the microscope and found them identical with blooms and bloomery iron of Europe from the early seventeenth century, which need not be surprising as the methods were alike.

Cline's conclusions agree very well both with older publications (88) and more recent ones (89) which tend to recognize the first metalworkers in the Southeast in the Bush-Hottentot people with Negroid admixture who were in N. Rhodesia in the first century A.D. and crossed the Zambesi (700 A.D.) and the Limpopo (1055) to reach southeast Africa. South-Africa may have obtained its knowledge of metallurgy (iron!) via the Horn, on the one hand, and across the Sahara, on the other, somewhere during the first five centuries of our era, but the true Iron Age does not start here before the fifteenth century with the disappearance of the hunting groups. The probable centre of the diffusion of iron metallurgy to Africa was not Egypt but rather Meroë or Aethiopia, but in order to understand its proper chronological place in this story we must know more about the relations between Meroë and Egypt.

If we now turn to *Egypt* we enter a field where the story of iron has given rise to many unfounded statements and speculations. Hadfield (90) stated that the Egyptians could make steel tools and harden iron. This knowledge was obtained from India. Gsell (91) contended that they made wrought iron and also steel by the "wootz crucible process". Iron was, however, not found in early graves because of religious taboos, but iron-working was introduced by the Egyptians in Syria and thence found its way to the rest of the Near East. Bronze remained long in vogue because it could be remelted and because of aesthetic ideas. Finally the Hyksos reintroduced the worship of Seth and since his metal, iron, became common in Egypt. It took, however, a long time to reach the Aegean and Europe.

Burchardt (92) is quite right in warning the reader against Gsell's dissertation which all Egyptologists know to be worthless. The idea that iron was known in Egypt 2500 years earlier than in Europe and kept a tradesecret or did not spread as the other metals, is sheer nonsense. It is now generally considered impossible that iron objects were common in Egypt before say 1500 B.C. For though these tools and weapons may have been reused and reforged as some say, they must have been rejected at some time or got lost. If they rusted away, some trace of them must have remained for rust is chemically a most stable product and only acid water could have washed it away without leaving a trace. As nothing is perhaps better for the conservation of antiquities than Egyptian desert sand and even such delicate objects as pieces of cloth, etc. have been recovered from it, it is impossible that iron objects, even if rusted could have escaped our attention. These theories of early Egyptian iron descend from statements by Wilkinson and Lepsius, who considered the working of Egyptian granite impossible without iron tools. Formerly many authorities believed these statements when Belzoni brought the earliest polished granite objects to the British Museum, but afterwards similar objects were produced from Aberdeen granite first with modern tools later with simpler ones. Abrasive powders, perhaps obsidian and emery, copper grinders and cutters but above all almost infinite patience were the agents employed by the Egyptians (93). No trace of iron tools was ever found in the Sakkarah temple but plenty of stone and copper ones. Again these ancient authors forgot that iron tools would certainly not do the work but that steel was necessary in this case and hence the insistence by later authors who upheld the "granite-theory" that the Egyptians knew how to make steel. Again we must point out that the knowledge of iron does not imply that of steel. The Cordofan negroes who make excellent soft iron from poor ore do not know to make steel, and many other similar examples could be quoted from Africa.

Soldi, as early as 1881 (94) rejected early iron in Egypt and modern authorities now agree with him, though Flinders Petrie wavered and thought that iron may have come from the south as a tribute from Aethiopians, Nubians and Negroes either in the form of ore or as weapons, but the date of iron metallurgy in Nubia is now by common consent put much later than formerly. Not until 2000 B.C. did the blue-coloured implements appear on monuments (122) which may imply iron, but the true Iron age is the Saitic and Roman period (95), and as far as we know there was no religious taboo on iron in Egypt.

It is certain that the appearance of iron is curiously sporadic and not until 800 B.C. do we find an iron knife with a bronze handle to show us that iron was getting cheaper than the older alloy (96). Petrie who knew that the Egyptians never exploited the Sinai iron ores believed that they may have used occasional pockets of native iron in Sinai. He quotes Ridgeway's theory of the origin of the Greenland telluric iron and states that strata of carboniferous sandstone and black haematite may have been attacked by eruptions of thick basalt, which partly covers it in Sinai, and that here telluric iron may have been formed to serve as a source to the Egyptians but there is no proof forthcoming that telluric iron was ever found in these regions.

Since Predynastic times iron was used for charms, amulets and other small objects of hammered iron or meteoric iron were found. Now iron is at present still considered unlucky for certain ceremonies by the natives of Egypt, but it is said to dispel demons. Plutarch and Diodor both state that the Egyptians not only hated red hair, one of the attributes of the god Seth but also his metal, iron, which is called "bones of Seth", just as magnetic iron oxyde is called "bones of Horus". Plutarch's *de Iside et Osiride* speaks of "a hook of iron, of the iron which came out of Seth" (cap. 62). Amulets of magnetite were also used in ancient Egypt. Many statements of the religious significance or taboos of iron centre around the meaning of the Egyptian word *bi3*, which we believe to mean "copper, black copper".

The *Book of the Dead* mentions a wall of heaven made of *bi3* and also a chain of *bi3* put around the neck of the serpent Apep. The dead man is said to conquer heaven and to split its *bi3* (Pyr. 305). Since Hyksos times we encounter the expression *bi3. n. pt*, "iron from heaven" (HWB I. 436.14) (or perhaps better "metal, copper from heaven"). Other religious texts say that the sky is made of *bi3* ,though Zimmer's conclusion that this idea arose from its blue colour and from the fact that meteoric iron occasionally fell from the sky seems putting our ideas into these ancient texts. Friend thought that *bi3. n. pt* originally meant haematite, which can cut into statuettes, etc. like marble, then later "iron" (97). Wainwright set out to prove that *bi3* always had meant "iron" (98) and he started to show that the ceremony of the Opening of the Mouth, originally performed with a stone instrument, was later always executed with one made of *bi3*. All the magic instruments used in these ceremonies the *nw3*, the *mšḫtyw*, and later the chisel called *mḏtft*, were all said to be made of *bi3*. A Roman text speaks of the "instrument of *bi3* of the sacred shrine" which represented a thunderbolt. The small chisels of iron found in Tut-anch-amun's grave and other instruments seem to represent these magical instruments. The metal *bi3* is connected with heaven, with the waters of heaven or the wall around heaven, it is intimately linked with meteorites, which were probably the forms under which Amun and Seth were worshipped. The Theban fetish of Amun looks like a meteorite and so does the sacred object of the Cabasite nome. *Bi3* is not as Sethe thinks "metal in general", but a quite specific metal and as copper seems impossible it must be iron. *Bi3* is mentioned as offerings in the very early texts of the Unas and Pepi II pyramid (99). The man-made iron, the *bi3. n. t3* is first mentioned in a Denderah text of Neronic date (100). These data of Wainwright have been discussed by Cook (101) who quite aptly points out, that the equation thunderbolt : meteorite : omphalos is far from universally valid. Also we have no adequate proof that Min or Amun or Seth had any connections with meteorites and therefore Wainwright's reasoning stands only as an attractive hypothesis. Wainwright also never brought forward one text in which *bi3* must have meant iron, the old and recognised translation copper fits in just as well. If we take *bi3* to mean "copper, black (unrefined) copper" and if we remember that the Mexicans, for instance, call iron "tliltic teputzli" that is "black copper", there is no reason why we should not suppose that the

Egyptians thought their meteoric iron just a form of black, unrefined copper and that they only recognised its celestial origin much later and dubbed it *bi3. n. pt*, that is copper from heaven. Only when they had attained the full Iron Age and iron was smelted and worked in Egypt itself were copper and iron distinguished as separate metals and the expression *bi3. n. t3*, that is "iron from the earth" was coined. As long as there is no positive proof of another meaning and as long as it fits the translation without "technical impossibilities" we must translate *bi3* as "copper, black copper" though not as "metal (in general)" as Sethe proposed.

The oldest iron object from Egypt were predynastic beads from El Gerzeh (S.D. 72) found in a grave with an undisturbed mud layer covering it (102). Gowland still believed them to be man-made smelted iron, but Desch reported a nickel content of 7.5% which proves their meteoric origin. They were treated like other metal objects made from native metals and therefore have no special significance for the story of metallurgy (103). Other beads of the same period turned up in tombs no. 67 & 113 at El Gerzeh and tomb 1494 (Ermant).

The earliest man-made object of iron was formerly thought to be a piece of iron found by Vyse between the stones of the Great Pyramid, which many now believe to have been dropped by Vyse's own workmen (104), though his story of the discovery is remarkably complete and precise. Some think that it can not be explained away as a fragment of an excavating workmen's tool, as it is "a thin film of metallic iron with a more or less thick coating of its oxides". (105) But Rickard strongly doubts it and Lucas thinks that it is a recent piece of iron lost in the cracks during removal of the outer facing of the pyramid for modern construction, and it is now generally agreed that it is an intrusion. Dunham and Young (106) have drawn our attention to the fact G. A. Reisner excavating the rooms of the valley temple of the Third Pyramid on July 19, 1908 found "copper and stone vessels, together with a flint wand inscribed with the name of Cheops, and a mass of yellow colouring matter. Underneath were traces of decayed wood, and an oxidized red mineral not unlike iron rust; probably red oxide of copper (it was not attracted by a magnet)". Tests on the sample revealed the matter on the wand to be iron oxide and so was the "red oxidized matter". As nickel was absent they believe this to have been a piece of iron (terrestrial) used in the "opening of the mouth" ceremony in association with the magical set and a pśś-kf (flint wand). May be this was a piece of iron accidentally obtained in gold refining. A better attested piece is the Abydos lump found by Petrie in a hoard of copper objects in a VIth dynasty pyramid at Abydos (107). This lump of oxide is certainly of Old Kingdom date but there is no proof whether it was a tool or implement of any kind and we do not know why it was placed in this foundation deposit. It may have been a piece of iron produced accidentally.

Several other finds mentioned in literature can be traced back to writings by Maspéro, but his statements though apparently precise will not stand scrutiny, they are mostly cursory footnotes entirely written from memory and even the description of the same object varies in his different works, as Wainwright correctly remarks.

Fig. 42.
Small iron head rest and ring with wd3.t -eye of iron
both from tomb of Tutankhamun (After Carter)

A thin blade of meteoric iron (containing 9% of iron) inserted in a silver amulet in the form of a sphinx's head (Cairo Mus. No. J. 47314) may be of Old Kingdom date.

Another fiercely contested piece is the Buhen spear-head which Randall Mac Iver found at that site in Nubia opposite Wadi Halfa and which he assigns to the XIIth dynasty (at the latest XVIIIth dynasty). However, this socketed spearhead, one foot long, which certainly is man-made iron, looks very modern and is quite like the weapons still used by the natives of Nubia. Both shape and size make the find extremely doubtful, the more as Sudanese iron smelting proved much later than Gowland originally believed it to be and it is either a late intrusion in the grave where it was found or it belong to a later date and is an import from the north.

Prezworski mentions texts of the XIIth dynasty which are said to state that Egyptian ambassadors were sent to Nubia to get gold and iron ore but these can not be traced. The oldest text which may mention iron is the Abu Simbel text of the XIXth dynasty.

All the finds before the XVIIIth dynasty (and the New Kingdom), therefore were proved to be meteoric iron or else stand in grave doubt.

But the contact with the Hittites and the Amarna Age mean a great change for Egyptian metallurgy. Griffith found at Tell el Amarna a lump of oxidised iron firmly stuck to a bronze axe-head (1924) and there is a pair of iron bracelets roughly worked with dog's heads in the collection of Mrs. J. H. Rea (XVIIIth dynasty). Then there are the iron objects found by Carter in Tut-anch-amun's grave, a small amuletic iron head-rest, a gold bangle with a *wd3. t* eye of iron and an iron dagger, all made of wrought iron according to Lucas (108). The small implements found on the mummy are too slight to be used as tools and have some magical intention, perhaps for the "Opening of the Mouth" as Wainwright proposed, though there is no certainty whether the metal iron itself had a magical meaning in those days in Egypt. These iron objects may have been presented to Tut-anch-amun (as some others were presented to Amenhotep III according to the Amarna letters) by one of the kings of Western Asia. In Syria and Palestine iron, however, must still have been quite a new discovery in the early part of the XVIIIth dynasty as it is not included in the tribute lists from these parts.

Iron is said to be mentioned twice in the Ebers papyrus, but the *bi3 kśj* of Ebers 48.19 is not iron from Qesi in Upper Egypt (von Lippmann) but magnetite (Ebbell), and the *ir. pt* (Joachim's art-pet and translated "heaven-made iron") of Ebers 92.16 is some medicine (Ebbell).

By the end of the XVIIIth dynasty blue objects on the monuments are generally thought to represent iron implements, but no Egyptian text tells us of the introduction of iron and hair and eyebrows are also coloured blue. Lepsius had contended that wrought iron was coloured brown and "pure, true iron" or steel blue, just as the Homeric Age distinguished grey and violet-blue iron.

The slight imports of iron objects from the Hittites and from Mitanni, perhaps, also from Palestine have no great effect on the use of bronze, iron remained scarce for many centuries. In the battles against the Lybians only bronze weapons are taken and no iron object nor any trace of rust was found in the town of Gurob. Still there are the military forges of Gerar near the Egyptian frontier and in the papyrus Anastasi I a royal messenger has his chariots repaired in Joppa by iron-workers. An iron halberd was found in the sand foundation of Ramses III's temple at Abydos and an iron sword of Cretan type dates from the reign of Seti I, all about 1200 B.C. A century later are iron knives found in the bright arches of the Ramesseum. Carpenter's researches pointed out that between 1200 and 900 B.C. iron objects were carburised and quenched in Egypt, probably by foreign experts.

Perhaps by this time iron ores were worked in the eastern desert and near Aswan, though the former deposits are generally said to have been worked by the Romans only. The new methods of treating iron and the possibility of making steel were of course important, but bronze remained superior as a base material as it could be cast.

The first real set of iron tools dates from the Assyrian domination. They were found together with an Assyrian helmet at Thebes and they have a quite modern appearance, and may be of Syrian manufacture. They are probably remnants of Assurbanipal's expedition (666 B.C.).

By Saitic times iron becomes more common and we can say that Egypt entered the Iron Age in the course of the seventh century B.C. A scale of armour found in the palace of Apries (XXXVIth dynasty) is probably of Persian manufacture. But even the Carian and Ionian invaders of Egypt in this same century still carry offensive weapons made of bronze (109)! Herodotus finds iron quite common in Egypt. He tells us that the priests engaged in mummification "take a crooked piece of iron and with it draw out the brain" and in his discussion on the pyramids he sighs: "If this then is a true record, what a vast sum must have been spent on the iron tools used in the work and on the feeding and clothing of the labourers" (110). The latter passage is often taken as a proof that iron tools were used in building the pyramids, but of course Herodotus just talks in terms of his age, when iron tools were common even in Egypt. The Assyrian tools which we have mentioned are partly made of mild steel since the tools have been given an edge and they can be permanently magnetised. The source of this steel seems to be Assyria or Syria.

Iron statues are mentioned in the Harris papyrus (40. b. 11), but it is very doubtful whether cast iron is meant, they were probably chased from wrought iron or may even have been cut from haematite.

In the meantime an extensive iron industry developed on the rich deposits of ore mentioned by Strabo in the "island of Meroë" in Nubia. Garstang and Sayce have dated the beginnings of this industry in the ninth century B.C. (111), but they are now generally thought to be later than 700 B.C. Great mounds of slag enclose the city walls and by the "Birmingham of ancient Africa" this country passed from the Stone Age to the Iron Age. Perhaps this was the source from which the Sudan got its early iron-workers. Iron slag and crucibles have been found at Kerma, Kawa and the islands of Argo too. Formerly it was thought that this was the centre for the early iron in Egypt, but this can no longer be maintained now the chronology of the earlier remains in Nubia is placed on a better footing. Recent research (112) has proved that iron metallurgy spread from Egypt into Ethiopia (Kush), notably during the joint reign of the Ethiopian dynasty (XXVth) of Taharka (689—663 B.C.). Ingots of iron were found in the contemporary treasury of Sanam. Still iron remains rare in tombs anterior to king Amtalka (558—553 B.C.) when it becomes more frequent in the capital of Napata. On the other hand Herodotus (113) mentions that the "Ethiopians" in the army of Xerxes still have flint arrow-heads, but then these may have been more effective seeing the quality of contemporary iron. Iron had already become a trade object in the silent trade carried on with the inland tribes for gold. A true Iron Age started in Ptolemaic times when the kings of Egypt organised hunting expeditions for the capture of elephants. During the third century B.C., the reigns of Ptolemy III (245—222) to Ptolemy V (203—181) new towns arose such as Adulis, later Aksum, which became the holy city of the Ethiopians. Now Ethiopia became the centre of the trade with Africa. The Periplus of the Erythraean Sea mentions iron (to be made into spears by the natives), small axes, adzes and swords being imported in the region (A.D. 60) and later Indian iron and steel ("stomoma") sail up the Red Sea to Egypt. By 350 A.D. Meroë is an important production centre of iron and steel and Cosmas Indicopleutes (522 A.D.) reports that Meroë caravans trade salt and iron for the gold of the Fazoqli.

The Roman-Nubian remains of Karanog contain plentiful iron anklets and bracelets, etc. Thin sheet iron was cut into the shape of rounded arrow-heads about 3″ long, these objects are still used for money in Cordofan and called "hashish". Iron chisels were also found in the abandoned gold-mines of Aethiopia.

The Ptolemaic Age brings us the first proofs of local working of iron ores in Egypt. At Memphis, Daphnae and Naukratis slags and crucibles have been found. Papyri tell us that iron tools were served out to the quarrymen in this period (255—254 B.C., record in the Flinders Petrie Papyri II. 7). A grave-yard of the reign of Ptolemy II yielded a considerable quantity of iron. This local iron industry flourished in Ptolemaic and Roman times to disappear in the Late Empire and Byzantine period. The iron-smith is called chalkeus in the papyri and later siderourgoi, or siderochalkeis (IVth cy A.D.) Specialists as nailsmiths (helokopoi, kleidopoioi) (114) and also weapon-, knife- and strigil-smiths are mentioned. Every village seems to have had at least one smith, in larger places there were guilds who bought their bar-iron collectively. The work is paid for by weight. Tools and weapons are the earliest iron implements for such objects as vases, etc. bronze long remained in use. The prices of iron objects are known in the first three centuries A.D., also the taxes paid by a siderourgos or ironmon-ger, who pays 20 drachmae and 2 obols a year and iron figures in the lists of customs due on imports, for instance in the Fayum district (A.D. 104).

Palestine and Syria have yielded no objects of the third millennium, but the earliest finds date of the reign of Amenemhat III (about 1825 B.C.) This is a small inset of iron in a gold ring used as an amulet and found in a royal grave at Byblos (115). Next in age are seven iron objects mentioned in the temple inventory of Qatna in the days of Tothmes III (about 1475 B.C.). The Annals of Thotmes II mention among the booty of the seventeenth campaign in Syria "tribute of the chief of Ty. n'. y a silver vessel of the work of the Kftiyw together with vessels of bi3" which latter may well be iron objects, though there is no proof.

From Syria we have more evidence on early iron. At Ras Shamra (Minet el Beida) the excavators found a large ceremonial axe dating from the fifteenth or fourteenth century B.C. The iron blade is held in a copper mount inlaid with gold wire and ornamented with a boar's protome and the heads of two lions from whose mouths the blade emerges (116). From similar daggers represented on the walls of Yazi-likaya Schaeffer infers that such daggers or axes were gifts of the Mitanni to the Hittites or war-trophies.

Further evidence comes from the archives of Syrian towns. Docu-ments mainly of the middle of the second millennium B.C. were dis-covered at Qatna (the present Mishrifé), the most important of which are four inventories of the treasury of the goddess Nin-Egal. These mention seven small pieces of iron, six of which are mounted in gold like the Byblos amulet mentioned above (117). Other texts come from the archives of Alalakh (118) and Mari and date back to the fifteenth century B.C.

In one of the Alalakh tablets Ammitaku of Allalakh specifies that he has taken from "those who opposed him" a host of objects. This list ends with "ŠUKUR weapons: 3 of bronze, 5 of copper and 400 of *iron*". These ŠUKUR weapons were a kind of daggers, we also hear of a "chief of the swordsmen" (PA-GIŠ-ŠUKUR). The number of weapons captured may be exaggerated as is quite usual in ancient war-records, but here we undoubtedly have one of the earliest records of iron weapons in history. We would have liked to be informed on the region whence these ennemies came, probably this was the north. The Mari tablets too mention iron, for Aplachanda, king of Carcemish sends to his "brother" the viceroy of Mari by messenger certain delicacies and "an iron bracelet" (119), which clearly indicates the rarity of iron during this period.

Later Phoenician finds at Rachdieh and other places include arrow heads, rings and nails, but these are believed to be of later date (1000 B.C.).

In Palestine there is the Late Bronze Age ring found at Gezer, two axe blades from a watertunnel at the same site (about 1500 B.C.) and an implement with an iron shaft from Tell et-Mutesellim III (1500—1200).

We already discussed the iron workers at Joppa which are mentioned in the Papyrus Anastasi I about 1250 and certain proof of iron-working in Palestine was found at Gerar, Tell Džemme, which was occupied from the Hyksos period (perhaps later by the Philistines) onwards to Persian times. A broken steel dagger of 1350 was found there and another steel dagger (before 1300) in the neighbouring Beth-Pelet. Around 1200 iron is quite a common metal in this post on the Egyptian frontier and the period from 1200—1100 shows large objects, hoes, picks, plough irons, adzes, etc. One pick weighs about 7 lbs.! The earliest of these tools dates from about 1180—1170, as do the furnaces found in this place. Petrie thought that they were metallurgical furnaces smelting the ore from the Beersheba basin, but the absence of slags is fatal to his theory. More probably blooms or bars or iron were imported here from the north and reheated in the furnace, for proper fuel supplies for smelting are also far to seek. The large furnace was probably for forging and case-hardening weapons and tools. Hulme aptly compared them with the military *fabrica* of the Romans. The later furnaces are certainly just smith's hearths.

The Tell Qasila furnace, discovered by Maisler (120) is a crucible furnace, probably worked by copper- or bronze-smith and not suitable for smelting iron and hence this cannot be an argument to identify Tell Qasila with Early Israelite Jaffa, where iron-workers are mentioned by the Anastasi I papyrus about 1250 B.C.

A structure at Lachiš formerly thought to be a blast furnace, proved to be a pottery kiln, but iron was found here in the Fourth City (1400

B.C.) (121). From 1200 B.C. onwards, therefore, more iron objects begin to appear in Palestine like the lance-heads, knives, daggers and tools of Tell Džemme rings from Tell el-Fara, knives from Gezer, agricultural implements, adzes, axes and knives from Tell Beit Mirsim B, Tell et-Mutessilim IV (together with a smithy, iron slags and lumps of ore), Tell Ta'annek III and an iron knive from Jericho.

Then by 900 iron is very common at all these sites and the Iron Age can therefore be said to begin at least as early as 1000 B.C. with a transition period running from 1300 to 1000 B.C.

At Tell Beit Mirsim three ploughshares, a sickle and a knife dating back to the seventh century were found (122). Spectrographic analysis of this completely oxidized iron shows that it was an iron low in nickel and cobalt and hence terrestial, with a fairly low carbon content.

Now it is an interesting question whether the early smiths at Gerar were Philistines or whether they occupied the site at some later date. These Philistines either formed part of the Sea-peoples, who invaded Syria and Palestine and were held by Ramses III on the Egyptian frontier in 1194 B.C., or they came in their wake. At any rate they occupied the coastal plain between 1190 and 1160 and their power was not broken before the reign of Saul (1020). Though some like Witter have of late stated that these were of Illyrian stock and that they learnt iron-working from the Mitterberg people in their home country and then introduced iron into the Near East, it is now generally believed that they came from Western Asia Minor (Caria or Lycia) and that they were kinsmen of or befriended with the Minoans (123). The question of their superiority in iron-working is still difficult to solve for we have no archaeological traits of Philistine civilisation to guide us, in fact, we know next to nothing about their material culture. As they came from Asia Minor they may well have had contacts with this region and imported bar iron which they worked in Palestine. They certainly did not smelt it as their territory contained no ores worth mentioning. But we think that the finds at Gerar solve the question (if Petrie is right in supposing Philistine occupation there). The Philistines were blacksmiths as so many other peoples from Asia Minor. They certainly could not have worked the mines of the Lebanon, nor yet exploited then, as this region was outside their control. Still according to Scripture they had a "corner" in iron which was not broken until the reign of Saul (124) if we may believe i Sam. 13.19—22.

The Israelites were certainly unacquainted with iron at the time of their wanderings and they seem to have learnt the art from the Philistines and other pre-Israelite peoples by the time of their settlement (125) though many of the iron tools may have been bought or imported from the North or from the Philistines. In David's time the Hebrews had iron tools and weapons which his conquests in the north made familiar and which must have been advertised by the Hittite warriors in his service. Was not his friend called Barzillai, that is "man of iron" (126) like the famous Swedish chemist Berzelius?

The Israelites, however retained a strong religious feeling against iron forbidding the use of hewn stones for the altar (127) and though by the time of Amos (760) iron is in regular use even by the poorest and local smelting is quite common, there was no change in this taboo. Josephus says that not only was the altar in the Temple formed without iron tools, but this held too for the stones of the first temple. The Samaritan Pentateuch has an eleventh commandement prescribing the erection of two stones inscribed with the ten commandements on the plaster surface but "thou shalt not lift any iron thereon".

Still bronze must have remained in use quite long, the Bible mentioning it 83 times against iron weapons only four times. Iron ore is mentioned as plentiful and the iron smelting furnace rather than that of other metals is mentioned figuratively for great oppression (128). Iron is often used as a metaphor for unbreakable, strong, not to be pierced by arrows, hard, unyielding and unploughable earth. Of the objects manufactured from iron we are told of the sledge-hammer (*pattish*), anvil, knive, sharpening steel, cooking griddle, bars of the city gates, fetters and iron points for the threshing sledge. Armour was also made or imported (129). It appears in the lists of metals after copper but before lead and tin. Hellenistic treatises of Jewish-Egyptian origin refer to iron and steel as "*ballathà* of the Jews" (130), "steel" in the Authorised Version should often be read bronze or copper. The *paldâh* occuring in Nahum 11 : 3 is thought to mean the flashing steel scythe of the Assyrian war chariot.

The "northern iron" of Jer. 15 : 12 though given in the Vulgate as *ferrum ab aquilone* is probably Chalybian steel and the "bright iron" taken with cassia and calamus from the merchants of Dan and Javan (131) may refer to Ionian steel though others say that the Phoenicians got these materials from Uzal (S. Arabia) and that it might be Indian steel! The *ferrum infectum* in the stores of Massada (132) is certainly not cast iron but unworked wrought iron, nor should we read "cast iron" for the *sideros chytós* of the Septuagint version of Job 40 : 18, but bars of iron or blooms are meant.

The "iron bedstead of Og" (Deut. 3 : 11) is probably a basalt sar-cophagus, as the peasants east of the Jordan often call basalt iron, and this makes it probable too that the iron teeth of the threshing sledge (Amos 1 : 3) are really pieces of basalt which are still used for these instruments.

Sirach describes a blacksmith's shop in details (133) and also the cutting of the conduit to the pool of Siloam under Hezekiah with iron tools. The temple of Solomon is said to have contained no less than 100.000 talents of iron (134). The blacksmith is geherally called *charaš barzel* but also *nappach* (user of bellows) or *pechami* (user of charcoal). He must have been a familiar figure in the reigns of the later kings for Nebuchadnezzar sent thousands of smiths into exile (135).

Iron-working was also well established in the north. Philon of Byblos states on the authority of Sanchuniathon the Phoenician historian (1200 B.C.?) that his people were the inventors of iron working guided by a magician called Chrysor Chorosh and the Chronos of the Phoeni-cians (Melkart) shaped himself a spear and sword of iron on the advice of a goddess "Athene". In later times North Syria was famous as an iron-working centre. An Aramaic dedication of a Nabatean "*faber aerarius*" was found at Puteoli and Diocletian established large im-perial armament factories in Antioch, Damascus and Edessa, which must have had some connection with such private workshops of eralier centuries.

If we now turn to *India* we find that it is difficult to fix an exact date for the beginning of the Iron Age. There are strong proofs of the existence of iron in the Rgvedic age (136). Iron is described in these sacred writings as ayas. The "*asi*" or sacrficial knife, the "*svadhiti*", (sacrificial axe), the *ksura* or razor and the "*khâdi*", the quoit ring worn traditionally by every Hindu woman on the left hand are all made or iron. The metal serves as a metaphor for the legs of strong horses, weapons are tipped with ayas, etc. It is smelted by the karmâras or smiths. Both the *karmâra* and the *dhmât*! (literally "blower") are iron-smiths. *Ayas* is said to be hard, tough, strong, tenacious, ductile and malleable. Banerjee believes that steel was also already manufactured in this period by the wellknown "wootz crucible process", using the leaves of certain plants and bird's wings as carburizing matter.

It is certainly used and mentioned in the period when the Yayurveda and Atharvaveda were composed, its name is often given as *cyâma ayas* (dark copper). From other, later developments between this period and that of Alexander, it seems pretty certain that iron was introduced in Northern India sometime between 700 and 600 B.C. Another iron-using people, burying their dead in cairns arrived from Persia through Makran and Baluchistan into Sind and the North-West Frontier province of Pakistan somewhere between 700 and 400 B.C., the period when the Dravidians introduced iron metallurgy into the South. As our knowledge of Indian prehistory is still in a flux, this picture may change in the next few years (137).

Fig. 43.
Primitive Indian blast furnace, Nagpur (After Begbie)

Between 500 and 200 B.C. iron weapons became general. Iron swords and daggers were found in early graves at Tinnevelly (300 B.C. and at Buddha Gaya.

The earliest examples of wootz steel were weapons found in early graves of the seventh and sixth century B.C. for instance n the tombs of Wurri-Coan, Central India. However, most of the famous iron pillars and beams are much later than originally claimed, all of them date from the first century A.D. or later. By this time there was a flourishing iron industry, often practised by wandering iron-smiths and there are many references to their craft in the Upanishads, where for instance the production of a bloom is described as "a mass of iron overcome by the fire and hammered by the workmen takes numerous shapes and forms." The size of these pillars and beams points to a settled industry as well which in later centuries was able to copy European models very quickly. Stories have been circulated about the secret composition of the iron of these pillars and beams, because they have not rusted in the places where they were erected. Britton cleared up this problem by proving that it was only the climate that made them resistant to corrosion (138) not the composition. Samples taken to Europe rusted just as quickly as modern ones. They were all hammered, welded together from smaller pieces of iron produced directly from ores, and remain a marvellous example of the possibilities of primitive technique.

There are of course different readings of the wootz process and Ure gives one which differs slightly from that which we have discussed, but which adds some interesting details (139): The bloomery is pear-shaped, 5' at the base and 1' at the top, built up of clay in a few hours and ready the next day after firing to dry it. The front opening 1' wide is opened up after every smelting. The bellows are simple goat's skins. Bamboo nozzles end in tuyères of clay. The furnace is first filled with charcoal and lighted. The moistened ore is then filled on top of the coals without flux and covered by charcoal, and these are then supplied constantly during three to four hours. The furnace is then stopped, opened and the bloom is removed with a pair of tongs from the bottom of the furnace. The bloom is then cut up into small pieces to pack the crucible better. These crucibles are made of refractory clay. Mixed with the charred husks of rice, the leaves of Asclepios gigantea or Convulvulus laurifolia and the wood of Cassia auriculata they are packed tightly. The charge is seldom over one pound mixed with the proper amount of wood chopped in small pieces. The mouth of the crucible is stopped with a handful of tempered clay, which is rammed closely to exclude air. When the plugs are dry, 24 crucibles are built up in a furnace arch and kept covered with charcoal and now subjected to a fire aided with blast air for about $2\frac{1}{2}$ hours. Then the furnace is allowed to cool and the broken crucibles yield the wootz in the form of a cake. The whole process though seemingly simple is one of long standing and the result of considerable experience. The magnetite usually worked contains about 72% of iron, the yield is about 15%.

If not exported but worked on the spot, the steel, a mixture of carbon rich and carbon poor iron is forged many times and etched with acid to obtain the "damask" design. It is then glowed, not over 700° C and carefully cooled.

The resistence to rust of certain kinds of iron and steel did not escape the ancients, for we find Pliny telling us (140): "Iron is protected against rusting by white lead, gypsum and pitch. Rust is called by the Greeks the antipathy (natural opposite) of iron. It is said that rusting may be prevented by a suitable religious ceremony too and that an iron chain still exists, at the town of Zeugma on the Euphrates which was used by Alexander the Great in bridging the river there. Those links which have been renewed are a prey to rust, from which the original links are quite free." It is not stated whether this was Chalybian or Indian steel.

Herodotus tells us about the Indian contingent in the Persian army, that "the Indians wore arrows also of cane with iron at the point" (141) and indeed ten such arrow-tips were found on the battlefield of Marathon and now reside in the British Museum.

Ctesias mentions two wonderful swords of Indian steel given to the Persian king, and Quintius Curtius (142) says that a present of 100 talents of Indian steel was given to Alexander by Porus, the Indian king. The matter of some 30 lbs. of steel would hardly have been considered a present worthy of the conqueror of the world if this had not been a speciality not manufactured by any other nation in the world in his times. This has led many authors to exaggerate the antiquity of Indian steel and to claim, as we have seen, that the ancient Egyptians imported and used it. Another source of difficulties is the word *adamas* which does not yet always denote steel in these times. Ptolemy's *adamas* for instance may be steel, but it is more probably the diamond from Sabarae, Cosa and the Sankh branch of the Brahmani (143).

The fine swords made of Indian steel had been famous since the days of Ctesias and Roman trade in India steel and iron was important. We must take the Seres mentioned by Pliny as being the Cheras of the Malabar coast, though China had an early industry, which however, is localised in Shantung (144). But Indian is the epithet applied by the Periplus and other authors and by the Digest-list. Now the Periplus gives Indian iron with sword blades at Adulis and other African ports and the author knows that "likewise there are imported from the inland regions of Ariaca Indian iron and steel", yet he did not see any metal at Indian ports. So Indians sent their ships with steel to the Axumites, who kept it secret, perhaps allowing the Romans to attribute the metal to remote China. Today the Indians make steel at Madras, Mysore, Punjab, Kashmir, Bengal, Rajputna, Assam, Burma, but especially at Hyderabad, and it is no wonder, therefore, that the Greeks attributed it to Ariaca and the Chera kingdoms. Saumaise points out that a special Greek treatise was written in Antiquity on the tempering of Indian steel and Chwostow may be right in supposing that the bulk of the Roman imports consisted not in large quantities of ore or steel but of objects fashioned from iron

and steel. They worked them into fancy cutlery as Clemens shows
(145) and perhaps into armour in Damascus, whither Indian steel was
sent, and at Irenopolis. The iron and steel attributed to the Seres, therefore, comes from India, not from the Sind town of Haiderabad but
from the central district and it was exported solely from North-West
India (146). *Ferrum Indicum* figures on the list of articles subject to duty
it Alexandria. Later the cakes of wootz, called *kus*, were exported in
large quantities to Syria, Persia, and Arabia. Damascus continued to
be a centre of the working of Indian iron since Diocletian founded
his armament factories there, until these were carried off to Samar-
kand and Chorassan by Tamerlane in 1399. The damask steel is
therefore an Indian product, which is still appreciated by the tribes of
Assam, who work the imported iron rods into swords, etc. The value
of these weapons depends upon the number of the welding lines on the
blade (147).

The antiquity of the iron industry of *China* has been greatly exaggerated, the father of Confucius is said to have been strong enough to lift
an iron door, the Iron Age is said to date from the Chou dynasty and
to have been introduced into Japan by 500 B.C. Recently Needham
(148) published an up-to-date summary of our knowledge on this
point and these were his conclusions (as far as related to our subject-
matter):

1. In China metallic iron seems to have been known only from about
   the sixth century B.C. onwards. If the first products of smelting
   were blooms of carbon-free iron, as in the western part of the Old
   World, they and their "Stückofen" furnaces left no trace, either
   textual or archaeological, of their existence.

2. Cast iron appears from the fourth century B.C. onwards at latest,
   used both for agricultural implements, moulds for tools and implements, and weapons of war. Factors connected with this early
   appearance of the fully liquid metal (some seventeen centuries
   before it could be obtained at will in the West) probably included
   the following:

   a. the use of ores exceptionally rich in phosphorus, or the addition
      of small amounts of phosphorus-rich minerals to the blast-
      furnace charge,

   b. the availability of good refractory clays, permitting not only
      the construction of adequate though small blast-furnaces, but
      also the use of the crucible processes in some parts of the country,

   c. the application of reciprocating motion to double-cylinder bel-

lows for metallurgical purposes as early as the fourth century
B.C.

d. the invention of the double-acting single-cylinder piston bellows,
giving a strong and continuous blast, used probably from the
second century B.C. onwards, and provided with iron tuyères
at least as soon as the beginning of the third century A.D.,

e. the application of water-power to these bellows, or perhaps to
hinged types even larger, in the first century A.D. or a little
before,

Fig. 44.
Iron reduction furnace, Shansi, China (After Read)

f. the use of coal, at least from the fourth century A.D., perhaps
long before, permitting the building of a very hot pile arond
crucibles, the contents of which were protected from sulphur
by luting.

The consequent abundance of cast iron in ancient and medieval
China constituted a radical difference from the siderurgical industry
in the rest of the Old World, and led to many corollaries.

3. If steel was produced by cementation of wrought iron in the Chou
and Chhin periods (as would be expected from European parallels)
this left no traces, textual or archaeological, so far discoverable.

4. On the contrary, the characteristic Chinese process of steelmaking
was decarburisation direct from cast iron, not the addition of carbon
to pure iron. This method, known for many centuries as the "hundred refinings", depended on the discreet employment of an oxidizing blast of cold air, and developed side by side with the more

drastic process of fining cast iron to wrought iron. It seems to have been fully in use from the second century B.C. onwards.

5. By the seventeenth century A.D. this oxidizing technique had led to procedures in China and Japan whereby a mass of molten iron was subjected to cold blast so that something like cast steel resulted.

6. From the fifth century A.D. onwards a great deal of steel was made in China by a method which we call, inadequately, "co-fusion". In this technique, wrought iron and cast iron were heated together, the pasty lumps of the former being bathed in the fully liquid carbon-rich phase. Though in the eleventh and twelfth centuries sometimes considered of less high quality than the decarburization steel, it could, under suitable circumstances, match it, as we know from modern experimental work. A reconstruction of the mediaeval Chinese process has given good eutectoid steel. The co-fusion method may have been known to the Arabs in the eleventh century and was known and used in Europe from the sixteenth century, though probably not extensively.

7. The welding of hard and soft steels to make the blades of weapons was known and practised in China at least as early as the third century A.D. In the seventh century, the art was transmitted to the Japanese, who centuries later brought it to the height of perfection, though after the sixteenth century it was little cultivated in its Chinese home. Since the procedure was also widely known and widely used among the Western European peoples (though with certain differences of detail) from the first to the ninth centuries A.D., it seems likely that we must seek for the original focus in Central Asia, perhaps in some cities in Sinkiang, whence it could have spread in both directions from about the second century B.C.

8. The damascene pattern in the Chinese culture-area derived, how-ever, not only from the welding process just mentioned, but also (to a much lesser extent) from the importation of the hyper-eutectoid wootz steel of India, in relatively small amounts. This trade seems to have taken several routes; e.g. Persia and Kashmir as well as Malaya and Indonesia."

In this summary we have omitted such conclusions as would lead us to subjects belonging to later iron metallurgy. Read has devoted several studies to this early Chinese iron industry (149). In Shansi iron is still made as of old. Limonite and haematite are mixed with 50% by volume of coal in crucibles and burnt in furnaces. The bloom is sold to wrought iron smiths, smaller pieces go to the manufacturers of cast iron. These mix them with coal in crucibles and heat them in small furnaces worked with hand-bellows. The contents of several crucibles are poured into one, which is then used to fill the mould. The high phosphorus content of the coal makes casting easy, the cast-iron melts at 980° C that is lower than copper. Crucible steel is not made at present by the Chinese, they always resort to case-hardening. Pinel (150) examined nine specimens of Chinese cast iron ranging in date from 502 to 1093 and found that they had a remarkable low phosphorus content taking in mind that of the coal used. Three pieces were cast in a single piece, but in most cases the composition varies largely even in the piece itself. Sand moulds were used in the earlier periods. The five M. high Buddha from Tsinanfu dates of the sixth century; the biggest piece is a cast iron lion of 953 A.D. which is 20' high and 18' long! But even the early Han pieces are already large for a young technique. Iron bells were made early as they are said to chase spirits!

There it a remarkable document on the importance of early Chinese iron manufacture in the form of a treatise by Huan K'uan written in the later part of the first century B.C. and containing a discussion held in 81 B.C. on the salt and iron monopolies exploited by the state (151). Already two early Chinese industrialists, I-tun and Kuo Tsung, had amassed princely fortunes in the production of both commodities and other families are recorded as prosperous iron workers under the early Han dynasty. But after favouring agriculture under the early emperors the later princes had to resort to various expedients to replenish the treasury which was depleted by the reduction of the land tax. The Yen-T'ieh-Kuan offices were instituted in 119 B.C. under Han-Wu-Ti's reign to control the iron and salt industries and to sell these product at a high rate yielding a large profit. In the year 115 "officers to equalize distribution" were appointed and a "bureau of standardisation and equalisation" was set up in the capital (110 B.C.). Though the treasury deficits disappear soon, great discontent followed and the iron implements in use standardised by the state were greatly criticised. The discussion recorded in this document was commanded by the Emperor and was held between the Crown officers and representatives of the Literati and Worthy classes, which showed up all the defects of state monopolies. In this document castings are mentioned as "jung-chu" that is "meltfuse".

Stanislaus Julien says that the secret of casting iron was brought to Ferghana by Chinese deserters in the second century B.C. but he states no source for this contention. Anyway this was the route by which the process reached the West and the Arabs had adopted it from China long before Mohammed. Chinese iron and steel were exported both to the West and to the South. I-Tsing says that the inhabitants of the Eastern Ocean valued it very much (680 A.D.) and that the Malayans were afraid of its "poison". Marco Polo mentions the Chinese iron industries which in later centuries were mainly located in Shantung.

However famous Persian and Parthian steel was, the birth-date of the Iron Age in *Persia* is still uncertain, though it is quite close to the original centre of iron-working in the Armenian mountains. The excavations of Tepe Gyan I (1400—1100) showed that iron was still scarce in this site, a few daggers, spear- and arrow-heads, rings and bracelets were found but no tools. At Susa a lump of iron, an iron bar,

Fig. 45.
Chinese crucible furnace opened (After Read)

an oxidised ring, iron nails, etc. were found but they can not be earlier than 1100 B.C. Many iron finds come from the Talyš region, but iron weapons are still partly of bronze! Their date is certainly not 2500 B.C. as some would have it but probably 1200—1100 B.C. Syalk A (1100 B.C.) yielded only a dagger and a spear-head, but in Syalk B (850 B.C.) there is a great variety and quantity of iron objects. In Luristan though bronze still prevailed, many objects dating of 1000—750 B.C. have useful parts of iron and decorative parts of bronze and gradually the objects are entirely fashioned of iron (152). In the necropolis of Ab-i-Zal (eighth century) the adzes and axes are of iron as the greater part of the fibulae, though the bracelets are mainly made of bronze. These few data go to show that the Iron Age begins about 1000 B.C. The iron industry of north-western Persia is said to be very old. A century ago Robertson reported (153) on the iron mines of Caradagh near Tabriz. Magnetic iron predominates with haematite and a mixture of the two is used by the smelters. The furnaces contain two hearths, the smaller 14″ square and 9″ deep, the larger sunk 3′ more into the ground, and with walls 2-3′ high covered with stones capable of resisting fire. These are supposed by Hulme to be a natural draught furnace coupled later with the second blast-driven hearth. The packing with a central dam of charcoal recalls the Corsican method of smelting. The blooms produced are marked. Were these mines already the sources of supplies of Assyria? Robertson calculated that one mine with a pro-

Fig. 46.
Chinese iron stove (150 B.C.), probably the oldest cast-iron object still extant
(After Laufer)

duction of 200 Tons a year might have produced 2857 years from the area excavated.

It is certain that Iranian steel was famous early. Artaxerxes (about 450 B.C.) is said to have given Ctesias a sword of Indian steel, but the Roman authors praise Parthian steel second only to that of the Seres. This was even exported to China in later days under the name *pin t'ieh* or *ki-pin* (Kashmir) as a product of Sassanian Persia (154). The Ko-Ku-Yao says that its surface exhibited the patterns of the winding lines of a conch or that it was like "sesame seeds and snow". The price of swords inlaid with gold threads and polished to make the pattern visible was higher than that of silver. It was said to be so hard and sharp that it could cut stone. The term *pin* is probably derived from the Iranian '*spaina* and the Pamir *spin*. The Iranian *pûlâd* occurs in Tibetan, Armenian, Ossetic, Grusian, Turkish and Russian and the Mongol is *bolot*! In the Tsin period Chinese writings mention *hu t'ieh* (iron of the Hu in Turkestan) (265—419 A.D.).

As early as the Han dynasty the Chinese modelled their scale and chain armour on Parthian examples. The Persian troops of 480 B.C. had scale armour as in the time of Heliodorus, but the Parthians and later Persians had true mail with links rivetted together (Suidas), which was still famous and often praised by medieval writers. The Arabs borrowed the coat of mail from the Parthians and spread it. Thus the Sudanese names of weapons are all Arabic (155) and the thousand years of feudal Arabic domination had a great influence of the art of war of the Sudanese and other African tribes.

The Turks were also famous weaponsmiths who worked the iron ores of the Altaï for the Avars until their fall (552 A.D.). Their name seems to mean "iron helmets" (156).

The country of the largest iron output in Arabian time was Persis, but Beirut, Kabul and Kerman had important mines too. Of the latter province Marco Polo tells us (157): "In the kingdom of Kierman there are also veins of steel. They manufacture here in great perfection all articles necessary for warlike equipment" and he also mentions the mines of Kabul. The mines of Ferghâna were famous for a very ductile kind of iron which they produced. A yearly tribute of 1300 iron vases or pieces of sheet iron was sent thence to Baghdad.

In Arabia (Bahrein, Oman and Jemen) there was a very old iron industry working with iron and steel imported from India, Persia and China. Bahrein was the centre of the manufacture of lances, Jemen and Muta specialised in damascened steel. Syria and especially Damascus remained an important centre and in the West Arabs worked the iron mines of Sicily and even Africa, whence iron was exported to India for further treatment.

The desert warriors were always in need of iron. In 964 the Carmates sent to Saifeddaulah in Tiberias to demand iron and this prince took the iron gates of Raqqah and even the weights of the merchants and surrendered them. Then the Carmates sailed down the Euphrates to Hit and took this iron into the desert.

There are several references to iron in the Koran and more particularly the fifty-seventh Sura called Iron, but as it is a gift of Allah, the

Mohammedans have never tabood iron as other peoples have done.

Alkindi (873) wrote a book "on the properties of swords" in which he distinguishes female iron which can not be hardened (Mermahâni: that is nermâhen, soft iron) and the male kind which can easily be hardened (Sâburqâni probably "iron from Shaburan). Magnetic iron can be made by adding certain substances to wrought iron, certain others produce the silverwhite steel (fûlâd), sometimes green and blue-tinted steel, also the "damask type (Firindj) looking like veined malachite", which is used for needles and bells. The best iron is *al-hindî* (*al-hinduwânî*), which comes from Qalah, Ceylon, Jemen, Basrah, or Damascus, but above all from China.

Alfaqih (eighth century) says that iron is produced in Egypt and his contemporary Ibn Hauqal (902—968) states that "in Tûs they win a red-brown ochre like the Egyptian haematite, which sometimes gives the male, at other times the female iron."

In the Arabian Nights huge walls of iron are mentioned and also the old story of the magnetic mountain in the Indian Ocean. Iron also figures largely in Persian epic literature. Firdusi tells that Shah Dshemshid made iron weapons and Feridun had a banner made of the apron of his smith Kawe. Special weapons are made by hardening Indian and Chinese iron and steel with blood.

The story of iron in ancient *Mesopotamia* is still fragmentary too. Black pigment used on pottery at Al Ubaid and Tell Halaf proved to be magnetic oxide of iron, and haematite appears quite early as a seal-stone. An iron object found in a grave at Al Ubaid was examined by Desch and proved to have 10.9% of nickel. It is believed to have been forged from meteoric iron at a comparitively low temperature (158). Next come three early pieces of man-made iron all dating from the early dynastic period (3000-2700 B.C.) and all found quite recently. There is the fragment of iron found in grave G. 67, Tell Chagar Bazar, by Mallowan (159) which was analysed by Desch and can not possibly be of meteoric origin. Parrot reports fragments of iron found at Mari near the remains of the pre-Sargonic temple of Ishtar (160). Then there is the bronze open-work handle of a dagger found at Tell Asmar which contained the remains of an iron blade, that was certainly of terrestrial origin (161). Frankfort suggests that this knife is very likely an importation from the north and that iron was occasionally produced and used during the third millennium in Transcaucasia and Armenia but was not exported as it was less servicable than well-hammered copper or cast bronze. The spread of iron in the later second half of the second millenium is due not to the discovery of the smelting of iron ores but to new methods of working the metal ("steeling").

As no smelting sites of this early date were found near these pieces or in the rest of Mesopotamian sites, it is suggested that they were imported pieces, probably from the highlands as Frankfort suggested.

It is unknown to the author whether the word "parzillu" (iron) occurs in any text of Gudea's reign as Boson claimed (162), but the earliest use of this word is found in a fragment of a tablet of the first dynasty of Susa from that town, which mentions along with gold, silver and ivory a "ḫullam pa-ar-zi-li", an iron helmet, and it would seem from this text of the early second millennium that iron was still rare. (163). Mostly parzillu is not spelt out but written with the Sumerian signs AN.BAR the pronounciation of which is unknown in Sumerian, though it possibly reads bar.gal, a word adopted from the Accadian parzillu. This word has itself been borrowed from a non-Semitic language, for Hall, Dussaud and Zimmern point to the non-Semitic but Asianic ending-ill.

AN.BAR can be translated "heaven-metal" or "star-metal" and thus would point to the meteoric origin of early Sumerian iron according to some. In the famous epic of Gilgameš there is a reference to a "meteor falling from heaven" (2.i.6), but not as some state to "death by iron", as the relevant passage reads "death during battle".

That the Sumerians, however ignorant of terrestial iron, did distinguish the different iron ores will be clear from the table VII.

Even during the Sumerian Renaissance of the Ur III period iron seems to have remained scarce. At Telloh iron objects such as beads, hooks, a bracelet and a lump of ore were found and though said to belong to the Ur III or Larsa period, they are loosely catalogued among the objects which are "not Graeco-Aramean", an indication which makes them useless to archaeologists. Iron weapons and tools appear in the Kapara stratum at Tell Halaf together with a movable hearth with bars of iron, perhaps a brazier (2000 B.C.). But in Mesopotamia proper a few years later under the reign of Hammurabi iron is still valued at one-eighth of its weight in silver (164).

The excavations of Yorgan Tepe yielded a dagger blade of bronze in a haft of iron dating from the Churrite period (1600—1375); and an iron foundation tablet of Tukulti Ninurta I (1280—1261) was found at Assur.

The Amarna letters mention iron rings covered with gold and ceremonial daggers but the tablets of a big Babylonian banking firm a

Table VII

The nomenclature of the iron ores

Sumerian	Accadian	Modern
ZID . ZID . AN . BAR		powder of iron
AN . BAR	*parzillu*	iron
ªAN . BAR		iron stone, iron ore
ªKA		iron ore, ochre (esp. red ochre)
ªKA . GÍG		black ochre
ªKA . SIG₇		yellow ochre
ªKA . PAR		white ochre, spathic iron ore
ªKA . GI . NA	*ªšadânu*	hard (heavy) iron ore, haematit
ªKA . GI . NA . DIB . BA	*ªšargubbu*	magnetic iron ore
ªKA . GI . NA . TIL . LA		ferrum vivum
ªBIL	*ªšadânu baltu*	pyrites (iron), fire stone
ªŠÁR . GUB . BA	*ªšadânu ṣabitu*	iron pyrites and its decomposition products
(ªZUR . ŠÁR . GUB . BA;		
ªGI . RIM . ŠÁR . GUB . BA)	*ªmarḫaši*	marcasite

century later (1395—1242) mention all metals but iron. Still at this period more art objects appear with bronze and iron parts. In Assyria there is certainly no iron industry by the thirteenth century and it is suggested that Mesopotamia had still to turn to the west or the north for supplies. In northern Syria the iron-using culture is suddenly introduced in the twelfth century. It is possible that the migrations of the "Peoples of the Sea" are connected with the changes wrought by a more prevalent use of iron from this period onwards. The Assyrians certainly adapted the "harder" way of fighting like they previously had learnt the lessons of horsemanship and organisation from the Hittites (165). They adopted iron weapons, possibly importing them or bars of iron from the north and west and their use of the new iron weapons enabled them to start their extensive military conquests.

Shalmenaser I (1276—1257) records "foundation tablets or iron" buried when rebuilding the temple Eharsagkurkurra (ARL, I, 120). Tiglath Pileser I (1115—1103) tells of his hunting expedition "with my mighty bow, with my iron spear and with my sharp darts" (166).

With Tukulti Ninurta II (890—884) we enter the full Iron Age. This king mentions that he took "iron" from the inhabitants of the Nairi (Khabur) region (167) and that on a later expedition he cuts his

way through the mountains upstream of the Euphrates with axes and
"iron pickaxes" (168). But still 1 talent (60 Kgrs.) are assessed at sixteen
shekels of silver (about 120 grammes) and a slave at 30—40 shekels
(169), Assur-nasir-pal II (883—859) very often refers to iron in his
inscriptions. He takes iron from the city of Sûru (170) and the tribute
of Sangar, the king of the land of Hatte was 250 talents of iron (171), that
of Kunulua the royal city of Lubarna of Hattina 100 talents. Iron was
placed among the spoils in the new palace of Qalah (172) where it
was found by Layard in 1867! Hatchets of iron were used to pave the
way of the troops and from the Nairi lands he takes no less than 300
talents of iron (173). It will be observed that this iron always comes
from the mountain highlands to the north and the west of Assyria.

Shalmaneser III (858—824) receives iron as a tribute of the Cilician
cities and from Hattina (174) and later he takes 400 talents of iron from
the Hattinites, 30 from Haîanu of Mount Amanus and from Sangara cf
Carcemish 100 talents (175).
Adad Nirari III receives iron as a tribute from the town of Mari and
no less than 5000 talents from Damascus (176).

Sargon II (721—705) uses iron on a lavish scale. He takes it from
Khaldia near Lake Van, not only in the form of bars but iron ovens,
lamps, etc. (177). In his palace large quantities of weapons, armour,
rings, nails, picks, and tools were found, together with bars of unworked iron nearly 150 Tons, of good soft iron (not steel!), free of
nickel and manganese according to Desch. When used by a native
smith it proved as good as modern Persian iron (178). The rough bars
are 12 to 19″ long and $2\frac{1}{3}$—$5\frac{1}{2}$″ thick, roughly tapered at each end and
pierced by a single jagged hole, weighing from 8 to 44 lbs. Similar bars
and pieces are common in Roman times and the type of ingot survived
in Sweden and Finland until 1870. Sennacherib receives iron daggers
from the king Hezekiah and under his reign hard stone is quarried
with iron picks (179).

There are several interesting texts relating to iron from these days.
Tablets from Niniveh edited by Johns give the names of 17 smiths,
always called nappachu and never gurgurru or smelter, they are therefore real blacksmiths working with imported iron. One tablet mentions
purchases of iron in Commagene, Harran, Khalhi and other districts
to the north-west of Assyria. In Harran 75 talents of iron are bought
for sixteen shekels of silver through the intermediary of a smith and
the price of the iron goes down as iron tools become quite common.
A central storehouse for iron is mentioned in a tablet (181) which

speaks of a "wooden building wherein the iron is stored at Assur" that needs repairs very badly. And another text gives details on the theft and recovery of "iron which the king my lord gave to the smith" (182).

The Neo-Babylonian king Nabonidus (c. 550 B.C.) got his iron from Mount Amanus and Mount Lebanon. A text of this Neo-Babylonian period (625—538) refers to different qualities of iron which have varying prices accordingly (183). One weight of silver can buy 240 units of iron from Iamana, but 361 to 406 units from Labnana. There-

Fig. 47.
Pieces of wrought iron, found in Sargon's palace of Niniveh
(After V. Place, Niniveh)

fore the iron from Mount Amanus seems to have been of better quality than the Lebanon iron. In another text of the above-mentioned king silver is valued at 225 times its weight in iron (184), in a further text (185) at no less than 624 times its weight. This points to the identification of different qualities of iron on the market in some way or other. Iron was then already common as a building material, for instance iron clamps were used in the bridges of Babylon (186).

Very little is known of the story of iron in *Armenia and Caucasia* for the lack of proper archaeological data from these countries. From the Assyrian data we have seen how important this country must have been as a source of supply to Mesopotamia. The big city of Tušpa in Urartu (known under Shalmenaser I (1250)) was founded about 840 by new invaders in this region who were formerly thought to

have brought the knowledge of iron from their original home Thrace
(187). This is now generally rejected, for iron is very plentiful in these
regions as soon as it is mentioned in Assyrian texts. The inhabitants
hewed out rock dwellings with iron tools. Their gods, the Khaldi,
from the region often takes its name, are associated by some with the
Chaldians of Pontus, and they are perhaps borrowed from the Hittites
as they included their god Teshub. It is not know whether the aborigines of this country, Herodotus' Alorodians, had any connection with
iron-working or with the metal culture of Pontus. It has been suggested
that much of the metalwork attributed to Assyria was actually made
in Van, the artistic traditions of which were transmitted by the Medes
to Achaemenid Persia (Herzfeld). The introduction of the Iron Age
in Mesopotamia is certainly due to the extensive booty of iron taken
from these highlands. In classical times iron from these regions was
shipped in Sinope and Trebizond.

In Transcaucasia a few ornaments of iron appear in the thirteenth
century in the Gžanda-Karabeg region, then in the next two centuries
iron weapons which do not differ typologically from the bronze ones.
In Georgia and Armenia iron appears in the same period. The earliest
finds in the Kuban area are mostly incrustations and it looks as if iron
is much later here than in the south. Iron then grows common in the
ninth century, the Kasbek, Georgian and Lelvar region yielded plentiful iron weapons but the full Iron Age is the Scythian period. In Southern Russia iron penetrates by 800 and grows common in the sixth
century B.C.

Recent excavations in Azerbaijan have also yielded early samples
of terrestial iron. The report says (188): "All the early pieces of iron
in the Near East dating between 3000 and 2000 B.C. belong to the last
three centuries of that period except the piece found at Tell Asmar.
Such uniformity is not unlikely when it is realized how few examples
of the metal there are of third millennium date, and how improbable
it would be that they should be the result of independent invention
in a series of adjacent lands, especially since there are few known pieces
of iron from later centuries before 1200 B.C. It is possible to draw
the conclusion that the people who entered Azerbaijan at the time
when the culture of the D period was established, toward the end of
the third millennium (now more generally believed to be somewhat
later than 1500 B.C.), were the first people there to try to make objects
of iron. Since they and related folk may have spread very widely all
over the Near East, it is possible that the appearance of iron objects

in many countries is due to the arrival there of branches of these people". We are inclined to agree with Erich (189) and date this migration of iron-smiths into Azerbaijan back to at most 1500 B.C. and more probably some two centuries later.

We must now to *Asia Minor*, where we find information as to the occurence of early iron in Troy very confused and doubtful. Useful iron does not seem to appear before the destruction of Troy VI in the twelfth century (190).

The only early objects are small ornaments and a needle from Alaca Hüyük III (about 2500 B.C.) but many pieces formerly dated 2000 B.C. and earlier are now considered to be considerably later.

The Kültepe or Kaneš business letters of the end of the third millenium mention a metal "amutum" which is five times as expensive as gold and 40 times as expensive as silver. Goetze considers this metal to be iron and this was confirmed by later documents (191). Sayce has stated that iron was mentioned in two letters of this collection but the KÙ.AN of Clay No 50, 1.9 read by Sayce parzi-ili should be read kaspu and refers to silver, the same signs occur in lines 18, 25, and 26 of the same letter. Again in letter Clay No. 92.1.12 Sayce read barzi to mean iron but this word means impost (it reoccurs in CCT III.37.8).

We have mentioned that the word parzillu is first found in a tablet of the first Susan dynasty (2200—1962) and that it is probably of non-Semitic origin on account of the suffix -ill. The Hittite signs for iron are AN.BAR or AN.BAR.GE, though here again as in Sumerian the pronounciation is unknown. The earliest document in which this word occurs in Asia Minor is a text from the Boghaz-Keui archives (192) in which Anittaš of Kuššar (1950—1920) says that he brought as booty from Hattušaš: "Then the man of Purushkanda was commanded before me. He brought an iron throne and an iron sceptre as commanded". Between 1850 and 1400 several ceremonial weapons of iron were made and exported as it seems. Boghaz Keui texts mention iron statuettes and iron foundation tablets or tablets for treaties. Thus BK II No. 1, Rs. IV, 5 mentions 10 gold objects and 11 wrought iron "ALAM" (salmu), probably tablets for a temple. No reference is yet made to iron as a trade object but only articles fashioned from iron are mentioned. Richardson may be right in stating that the texts of the Teshub temple may be as late as the reign of Hattušiliš III (1283—1260), but he is wrong when he says that there are no earlier texts (193). We have already given the Anitaš text edited by Hrozny (194) and further texts are sure to appear as the documents from Hittite sites are published. There

is another text (195) (about 1300 B.C.) which runs: "They cover the
wooden beams with plates of silver and gold, the gold they bring
from the city of Bi..., the silver from Kuzza..., black iron of heaven
from the sky...". Campbell Thompson thinks that this meteoric iron
came with the copper from Mout Tagatta mentioned further on in
the text. Therefore the evidence is now overwhelming that iron was
known earlier than Richardson thought. "Black iron" is mentioned
in several texts of different date (196).

Next comes a much debated letter (197): "As to the good iron
(parzillu damqu) which you wrote me about, good iron in Kizzuwatna.
21 in my seal-house is not available. That it is a bad time for
22 producing iron I have written. (But) they will produce good iron;
    so far they will not have finished.
23 When they will have finished, I shall send (it) to you. Today now
24 I have an iron dagger blade brought on its way to you.
25 As for the (armour) which you have sent me (saying): for this
    (armour)
26 send blades in return, so far they have not finished producing (them)
27 (when they will have finished, I shall send) them to you...

Goetze points out that they are only stored in the king's seal-house
in Kizzuwatna but not produced there! He holds that the author of the
letter is Hattušiliš III (Urḫi-Teshup's sucessor), the addressee the Assyrian king Shalmaneser III (1265—1235 B.C.), who was interested
in the town of Turira mentioned in the same letter. The style imitates the
Assyrian document, which arrives at a moment when there is some
tension in the relations between the two kings. Formerly it was believed that the addressee was Ramses II and Meissner's opinion is
that the letter was written by the viceroy of Kizzuwatna to the Hittite
king himself. The second point of the debate was the exact situation
of Kizzuwatna, which Goetze and S. Smith placed in Cilicia in the
Taurus mountains, Winckler, Ed. Meyer, Bilabel, and others in Pontus and Wainwright in the north-eastern corner of Cilicia, as it was
later called Tabal. This name goes back to the Sumerian tibira (smith)
and Naram Sin already refers to a mountain Tibar apparently near
Aram in the far north-western corner of Mesopotamia. Later we find
in Pisidia the city of Seleucia called "Sidera". We, however, still follow
Schachrmeyr and say that at the present time the exact situation of
Kizzuwatna is unknown but it is enough for our story to know that
it is some part of the mountains between Taurus and Pontus (198).

This letter certainly proves, that at this time iron weapons were still rare, that the king of the Hittites had no easy access to the supplies of smelted iron and that the iron was smelted and worked in the region that had already produced copper, gold and silver for many centuries (199). Thus even in the later Hittite Empire iron was not yet very common and iron weapons were certainly not used by the Hittite armies in general before 1200 (200). Though there are iron objects from Tell Halaf around 2000 B.C. there are still scarce in Carcemish nearby eight hundred years later. But gradually more and more iron tools and weapons appear in the years between 1400 and 1200. In this period the bronze production seems to have run short and much old material was remelted and reused, and this was a stimulus to the growing iron industry. The necessity of having a good new material gave the impulse and overcame the objections of more fuel and greater skill that iron metallurgy demanded. Time taught the right processes of "steeling" and gave iron its superiority over bronze. The unrest following the fall of the Hittite Empire at the onslaught of the Peoples of the Sea stayed this evolution for a time, though it spread the knowledge of the smelting and working of iron. Afterwards trade and traffic had found new roads and the copper imports in Asia Minor ran still more short, which gave a new impulse to the iron industry especially after 1000 B.C. Then we first find iron objects imitating bronze types, then equal amounts of bronze and iron copies of the same objects in every site, as well as iron ornaments on bronze objects followed by the use of bronze for the ornamentation of iron and the repairing of bronze with iron parts. Then finally iron fully takes the place of bronze. Thus iron and iron wire are still used for the decoration of bronze weapons in Alishar Hüyük II and iron is still used for ornamental purposes in Koban and Thespiai around 1000 B.C. But between then and 800 there is a strong growth of the production of iron and we find many iron objects in such sites as Kerkenesdagh, Göllüdagh, Gordion, Gâvurkalesi, Gözlü Kule, Pazarli, Alishar Hüyük and Toprakkale, though bronze objects still form the majority still combinations of both metals run scarce and by 700 iron is absolutely supreme. There-fore 1400 to 1000 B.C. must be recognised as the transition from bronze to the full Iron Age. We also point to the Sword god of the Hittites pictured at Yasili-Kaya. Cuissin pointed out that this sword is entirely different from the Bronze Age types and that it belongs to typical iron-workers' products. This line is worth following up and we must remind the future student of this problem of the Scythians "who sacrified to an antique sword, an image of Ares (201) like the Khonds of Hindustani who have a god of iron, Loha-Pennu, who also is a god of war and who is represented in each village by a buried piece of iron.

The picture we gather from Northern Syria, later occupied by a Hittite state, Mitanni, and by smaller successors after its downfall is this. The list of the temple-treasure of Mishrifé-Qatna before the conquest of Thotmes III (1500) mentions seven objects of iron, six of which are set in gold, and it is possible that the *Ty . n' . y* of his seventeenth campaign was on the confines of Asia near Qatna, and that the *bi3* mentioned as a tribute is really iron. There are many iron deposits in Northern Syria and the later Doliche on the road between Cataonia and Tabal to Mitanni may already have played a part in the history of iron of those early times.

Anyhow, in the Amarna letters Mitanni figures as an iron-exporting and perhaps iron-producing country. The presents sent by Tušratta of Mitanni to Amenhotep III of Egypt embrace a *mittu* of *parzillu* covered with 15 shekels of gold (XXII, I, 38), two "handrings of *parzillu* sheeted with gold" (XXII, II, 1—4) and a "dagger the blade of which is made of *parzillu* and the haft of which is covered by lapis lazuli set in gold (XXII, II, 16). Again the presents sent by Tušratta to Amenhotep IV or Akhenaten consist of "ten thin handrings of iron covered with gold, using 30 shekels of gold" (XXV, II, 28). The first letter also mentions "a dagger made of *ḫa-bal-ki-nu*" (two more mentioned in the same letter) and also "ten *giakâtu* of the same material" (XXII, I. 32; III, 49, III, 6). This *ḫabalkin(n)u* is tentatively supposed to be steel for no more reason than that it is a dagger blade. At the same time it comes from a state not far from the Chalybes and there is a certain possible "merchant's garbling" in *ḫabalkinnu* and *chalibikos*. It is therefore permissible to leave the translation as it stands and take this unknown word to mean steel. Possibly the further decipherment of Hittite documents will one day show up the origin of this word.

This brings us again the problem of the Chalybes, those smithing tribes, about which we possess so many classical references (202). These *siderotektones* living in dens and caves on the Black Sea coast between Samsun and Trebizond are said to be "a Scythian tribe, living where the iron was born" (Etymologicon Magnum and Suidas). Sayce derived their name from *khale-wa*, that is "dwelling in the Khale or Halys basin", and he contends that their axe-hammer was not only a battle-weapon but served in smithing as well (203). We do not know whether they lived in Pontus already before the wanderings and in-

vasions of 1200 B.C. Possibly they are related to the Alorodians or
they may be remains of the Khaldi of Lake Van dispersed over a larger
area. But whatever their story may be, it is certain that the Pontic
region played and important part in the history of metallurgy long
before 1200 B.C. and we have dubbed the aborigines of Pontus Chalybes
as long as no other data are forthcoming. Relations between the Chalybes and the inhabitants of the Kuban area and diffusion of iron to
Europe by the way of the Russian steppes remain entirely hypothetical.
It is certain that after 1200 B.C. the Chalybes were working for their
new masters, the Mushki and the Tibareni and therefore it seems more
probable that they were the original inhabitants of the country. The
classical reports which make the Chalybes Scythians has led Hulme
to suppose possible connections with India, not only because of the
connections of the magnetite process of the Chalybes with the Indian
wootz process but also because of the curious story of mice nibbling
iron, which also occurs in Indian tales and may denote the finely divided
state of the magnetite worked. This legend given by pseudo-Aristotle
is, however, more common in the West than usually supposed. Aelian
reports the same peculiar taste of the mice of Teredon in Babylonia and
Theophrastus (204) who adds that the mice devored the iron and steel
of the forges of the Chalybes. Further study of this problem, comparing
the classical reports with the role of mice in the legends of the Near
East will probably throw more light on this question. The Greeks had
some faint ideas on the invention of iron in Asia Minor for the Parian
chronicle on the marble slab now in Oxford records as item 11: "From
the times when Minos the elder was king of Crete and built Apollonia,
and iron was discovered in Ida, the discoverers being the Idaean Dactyls, Kelmis and Damnameneus, in the reign of Pandaion of Athens
(1462—1423 B.C.)".

Though the Cretan Mount Ida is wrongly mentioned instead of
the Phrygian mountain of the same name, the report contains a vague indication that the Greeks believed iron metallurgy to have been evolved
in Asia Minor somewhere around 1400 B.C., which fits in quite well
with the archaeological data for the rise of iron industry in these regions. Apart from the sword-god already mentioned the Hittites possessed a god of the thunderstorm, Teshub, who is also closely connected with iron. In the troubled years around 1200 B.C. a group of
Chalybes migrated to Doliche, bringing their god Teshub of the
double-axe with them and thus they started the cult of the "Baal of
Doliche", who invented iron and who was still worshipped in Roman

times as the "Jupiter Optimus Maximus Dolichenus natus ubi ferrum nascitur". His cult spread in the Roman Empire and we find him as the god of the tree-fellers for the Roman troops in Germany!

The wanderings and invasions of the Peoples of the Sea broke the Hittite monopoly of iron and steel manufacture and iron spread quickly over the Near East. The Shardana of Libya(?) forming part of these peoples are shown on the Egyptian monuments as carrying blue (steel?) weapons, and in Asia Minor the production of iron and steel was taken over by the Traco-Phrygian invaders and spread all over Asi Minor. Thus the industry of Phrygia, Ionia, and Lydia started. Iron tools and weapons are now very common the post-Hittite and Phrygian strata of Alishar Hüyük IV and V contain no less than three times the amount of iron as compared with the older strata. Phrygian slag from working haematite was found in the tumulus of Bos-hüyük (Lamunia). Iron working spread to Europe between 1300 and 700 and we find the Dipylon, Villanova, and Hallstatt civilisations, practically continuations of the Bronze Age, using both iron and bronze weapons. There are typological proofs of the influence of Anatolian bronze types of the first quarter of the first millennium in the Aegean up to Italy and as there are close trade connections with Thrace and the Middle Balkans, there are possibly the lines along which the knowledge of the new metal was carried to Europe (205). Though the iron industry in Asia Minor suffered greatly by the new invasions of Cimmerians, Scythians and Assyrians about 700 and the ores of Central Europe and Spain became more important, partly because of their natural steel production, the industry in Asia Minor still survived and remained important even in classical times. Pontic iron was still most favoured, the best iron for building purposes was Sinopic and Chalybian, while the Lydian iron was favoured for rasps, swords, razors and graving tools. This difference was probably due to both chemical composition and to different methods of tempering, a point which deserves further research. Possibly the difficulty of producing iron made local industry less prevalent than that of copper or bronze and certain great centres remained the producers for the civilised world.

Still there was a blacksmith or two in every town and one must naturally assume that few objects in ordinary use were imported in finished form but that they were made by the local smith in the form or shape desired by the customer from bar-iron. Bronze and iron lay in the workshops of the Cilician pirates (206) and Vespasian had arms made in the most important cities of Asia Minor (207). Cyzicus and

Rhodes were famous for weapons probably on account of their trade with the Black Sea. In Late Republican times Cibyra was especially noted for its chasing and embossing of iron (208) and the Roman publicani exploited the products of the province and also the iron work of Cibyra.

Our conclusion is that ironsmiths in the mountains between Taurus and Caspian Sea experimented with the smelting of iron ores, discovering the trick of making wrought iron and carburising it, possibly by 1800 B.C., and guarding it as a close secret. They started to turn it into tools and weapons by 1400 B.C. or trading it in the form of strips or bars, such as the "currency bars" we will discuss later on. The migrations about 1200 B.C., however, let the cat out of the bag and ironworking spread east and west.

The iron industry of *Cyprus* had no great importance but the constant contacts of this island with Anatolia introduced iron there. Pococke saw iron mines at Paphos, Soli and Bole. The iron working areas were concentrated at Tamassos and Soli. Brown iron ore of some richness is found in the pyritic masses of the igneous regions. Magnetite and specular haematite are also found on the northern slopes of Mavrovouni (209), so there was no need for the islanders to import the metal (210). There is the legend given by Strabo that the Telchines invented copper and iron working in Crete and came to Cyprus by the way of Rhodes, but the archaeological data show quite clearly that iron penetrated Cyprus from the Anatolian hinterland.

Iron figures as a precious metal in jewelry since 1400 B.C. There is the agate sceptre of Kurion now in the Cesnola collection, the sockets of which show traces of iron. An iron arrow-head was found in an old grave of Tamassos and a plated ring at Salamis and also two iron knives with ivory handles in a 1200 B.C. tomb. After 1000 B.C. it is generally used for knives and swords though other objects are still mostly made of bronze, and both metals continue to be used side by side for a very long time even in the Geometric period when there are plentiful types of weapons and tools.

Crete is not very prominent in the story of iron notwithstanding the classical traditions which localise its invention in Crete instead of on the Anatolian mainland. Though Meyer mentions traces of old mines, there are no notable deposits in Crete and Mount Ida is covered with timber but there are no signs of smelting sites. There is no doubt that iron was a foreign metal in the early Aegean. Mosso's lump of un-smelted iron of Neolithic date (Phaistos) turned out to be magnetite (211).

In a tholos of Hagia Triada slags of iron working were found (2000 B.C.) and there is some meteoric iron of the same date in a tholos of Platanos. The Grotto Mavro Spelio at Knossos yielded a cube of iron of MM II date (1800 B.C.). Eight finds of iron finger rings from the Aegean from the period between 1500 and 1200 B.C. are listed by Person (212). But the metal becomes more plentiful after 1200 in the transitional period before the Geometric age. Iron weapons from Muliana, Kavusi, and Knossos are still "bronze types", and bronze tools and weapons continue to be used long side by side with iron ones. Iron gradually becomes supreme in the eight century and a hundred years later iron was used for all kinds of utensils and art objects as the excavations of Olympia show. The Doric invasions brought iron to Crete as is shown by the affinity of the early weapons with Central European types.

Meteorites were known and worshipped in ancient *Greece*. The Iliad describes Athena darting from heaven like a meteor and in the Hymn to the Pythian Apollo the god is represented as having reached Krissa in the same meteoric form. Many meteorites were worshipped in Antiquity for instance the stone of Elagabalos and the stone of Chronos.

Still no objects fashioned of meteoric iron have been found in Greece. The earliest iron workings (slags of Vardarovca C) dates from the twelfth to eleventh century B.C. In Thrace they are hardly older than the ninth (Swords of Alexandrovo and Popovo of typical bronze forms). The general spread of iron in the Aegean in the twelfth century B.C. may be actually connected with the Dorian invasion. Iron may well have spread across the Aegean back along this paths travelled by the Aeolian, Ionian, and Dorian colonists. The last invaders, traditionally the Dorians, may have introduced it in Hellas, which previously received it from Anatolia via Thrace and Macedonia. They merely popularised what was already in use in southern Hellas.

In the Mycenian period iron was still as costly as gold. We have already mentioned the finger rings catalogued by Person and at Mycena Tsountas found some iron chains along with gold chains in late tombs. Iron is used with strips of gold, copper and bronze inlay. Iron did not come from Egypt to Greece as some supposed, for the earliest iron types of Daphnae and Naukratis are definitely Greek or European forms.

From the Geometric period upto the sixth century iron became more and more common. The metal was possibly smelted at Tyrins. Athens and in the Dorian plain from the tenth century onwards (213).

The Greeks knew very well that mankind had passed a period in which iron was unknown. Hesiod (214) speaks of a period "in which there was no dark iron" and Herodotus (215) says that "iron had not yet been discovered to the hurt of man". But in the Homeric Age iron, though wellknown, was still on its probation (216). Men of the sword preferred bronze and Sir John Evans thought that even in 600—500 B.C. steel and iron were common but had not yet superseded bronze entirely.

Iron is mentioned some 49 times in Iliad and Odyssey but it was not a useful metal much earlier than the ninth century B.C. Most of the details which Homer gives such as the tempering of steel by the smith are anachronisms, for they were drawn from contemporary life of the poet. When Homer pictures the wainwright with an iron axe he surely speaks of his own experience. The metal is mentioned several times along with bronze and gold as a form of wealth and therefore it is still a rarity in Late Mycenaean times. The "much-belaboured" lump of "iron" offered at the funeral games is probably a bloom rather than a piece of meteoric iron. Only in one place does the poet describe its manufacture, when he tells us of the divine smith, Hephaestus, and the things he wrought. When the poet speaks of iron arrow-heads, an iron mace or iron axes as used in the shooting contest at the end of the Odyssey, he is certainly quoting from his own experience and draws a false picture of the Mycenaean Age.

Though in the Homeric poems the chalkeus is already a blacksmith, the prizes set by Achilles are a bloom or implements but not iron weapons. The further references to iron in the Iliad and Odyssey merely indicate what Homer though of the use of this new metal and they prove little of its production. The iron which Mentes the Taphian brings to Temesa in Cyprus (or Tempsa in Bruttium as Willamowitz believes) is thought by some to come from the Illyrians!

The Greeks were never prominent in metallurgy and imported their iron mostly in semi-finished condition. It is doubtful whether the Greeks of the epic were very familiar with its production, but the generation of Hesiod already possessed a considerable knowledge of "the softening of iron in glowing mountain fires" (217). The earliest exploitation of ore deposits after 1000 B.C. was probably in the islands rich in ores such as Samothrakè and Euboea and in Sparta and Boeotia.

Here the sagas later bring figures from Pontus, Colchis, Syria and Cyprus but above all from Phrygia. We have pointed out several of them and, therefore refer only to Hellanikos' Phronikos which tells of the Dactyls.

The earliest smelting seems to have been of a simple kind, smelting in small pits with charcoal and forging the still glowing white "mydros" (mass) to wrought iron, a sight still new and wonderful to the man in the street in Croesus' time (218). This iron was not always very good and contained many bits of slag and holes (diplóe). It was often traded in the form of bars like the Spartan obeloi or obeliskoi which may have also served as "roasting-spits" as some contend, but which surely served as money in Sparta and other Peloponesian states before the earliest coinage. Some cult-ceremonies still forbade the use of iron or the touching of iron was taboo for the officiants.

The blacksmith hardened his iron and quenched it, using a "pharmakon" or secret remedy, in cold water. The steel weapons and tools were described as "ioeis" or violet-coloured, common iron being "poliós" or grey but both remain "polúkmetos", difficult to work. The word adamas, untamable, for steel first appears in the writings of Hesiod. Chalybian steel was probably introduced after the colonisation of the Pontic coast.

Periclean iron is often loosely classified as steel, but it should be remembered that the carbon content of ancient iron is often entirely fortitious and tempering remained a difficult art. Therefore the word steel should only be applied if an analysis has shown it to be such. By the end of the seventh century Glaukos of Chios had invented "kóllesis" (welding) and the Samians are said to have discovered (or borrowed) the process of hollow casting for bronze, not iron as the texts claim. Aristarchos of Alexandria (220—145) says that "iron is not cast as bronze" and this certainly remains true for Greek metallurgy.

Laconia, later famous for its steel, may not have begun industrial production before 550 B.C. from the deposits of Portokalio and Kulenda. Lesbos and some of the Cyclades (Cythnos, Seriphos, Siphnos) contain iron ore but there are no certain traces of ancient workings, neither was the splendid chromite ore of Rhodes worked by the ancients.

Euboea and Boeotia were also famous for their iron. Gradually the quality of Greek iron imported. The older samples contain "streaks of raw steel, showing that the carburization took place probably when the bloom was made, rather than during reheating, because these streaks are well below the surface" (219). However, samples of the dowels and clamps used to fasten the blocks of Penthelic marble of the Parthenon together (220) are as a rule carbon-free iron and in some places a steel with a variable carbon content (traces to 0.9%), in other places they also contain slag inclusions. The lack in uniformity in grain is due to overheating. Generally speaking the iron was reheated in a charcoal fire at about 900° C and this gave the varying local carburi-- zation of the surface only as the contact with the charcoal lasted too short a time. Temperature control was of course always the difficulty of the ancient smith! Clamps and dowels from the Artemis temple of

Fig. 48.
Hephaistos, the lame Greek god of the smithy

Magnesia (221) also show a good pure wrought iron with up to 0.9 % of carbon made from pure Greek ores, as the phosphorus characteristic of contemporary Central European iron is absent here.

In the Athens of Pericles iron was worked by foreign residents. Pasion and Kephalos owned armour factories and Sophocles' father is said to have been a blacksmith. The patrimony of Demosthenes includes a sword factory. Pseudo-Aristotle in his passage on Chalybian iron tells us that a fourth-century Sicilian banker made a nice little "corner" in iron "recognizing that iron was an indispensible commodity he once succeeded in buying up the produce of all the smelters of iron and made a profit of 200% when a scarcity arose".

The iron mines of Macedonia were worked in Roman times to, when the charges imposed were half of what had formerly been paid to the kings (222).

In *Italy* the transition to the Iron Age starts between 1100 and 1000, but until 1000 B.C. bronze is still supreme in Etruscan necropoles. In Bologna and its Villanovan civilization iron was quite common about 900 B.C. It is this Villanovan civilisation in its Etruscan form that created Rome, it started the Elban and Tuscan mines (223). The early history of Rome can certainly be seen as Rome striking out for the Etruscan ore deposit. But until the closing years of the Republic iron working remained rustic in its simplicity as we can see from Varro's report on the travelling smiths of his days (224).

Early Rome had its iron-smiths and Porsenna forbade the use of iron except for agriculture (225). The Fratres Aravales had a strict taboo on using iron in many ceremonies and a similar taboo held good for other cult-ceremonies. Iron was said to destroy the work of the spirits who hated it, then it was used to counteract the influence of base spirits.

The people of Populonia furnished iron (226) for the levy in 205 B.C. for Scipio's invasion of Africa, probably from the Elban mines. In the period of 200—150 B.C., the war period, the manufacture of arms must have been extensive. Probably Rome and the municipalities between Rome and Capua supplied most of the weapons needed. Many implements and tools were also in demand if we compare Cato's equipment for his olive orchard (227).

When by senatorial decree Italy was closed for private mining, this did not apply to the iron mines of Elba, the product of which was of the highest importance to the army and the agriculturists. Pliny calls the decree old and we may assume a second-century date. Later references prove that the Elban mines continued their operations, at least they were worked throughout the Gracchan period (150—80 B.C.) and well into the Empire. Elba was one of the earliest Greek places in Italy. Diodor reports on this Elban mining (228): "Near the town of Etruria called Populonia lies the island of Ilva. It abounds in siderite which they mine for smelting and making of iron, since it contains much of this metal. Those engaged in the work crush the rock and roast it in furnaces skilfully made for the purpose. When it has been melted in a strong fire, they cut the matter into parts that look like large sponges. Merchants buy these with money or an exchange of goods and carry them to Dicaearchaea (Puteoli) and other ports. Men who engage the labour of smiths buy these masses of ore and make all kinds of implements of them. Some parts they hammer into weapons, others into hoes, sickles and other useful implements and the merchants carry these everywhere and they are used in every part of the world." It is possible that the iron industry did much to support Puteolian shipping and had already begun in the second century, since Cato finds some of his implements in the Campanian region. The forests of the islands and the mainland coast nearby were not very abundant and the factories of Puteoli (where there was timber and a good harbour) had taken over the work of producing wares from the blooms produced in Elba.

Diodor's report is confirmed by Varro and by Strabo (229).

The State had armories of its own before 100 B.C. (230). Military necessity leads to concentration of the industry in Puteoli, Syracuse, Rhegium, Venafrum, and other centres like Populonia, Volterra, and Minturnae. Thus the way was paved for later government control. Then gradually the industry was transplanted to the provinces in the neighbourhood of the mines. In general there was only a broadening field of industrial application, no technical progress, for there was abundance and the ruling classes had only contempt for industry. The Roman Empire possessed mines of all metals used anciently and was selfsufficient, though certain quality products such as Seric steel might be imported occasionally. State organisation was applied to the largest deposits, but iron was still normally produced by independent labour in many forest regions. Furnaces of itinerant smiths were usual in the Weald, the Jura, Loire Inférieure, and Yonne. In Bosnia, Chalcidice, and England slag derived from smelting is frequent on both Roman and pre-Roman sites, showing that the ore was collected locally and reduced as needed, just like the bog ores of Germany. Gaul supplied itself and the armies on the Rhine. Only in times of war in towns like Beuvray or when the ore was abundant and of good quality, especially if it occured in massive formation and not in thick beds which could be attacked by shallow pitting, the Romans confiscated the mines, as in Aude or Carinthia, and entrusted the management to imperial lessees.

The blooms from forest furnaces were welded together into large blocks as current in Roman trade in such installations as found in Corbridge, Cedworth, and Sarmizegethusa. They were often bought by the military, who had a smithy in every important station, which thus accounts for the slag so frequent in Roman forts in England and elsewhere. It was also common in Roman villas, where the ordinary tools, required locally, were manufactured or repaired as had been usual even in Homeric days. The magnetite sand from Avellino, east of Naples may have fed part of the iron industry of Southern Italy.

Iron slag found in association with small brick-lined furnaces under St. Saba church proves that forges existed in the capital.

In the Early Empire there was a very large guild of fabri at Milan and also an unusually large number at Brescia (Brizia). Como was famous in Pliny's days for its iron industry. Aquilea was probably deeply interested in the famous iron mines of Noricum; Roman state-contractors who handled the mines lived there but very few fabri! Populonia has still a few iron-workers but most of the iron trade had gone to Puteoli. Since inscriptions there mention no guilds of fabri, it is probable that slave-labour manned the numerous smithies of the town.

Still, to a far greater extent articles were made and sold in small shops. It would seem that the making of iron tools was partly in the hand of individual smiths, partly in the hands of firms who produced articles in large amounts under a system half-way advanced towards factory production. Even at Capua where silver-plate was more or less a factory product, iron utensils were made more often in small shops and Rome itself had many individual iron-workers. The capital has a strong guild of fabri ferrarii (231) with specialists making only helmets, shields, swords, knives, locks and nails. Rome had even a street names Vicus...ionum Ferrariarum (232). Probably there was a chalkeus or two in every town, Vespasian found sufficient smiths to make his arms (233).

Pontic iron was still most favoured, Sinopic and Chalybian iron were used for building purposes, Lydian iron was favoured for rasps, swords, razors and graving tools (234).

The Romans of the Imperial Period understood the making of different kinds of steel, having adopted many methods of the Celtic smiths. Roman swords of the Nydam find were analysed by Neumann (235) who found that three methods were followed: a) welding on damask-strips on both sides of a hard steel blade; b) cutting edges of hard steel welded on iron and c) case-hardening and forging iron. He showed that some of the typical structures changed into more stable forms in these old samples buried so long in the soil. During the conquest of Roman *Spain* direct State exploitation was no doubt the rule notwithstanding Diodor V. 36., though modern exploration does not bear out the classical reports on "richness in iron", except in the Basque provinces which were hardly explored before the middle of the first century A.D. (236). But the Early Empire found iron in the large area stretching from Baetica through Dianium, Bilbilis and Cantabria to the coasts of Gallaecia (237) though it was best known to the world in its manufactured form. Arms and cutlery were the articles ordinary exported. The fame was mostly due to particular manufacturing met-

hods such as steeling by burial (238) or to the special quenching qualities of certain waters (Martial, Justin, Pliny). The importance of this
industry to Rome is attested by a wealth of records of societies, officials
and private individuals connected with the extraction, manufacture
or distribution of the iron. Certain alluvial beds like those of Catalonia
and Alicante and also Toledo were worked in the Later Empire and
the Middle Ages.

Roman *Gaul* contained the relics of many older smelting sites and
enormous masses of slags have been found which can not be dated
precisely. Many blooms of Celtic date have been found spread all
over the country, though there is possibly some connection between
the bloomeries and the rise of some towns. Some oppidae like Bibracte
had an important iron industry and Caesar mentions the ingenuity
of the Bituriges and their iron mines in the country surrounding the
present Bourges (239).

Maréchal (240) believes that he found proofs that iron was treated
with nitrogen-compounds to increase hardness (and brittleness!) in
objects of La Tène from France, Bohemia and Poland.

In Roman *Britain* the important phase of the Roman industry falls
between 250 and 360 A.D., when iron slags were also used for road
repairs. Iron was mined in many places especially the Weald and the
forest of Dean in Roman times. Caesar's "coastal regions of Britain"
(241) probably refer to the former. These deposits were, however,
inconsiderable when compared with the central iron deposits exploited
by the Romans. The iron ores first used were evidently clay ironstones
from the Lower Cretaceous Wealden forest area in Kent and Sussex,
some of the Jurassic weathered oolites (that is, limonites) outcropping
under the Ooltic Limestone between Oxfordshire and Lincoln, Lower
Lias south of the Humber — all low grade deposits but more manage-
able than better ores. There is evidence of working, in all cases mentioned, by Roman times, when also haematite in the Carboniferous
Limestone of the Forest of Dean and the Vale of Glamorgan, near
Barrow-in-Furness and in Cumberland was used on a large scale (242).

The iron production of Britain was quite considerable, as Colling-
wood has it "every town had its blacksmiths, every fort its regimental
smithy, every villa its forge".

The slag heaps of the forest of Dean range from the first to the fourth
century in date, traces of smelting also exist in Glamorganshire. Pre-
Roman smelting sites were found in the Mendips and near Glaston-
bury. Other Roman smelting sites were found in Lincolnshire, Not-

tingham, North Wales and on the Lancashire-Cheshire border. In the forests of the North iron slag is not infrequently found in circumstances which prove that iron was produced locally for the use of the garrison. Iron-smelting was done at some villas (At Ely near Cardiff, etc.). The use of malleable iron by the blacksmith in making various kinds of objects is attested by vast quantities found at different sites. But often they have not been analysed owing to their rusty condition and their bulk and variety have been overlooked. Here and there we can trace blacksmith's work which seems to have been done commercially, the Wroxeter finds were hardly meant for local shops only. Again some iron objects especially knives and centre-bits bear the maker's name!

In *Central Europe* the Iron Age begins with the Hallstatt period (1000 B.C.) which preceeds the La Tène civilisation (400 B.C.). The bearers of the Hallstatt civilisation were the Illyrians, but the La Tène period is that of the Celts who were the clever smiths, making tools, weapons and bars of iron for trade purposes, with whom Caesar had to contend. "Their steel is hard and pliable" says Philon when telling of the method of burying the wrought iron before the forging of steel. Carinthia, Carniola and Styria as well as Tyrol abound with useful iron ores such as magnetite, haematite, limonite and above all the famous spathic iron. The furnaces are either of the simple pot-bowl type or the more complicated shaftfurnace and primitive forms of Stückofen seem to have been used in the Later La Tène period. The Hallstatt civilisation knew case-hardening only, but the Celts had various methods of "steeling" such as the false-damascening which consisted in welding harder and softer strips together. Some of the natural steel quite free of sulphur and phosphorus must have been difficult to forge as it was liable to form cracks. As the hardening can be easily found under the microscope it is proved that we can still analyse the ancient methods of working iron and steel on the excavated samples though sometimes the structure is slightly changed by time.

The bog-iron industry of Europe has the character of village iron-smelting. In Noricum much smelting is done in the hill-top settlements, the mines being worked from Hallstatt to well into Roman times.

The Romans controlled the Noric fields directly just like the Sana valley in Bosnia, local workings were gradually concentrated into larger fields. The slag found in Noricum amounts to some 100.000 Tons which may be equivalent to 30.000 Tons of iron, lime was the usual flux as proved by finds at Eisenberg. In Noricum most traces of

the older workings disappeared where the Romans started exploitation (Huttenberg); only the Romans do seem to have preferred the
whether yellow and white ores, while rejecting the spathic iron. Some
of these ores contain titanium, an excellent component to make steel
with. The bars or blooms of iron were probably no longer worked on
the spot but exported to Aquilea. Iron was also mined on the Styrian
Erzberg between Eisenerz and Vordernberg, where coins prove exploitation upto at least 316 A.D. Further north there were many
Roman workings in Central Jura, North-Eastern Gaul, Luxemburg,
Northern Alsace, near Trier and in the Eiffel. In Central Germany the
bog-ore was exploited locally.

The Romans adapted not only the methods but also many of the
tools of the Celtic smith (243). Only the form of bars of crude iron
do not seem to have been imitated for the Celts used a peculiar double-
pyramid form. There are two types of Celtic bars (244), the short ones
from the south about 30 cms long and the longer ones of the north
ranging from 40 to 60 cms. They weigh about 3—10 Kgrs. Both
belong to the Illyrian-Celtic civilisation as they are found in Germany
inside of the Limes. As many of these bars are adjusted to a certain
weight and sometimes bear stamps of guarantee they also seem to have
served as precursors of money like the currency bars and "Schwur-
schwerter" of prehistoric Europe.

The Hallstatt period (and the Iron Age) may have begun in 1000
B.C. but up to about 750 B.C. iron objects were mainly ornaments,
only after 750 the proportion of iron versus bronze objects begins to
rise markedly, and the true Iron Age is the La Tène period, in which
the Celtic smith dominates. Thus though iron is introduced into Britain
about 450 B.C., large scale smelting begins only by 200 B.C. By that
time the iron-smiths of Europe were turning out iron in the form of
strips of forged iron of about eleven ounces each, "currency bars"
in unit values of $\frac{1}{4}$, $\frac{1}{2}$, 1, $1\frac{1}{2}$, 2 and 4 units.

The Germans originally did not know iron but began to work it
in the fourth century and produced iron and steel locally mainly from
bog-ore. The smelting was conducted in forest-smithies which form
remained popular in Germany until well in the Middle Ages (245).
In Siegerland both the primitive pot-bowl furnaces and small Stuck-
ofen are found (246). Good manganese-holding ores and oak charcoal
produced iron and steel of widely varying composition. At Hallstatt
the native smelting furnaces usually worked spathic iron ore with a
high manganese content, but the slags from the Roman settlement show

that they smelted a haematite with a low manganese, lime and magnesium content (247). All over Europe the smiths usually took what
ore they could lay their hand on, thus in the Low Countries sphaero-
siderites (locally called "klapperstenen") were collected on the high
grounds and smelted in small bowl-furnaces (248). Stückofen were
introduced into Central Germany about 300—100 B.C. (249), earlier
types include shaft-furnaces. In some cases such as the smelting site
at Goldebeck we can study these bowl-furnaces (with a very thin coat
of loam) quite closely as the chimney fell down and covered the remains of the working furnace (250).

Iron metallurgy in Noricum was based on the skill of the best copper-
smiths of pre-historic Europe (251), though Witter wrongly believed
that they invented iron metallurgy and brought it to the east. The
Celtic smiths of this region certainly inspired the rest of Europe and
their work is as good as the simple furnaces and tools they had allowed
them to make. La Tène objects consist of wrought iron, sometimes of
steel, some of the latter having been hardened (252). The process of
making proper steel from iron was indeed understood as was the art
of providing knives and files with proper cutting edges. Hardening
was applied to such parts only which needed it, but tempering does not
seem to have been known or applied before the beginning of our era.
The typical bars of iron weighing some 3—10 kg. were carburised
steel but included slags and other impurities, experiments to forge
them properly proved that the La Tène smith must have been an excellent craftsman with much experience to select the proper type of
bars from such varying steel trade samples.

Gradual improvement of these techniques is shown by the examination of later samples of iron. A nail of the Oseberg ship of Viking
date (253) proved to be a steel with 0.2% carbon and 0.1% phosphorus.
It was made either from the bog ore (myrmalm) of southern Sweden
or the lake-ore (sjomalm) of north-central Scandinavia. The nail was
worked at temperatures above 925°C, forged and then simply air-
cooled or may be dropped in a bucket. Oldeberg has collected the most
important data on the rise of iron metallurgy in Scandinavia (254).
Pleiner (255) has done similar work for iron in Tchechoslovakia, where
a Bronze Age iron-rivetted haft of a dagger was found at Gánovce
(northern Slovakia) but where the real Iron Age comes in the Hallstatt
period only. The ring (sixth century B.C.) from Byči Skála, formerly
believed to have been cast, was proved to have been drop-forged in
dies in two halves and then fire-welded. Piaskowski has done very

extensive work on the rise of iron technology in Poland and he has examined many ancient objects after first studying the methods and theories of the classical period (256). He concludes that there is a steady progress in technique and by the eleventh century the arts of carburization, welding and heat treatment are mastered perfectly (257). Research on ancient Hungarian blooms is now on its way (258).

The Finns, at least the West-Finns, are said to have learnt iron working from the Germans, calling the new metal *rauta* (copper), but by the fourth century A.D. they were already good blacksmiths. From the Kalewala which treats of the origin of iron (Runo IX) we learn that the Finns smelted bog ore.

8. *Steel for Swords*

We have repeatedly mentioned the difficulties of carburizing wrought iron properly in the simple means at the disposal of the ancient smiths and their attempts to develop a good cementation process or a process to manufacture crucible steel. Also we have pointed out that the unequal distribution of the carbon in the "steeled" iron strips and the peculiar structure of the "wootz" cakes of steel tended to produce a pattern on the metal surface which pleased the ancient smiths and which they tended to enhance or embellish. In the course of history several schools arose producing such "damascened" blades of steel or more often composed of a core showing the damascene pattern onto which were welded separately made cutting edges (259). These different schools were:

1. The Caucasus, from which region we have only fairly late examples of this technique (seventeenth to nineteenth century), based on a core of welded damask steel and cutting edges welded in imitation of hypereutectic steel. The decoration is often effected by treatment with acid, giving the metal surface the "pamor" effect of the Javanese kris.

2. In Iran such blades were made of hypereutectic crucible steel with 1.0—1.8% of carbon. The carbide particles are not distributed evenly through the mass but wave-like to form the "poulad" pattern, they have formed dendrites, and the smiths strive after a fibrous structure of their blade.

3. In Malaya and Indonesia welding is applied to achieve the "pamor" effect either by welding together strips of a fibrous structure or by using very thin strips of various surface designs welded together

in wavy designs. The latter method is preferred in Java and Celebes but in Sumatra a homogeneous average carbon steel is the basic strip from which the design is built up. Some believe that this was a local development independent of India or China (260).

4. The Indo-Tibetan region is probably the country of origin of the "Poulad" type of damascened blade.

5. Central Asia and Siberia produced blades of steel cutting edges welded to a wrought iron core and from this still largely unknown centre the damascened blade technique went to China (third century A.D.) and Japan (eighth century).

6. The European school which began in Hallstatt and Etruria and ended in the efforts of the Merovingian and Viking smiths, which we will now discuss in somewhat more detail.

The low and irregular carburisation of early iron could be partly overcome by the primitive smith by using tricks only. Good cutting steel should contain at least 1% of carbon, which is distributed equally over the entire piece of iron only when there is proper and long contact with the hot charcoal. In case-hardened steel, which remains for 4—5 hours at 950° C in contact with the charcoal, the carbon penetrates only about 1/16″ below the surface. Hence the ancient smiths obtained only superficially "steeled" iron, the core remained uncarburized. He could overcome this partial and unequal distribution of the carbon by using the "piled structure" method of "fagotted iron". If a number of thin plates of iron are separately carburized, piled on one other and forge-welded together, the forging so obtained will have much better distribution of carbon throughout its mass. This technique was already used in forging a Luristan sword (seventh century B.C.) which shows a pile of eight strips, hot-forged but cooled in the air (261).

Having succeeded in raising the carbon content of his iron and having brought some portion of it within the range of a steel (262), the prehistoric smith was in possession of a harder material and, due to the presence of the iron carbides, a material with better wear resistance properties. But only by proper quenching and tempering a better cutting tool could be made and this final heat-treatment of his carburized iron was the most difficult and irregular process. The carburization technique certainly goes back to about 1200 B.C., but quenching, for which Carpenter suggested 900 B.C., is now believed to go back to the sixth century B.C. only. This conclusion is more safely based on the examination of early blades. We have already mentioned the Luristan sword as an early example of "piled-structure", another example is the sixth century B.C. spear from Deve Hüyük, and it would seem that this technique goes back to the eighth century B.C.

Without our background of knowledge of the physics and chemistry of metals and guided by practical and visual experience only the ancient smiths could hardly be expected to conquer the techniques of fagotting, carburizing, quenching and tempering quickly. Indeed several Roman objects clearly show how they struggled to find the proper conditions for the various iron objects they made. Thus a Roman chisel (263) proved to have insufficient carburisation and hence the local heat treatment applied to the cutting edge in order to harden it failed!

From our rapidly growing evidence it is now clear that the best approach was started by the Celtic smiths of the La Tène period, who by the third century B.C. had effective ways of forging the slag out of the iron bars and who understood to weld a pile-structure of strips together in order to obtain a more equally carburized blade with sufficient resistance and elasticity. They also applied forging at high temperatures, quenching and annealing with different degrees of success. They learnt also to treat the core separately from the cutting edges starting with a wrought iron, nearly free of carbon, from which the scoria had to be removed by hot-forging.

These techniques were also used by the Etruscans (265) and by the Iberians. The typical Etruscan "spada falcata" is made by welding together layers of soft iron and steel. The Iberian work seems to be of poor metallurgical technique, but it is finely decorated and apparent artificially patinated. Gallic swords found in northern Italy show considerable carburisation (0.5% on the average), a Gallic sword of the first century B.C. even consists of eutectic perlitic steel with 0.7—0.8% of carbon!

Gallo-Roman techniques were no longer based on the use of wrought forged iron strips, but on the use of quenched steel strips. The second to fourth century A.D. is a period of technical revolution amongst the barbarian tribes of Europe on whom Eastern influences begin to impinge. The new blades combine a mild iron or steel (giving the elasticity to sword or dagger) with a steel cutting edge (not quenched in the modern way to give a martensite structure) with a homogeneous grain structure to combine a maximum hardness with a minimum of brittleness. The new impulses in Celtic civilisation and art had definite influence on the Germanic peoples of the north (266) and the typical Celtic sword is now being manufactured there too, vide the Trinnemore find in a peat bog of North Jutland. The later Merovingian and Viking smiths use a similar very homogeneous low-carbon iron for the cutting edges together with a core consisting of strips of high-carbon soft metal, often folded and welded to obtain the desired pattern. The cutting edge is obtained by strong forging. New weapons are developed such as the "fransisca" (a missile axe of asymetric structure, the cutting edge of which is usually carburized by a cementation process), the "scramasax" and the "long-sword" which was soon a favourite weapon not only in Europe but also in the region of the steppes (267). The Arab sources speak of the "Rus" and the "Farang" smiths who excelled in their art and their techniques are copied in the Orient. The "Rus" were the Scandinavian smiths who had adopted the Celtic techniques. From Europe the Arab and Syrian traders import the "blades of the Francs" and the "blades of Cologne".

9. *The nomenclature of iron*

Again we must devote a few lines to the ancient *nomenclature of iron*. The etymology of many ancient words for iron is far from clear. The Sumerian AN . BAR is generally interpreted as "heaven-metal" or "star-metal", but Campbell Thompson believes it to mean "heaven-flash (of the meteor)". But these explanations would infer a very early knowledge of the celestial origin of meteorites. Possibly there is some colour-association in the element "heaven" in this word. It certainly does not mean "foreign metal" as Kirsten contended (268).

Since Hommel (269) gave his etymology of the Semitic forms *par-zillu*, *barzel*, etc., the word *parzillu* has been the subjects of many speculations. Though some still believe that it is derived from a Sumerian BAR . GAL (270) it is now generally believed to be a non-Semitic, Asianic word on account of the ending *-ill*. Bork and Gaerte (271) believed in a Caucasian origin and mention a Caucasian "varkil" for iron as the ancestor of a series of terms for this metal, to which belong both parzillu and ferrum! In Pehlevi steel is called pulafat, New Persian pûlâd, Russian bulatu, Mongol bolot, while similar words are found in Tibetan, Armenian, Ossetic, Grusian and Turkish. In the Old Testament we find "p.lādōt" for steel (272).

Another Iranian expression for steel is al-hindî, al-hinduwânî (the Indian) which occurs in later writings as Hindiah, andaine, andoine, andun or ondanique, the latter four especially in books by European medieval writers on Oriental subjects.

Max Muller (273) suspected that ayas originally meant copper in

Sanskrit and that as iron took its place the meaning of ayas changed and specified.

In passages of the Atharva Veda (11.3) and the Vâgasaneysanhitâ (18.13) a distinction is made between syâman ayas, dark-brown metal, and loham (lohitam) ayas, bright metal; the former meaning copper, the latter iron. This shows that the exclusive meaning of ayas, iron was of later growth and renders it probable that the original Aryan "'ayos" meant the metal par excellence, copper. In Old High-German a new word for metal in general was formed ar-uzi, the modern Erz. Our present Eisen seems to have descended from ayas too. These conclusions are confirmed by Schrader (274) who finds that there was no general Aryan term for iron and that a new word for this metal was formed independently in each of the Aryan languages who originally had words for gold, silver and copper only!

In the Avesta ayah is permanently used for iron, like the later Sanskrit use of ayas.

Sideros has been connected with sidus, star by Pott and Lenormant in analogy with such expressions as AN . BAR, etc. But Tomaschek and Schrader have derived it from a Caucasian or Udic zido! Others again consider zido to have been derived from sideros and Pauli thinks that the latter goes back to a Cretan-Etruscan word(?) and cites a similar Lycian term, the Etruscan sethala, sethlans (Vulcan) and the names Haithalia, Saithalia, Aitháleis used for the islands Lemmos and Elba. On the other hand modern writers such as Muller derive it from "'suîdē-ro-", compare the Lithaunian svidēti, glittering, thus giving it the meaning "glittering metal", a name associated with its colour like that of the other metals.

Chalybs is connected by the scholiasts with Chalyps, son of Ares, but it is probably born in the trade between the Greeks and the Chalybes.

The French *acier*, Italian *acciajo*, Spanish *acero* have been derived from the Latin *acies* (Pliny, *Nat. Hist.* 34, 141, etc.) but others (275) connect it with the Middle-Latin *aciarium*. It certainly first meant the sharp edge, then the steel itself!

The etymology of *ferrum*, the Latin for sword, is still doubtfull The links forged by Bork between *ferrum* and the Semitic *parzillu* of *barzel* remain very weak. Hintner connects it with *videdhrti, fertum*, and says *ferrum* means "the solid"!

Neither is the origin of the modern German *Eisen* fully explained. Pokorny (276) connects *Eisen*, Gothic *eisarn, ísarn*, Celtic *isarnon*, with an Illyrian *'eisâ-rno-m*, which means "the strong" (as compared with bronze) and therefore connected with the Greek *hierós*, strong. The Celts may have taken this name from the Illyrian Veneti who were the bearers of the iron-working Hallstatt culture! The compound-names with the Celtic *isarâ*, strong, are very frequent in place-names or the names of rivers. Grimm, Schrader, and others, however, consider the Gothic *eisarn* as a derivative form of *aiz*, *'ayos*, the Aryan term for copper. *Eisarn* was then later changed in Old High-German to *îsarn*, then to *isan*, the modern *Eisen*, while the Anglo-Saxon *îsern* leads to *îren* and *iron*. It would seem that the latter derivation is the most probable of all.

Having run with seven-league boots through the story of iron we have detected many weak points and many blanks. It would seem to us that exact data on smelting sites and furnaces of iron-workings are possibly still more scarce than in the case of other metals and unless this is repaired by future students we can hardly say with the aged Ilmarinen, the supersmith of the Kalewala:

> "Now I know whence comes the Iron
> And of Steel the evil customs."
>
> (*Kalewala*, Runo IX, lines 269—270)

BIBLIOGRAPHY

(Further details see my Bibliographia Antiqua, Philosophia Naturalis
and its Supplements I (1950) and II (1963))

1. KORAN, *Sura* 57, 25
2. PLINY, *Nat. Hist.* XXXIV. 139
3. BRAUN, P., *Les Tabous des Feriae* (Année Sociologique 1959, 49—
   125)
   DUNBAR, G., *Other Men's Lives* (London, 1939, 259)
   GOLDZIHER, I., *Eisen als Schutz gegen Dämonen* (Arch. Relig. wiss.
   X, 1907, 41)
   THORNDIKE, L., *History of magic and experimental science* (London,
   1929, 2 vols.)
   KENNETT, R. H., *Ancient Hebrew social life* (London, 1933)
4. PLINY, *Nat. Hist.* XXX. 17; XXXVII. 60
5. PLINY, *Nat. Hist.* XXIII. 81
6. PLINY, *Nat. Hist.* XXIV. 17; XXV, 106
7. PLINY, *Nat. Hist.* XXXIV. 149
8. PLINY, *Nat. Hist.* XXXIV. 142
9. PLINY, *Nat. Hist.* XXXIV. 147—148
10. PLINY, *Nat. Hist.* XXXVI. 126—130
11. PLINY, *Nat. Hist.* XXXVI. 145
12. PLINY, *Nat. Hist.* XXXVI. 149
13. PLINY, *Nat. Hist.* XXXIV, 117
14. PLINY, *Nat. Hist.* II. 147
15. PLINY, *Nat. Hist.* XXXIV. 143
16. PLINY, *Nat. Hist.* XXXIV. 142
17. DIODOR, V. 13
18. PLINY, *Nat. Hist.* XXXIV. 151—155; DIOSCORIDES, V. 93—94
19. VITRUV, VII. 7. 2
20. STRABO, 17. 2. 2. cap. 821
21. DEUT. 8. 9
22. JOSEPHUS, WARS 4. 8. 2
23. PLINY, *Nat. Hist.* XXXVI 4. 128; STRABO, 13. 1. 56. cap. 610
24. APOLL. RHOD., *Argon.* II. 141
25. PLINY, *Nat. Hist.* XXXVI. 128
26. STRABO, 13, 4. 17. cap. 631
27. STRABO, 14. 2. 7. cap. 654
28. STRABO, 10. 3. 22. cap. 473
29. XENOPHON, *Anabasis* V. 5. 1; STRABO, 12. 3. 19; PLINY, *Nat.
    Hist.* XXXIV. 142
30. STRABO, 5. 1. 8. cap. 214
31. STRABO, 3. 4. 17. cap. 164; 4. 2. 2. cap. 191

32. STRABO, 4. 5. 2. cap. 199
33. STRABO, 3. 2. cap. 146; 3. 4. 6. cap. 159
34. STRABO, 5. 2. 6. cap. 223; DIODOR, V. 13
35. GILLE, B., *Le moulin à fer et le haut-fourneau* (Métaux et Civilisations I., 1946, 89—94)
    JOHANNSEN, O., *Zur Geschichte des Hochofens* (Stahl und Eisen 28, 1908, 786)
    PASCHKE, M., *Eisen in geschichtlicher Darstellung* (Giesserei 22, 1935, 535—561)
36. PLINY, *Nat. Hist.* XXXIV. 143—146
37. ARISTOTLE, *Meteor.* IV. 6. 11
38. THEOPHRASTUS, *On Stones* cap. 9
39. PLINY, *Nat. Hist.* XXXIV. 149
40. PLINY, *Nat. Hist.* XXXIV. 141
41. APOLL. RHOD., *Argon.* II. 1001—1007
42. RICKARD, T. A., *Man and Metals* (London, 1932, 2 vols.)
    RICKARD, T. A., *The early use of metals* (J. Instit. Metals, 43, 1930, 297)
    RICKARD, T. A., *Iron in Antiquity* (J. Iron Steel Inst. 120, 1929, 323)
    ZIMMER, G. F., *The use of meteoric iron by primitive men* (J. Iron Steel Inst. 94, 1916, 306)
43. RICKARD, T. A., *Drift iron* (Geogr. Review XXIV, 1934, 525)
    SAYCE, R. U., *Primitive arts and crafts* (Cambridge, 1933)
    RICKARD, T. A., *The knowledge and use of iron among the South Sea islanders* (JRAI 62, 1932, 1—32)
44. HEIDE, Fr., *Kleine Meteoritenkunde* (Berlin, 1934)
    RAYLEIGH, LORD, *Meteorites and some problems which they present* (Endeavour Oct. 1944, 127—134)
    BUDDHUE, J. D., *Synthetic Metallic Meteorites* (Pop. Astron. LVI, 1948, 105—108)
45. PLINY, *Nat. Hist.* II. 147
46. LARKE, W. J., *Iron and Steel* (Nature 186, 1935, Suppl. to no. 3427)
47. CARPENTER, SIR H., *Native Iron from Greenland* (Nature July 27, 1935, 152)
48. NIELSEN, N., *Evidence on the extraction of iron in Greenland by the Norsemen* (Meddelelser om Grønland 76, 1930, 193)
49. HULME, E. WYNDHAM, *Early iron-smelting in Egypt* (Antiquity XI, 1937, 222)
    PEAKE, H., *The spread of iron-working* (Geogr. Review XIII, 1933, 63)
    QUIRING, H., *Die Erzgrundlagen der ältesten Eisengewinnung* (Z. f. prakt. Geol. 41, 1933, 128)
50. HULME, E. WYNDHAM, *Prehistoric and primitive iron smelting* (Engineering 146, 1938; 632; 148, 1940, 498—500)
51. ARISTOTLE, *de Mirab. ausc.* 25—26
52. PLINY, *Nat. Hist.* XXXIV. 141
53. HULME, E. WYNDHAM, *Iron-smelting with lake and bog-iron ores* (Antiquity XI, 1937, 221—222)

54. AGRICOLA, G., *Zwölf Bücher vom Berg- und Hüttenwesen* (De Re Metallica) (Berlin, 1929)
BIRINGUCCIO, V., *Pirotechnia* (edit. Johannsen, Braunschweig, 1925)
THEOBALD, W., *Des Theophilus Presbyter Diversarium Artium Schedula* (Berlin, 1933, 165—168)
55. HULME, E. WYNDHAM, *Antiquity* VII, 1933, 363
56. PAUSANIAS, X. 18. 6
57. LUCAN, VI. 403
58. PLINY, *Nat. Hist.* XXXIII. 30
59. HESIOD, *Theogony* 864—868
60. ILIAD, XXIII. 826
61. ARISTOTLE, *Meteor.* IV. 6
62. DANIEL, II. 31—41
63. PLINY, *Nat. Hist.* XXXIV. 141
64. HULME, E. WYNDHAM, *Prehistoric and primitive iron-smelting* (Trans. Newcomen Soc. XVIII, 1937/38, 181—192)
65. SCHMITZ, F., *Orientalischer Damaststahl* (Beitr. Gesch. Techn. Ind. XX, 1930, 81—86)
66. DESCH, C. H., *Some properties of steel with globular cementite* (J. Iron Steel Inst. 107, 1923, 249—266)
67. HADFIELD, R., *Sinhalese iron and steel* (J. Iron Steel Inst. 1912, 134)
68. JOHANNSEN, O., *Die Erfindung der Eisengusstechnik* (Stahl und Eisen 40, 1930, 401)
REZORI, H. VON, *Das Gussrohr* (Gas-Wasserfach 93, 1952, 295—297)
69. CARPENTER, H. C. H., and ROBERTSON, J. M., *The metallography of some ancient Egyptian implements* (J. Iron Steel Instit. 121, 1930, 417)
BROWNLIE, D., *History of the cementation process of steel manufacture* (J. Iron Steel Instit. 121, 1930, p. 455)
HADFIELD, R., *Metallurgy and its influence on modern progress* (London, 1933, 2nd edit.)
HADFIELD, R., *History of the cementation process of steel* (J. Iron Steel Instit., vol. 121, 1930, p. 345)
70. PEARSON, C. E. and SMYTHE, J. A., *Examination of a Roman chisel from Chesterholm* (Proc. Univ. Durham Phil. Soc. IX, 1934, 141)
71. ODYSSEY, IX. 459; SOPHOCLES, *Aiax* 650
72. VIRGIL, *Georgics*, IV. 172
73. PLINY, *Nat. Hist.* XXXIV. 146
74. PLINY, *Nat. Hist.* XXXIV. 145, ISIDORE, *Orig.* XVI. 20. 1; MARTIAL IV. 55. 15
75. PLINY, *Nat. Hist.* XXXIV. 146; HIPPOCRATES, *coic. praenot.* 384; PLUTARCH, *de prim. frig.* 13, p. 950 C
76. JUSTIN, XLIV, 3. 8
77. COGHLAN, H. H., *Notes on prehistoric and early iron in the Old World* (Oxford, 1956)
GILLE, B., *La Technique Sidérurgique et son évolution* (Nancy, 1955)

GOURHAN, A. LEROI, *Notes pour une historie des aciers* (Techniques et Civilisations II, 1951, 4—10)

JOHANNSEN, O., *Geschichte des Eisens* (Düsseldorf, 1953)

LYTTELTON, R. G., *Social consequences of iron and steel* (Engineering 177, 1954, no. 4610, 713—714)

PECO, F., *L'industria siderurgia nel milanese* (Metall. Ital. 1956, 188ff)

SCHULZ, E. H., *Ueber den Werkstoff des Schweisseisen Zeitalters* (Arch. f. Eisenhüttenwesen 26, 1955, 7, 365ff)

SCHULZ, E. H., *Zur Frage der Entwicklung des Stahles für ärtzliche Instrumente* (Sudhoffs Arch. Gesch. Med. Naturw., April 1955)

78. RICKARD, T. A., *The knowledge and use of iron among the South Sea islanders* (JRAI 62, 1932, 1—32)

RICKARD, T. A., *Drift iron* (Geogr. Review XXIV, 1934, 525)

79. BECK, L., *Die Geschichte des Eisens* (Berlin, 1892)

GOWLAND, W., *Metals in Antiquity* (JRAI 1912, 285)

80. SMITH, R. A., *A guide to the Bronze Age Antiquities* (British Museum, 1920)

81. *Ant. J.*, V, 1925, 391

82. RICHARDSON, H. C., *Iron, prehistoric and ancient* (AJA XXVIII, 1934, 555; XLI, 1937, 447)

83. HERTZ, A., *Histoire de l'outil en fer* (Anthropologie 35, 1925, 75)

HERTZ, A., *Iron, prehistoric and historic* (AJA, 1937, 441)

WRIGHT, G. E., *Iron, the date of its introduction into common use in Palestine* (AJA 43, 1939, 458)

HARLAND, J. P., *The use of iron in the Bronze Age* (AJA, 1039, 59)

PRZEWORSKI, ST., *Die Metallindustrie Anatoliens in der Zeit von 1500 bis 700 v. Chr.* (Leiden, 1939)

SMITH, R. A., *Guide to the Antiquities of the Iron Age* (British Museum, 1905, 1)

WAINWRIGHT, G. A., *The coming of iron* (Antiquity X, 1936, 5—25)

SCHACHRMEYER, F., *Herkunft und Verbreitung des Eisens* (Athen. Mitt. 41, 1906, 409)

QUIRING, H., *Über die älteste Verwendung und Darstellung von Eisen und Stahl* (Beitr. Gesch. Ind. Techn. XXII, 1933, 29)

KOSSINA, G., *Die Anfänge der Eisengewinnung und der Eisenbearbeitung* (Mannus, Erg. Bd. VIII, 1931, 1)

KIRSTEN, A., *Persson's Eisen und Eisenbereitung* (Gnomon XI, 1935, 43)

BURCHARDT, M., *Die Eisenzeit in Aegypten* (Präh. Z. IV, 1912, 447)

CHILDE, V. GORDON, *Man makes himself* (London, 1936, 41, 135, 167, 258)

NEUMANN, B., *Die ältesten Verfahren der Erzeugung technischen Eisens* (Berlin, 1954)

MONTELIUS, O., *Wann begann die Verwendung des Eisens* (Präh. Z.V, 1913, 289)

84. ILIAD, VI. 58; XI. 146; X. 425

85. *J. Iron Steel Inst.* 66, 1904, 99
86. CLINE, W., *Mining and metallurgy in Negro Africa* (Paris, 1937)
87. LUSCHAN, E. VON, *Eisentechnik in Afrika* (Z. f. Ethn. 41, 1909, 22—49)
    BALFOUR, J. Inst. Metals 43, 1930, 350
88. FOY, W., *Zur Geschichte der Eisentechnik, insbesonders des Gebläses* (Ethnologica I, 1909, 185)
    FROBENIUS, L., *Kulturgeschichte Afrikas* (Berlin, 1933, 197)
89. BRAIDWOOD, R. J. and WILLEY, G. R., *Courses toward Urban Life* (Edinburgh, 1962, 24)
    CARL, L. and PETIT, J., *Une technique archaïque de la fabrication du fer dans le Mourdi* (Sahara Oriental) (Ethnographie 50, 1955, 60—81)
    FAGG, W., *Ironworking with a stone hammer among the Tula of Nigeria* (Man 1952, no. 76)
    JEFFREYS, M. D. W., *Some notes on the Bikom Blacksmiths* (Man 1952, no. 75)
    WAINWRIGHT, G. A., *The coming of iron to some African peoples* (Man 42, 1942, 61, 103—108)
90. HADFIELD, R., *Egyptian iron* (Trans. Faraday Soc. XI, 1916, 183)
91. GSELL, M., *Eisen, Kupfer und Bronze bei den alten Aegyptern* (Diss. Karlsruhe, 1910)
92. BURCHARDT, M., *Die Eisenzeit in Aegypten* (Präh. Z. IV, 1912, 447)
93. GRIFFITHS, J. GWYN, *The tools of the Pyramid builders* (ASAE 53, 1955, 149)
94. SOLDI, E., *Sur l'hypothèse du fer en Egypte pendant les premières dynasties* (Bull. Soc. Anthrop. (3) IV, 1881, 34)
    LEPSIUS, C. R., *Die Metalle in de Aegyptischen Texten* (Berlin, 1878)
    GRAPOW, H., *Die bildlichen Ausdrücke des Aegyptischen* (Leipzig, 1924, 59)
95. DYKMANS, G., *Histoire économique et sociale de l'ancienne Egypte* (Paris, 1936, I. 202; II. 151)
    LUCAS, A., *Ancient Egyptian Materials and Industries* (London, 1934, 151, 153, 193, 405)
96. PETRIE, SIR W. FLINDERS, *Arts and Crafts of Ancient Egypt* (Edinburgh, 1909)
97. FRIEND, J. NEWTON, *Iron in Antiquity* (London, 1926)
98. WAINWRIGHT, G. A., *Iron in Egypt* (JEA XVIII, 1932, 3—15)
    WAINWRIGHT, G. A., *Amun's Meteorite and Omphaloi* (Z. Aeg. Spr. 71, 1935, 41)
99. HERTZ, A., *Iron, prehistoric and historic* (AJA 1937, 441)
100. DÜMICHEN, J., *Hist. Inscr.* II, 1869, 56
101. COOK, *Zeus* II, 1940, 885
102. WAINWRIGHT, G. A., *Predynastic iron beads in Egypt* (Man XI, 1911, no. 100)
103. CHILDE, V. GORDON, *The Most Ancient East* (London, 1934, 114, 118, 189)
104. WAINWRIGHT, G. A., *The coming of iron* (Antiquity X, 1936, 5—25)

105. HAWKES, C., *Early iron in Egypt* (Antiquity X, 1936, 355)
106. DUNHAM, DOWS, and YOUNG, W. J., *An occurence of iron in the fourth dynasty* (JEA 28, 1942, 57—58)
107. HALL, H. R., *Note on the early use of iron in Egypt* (Man, III, 1903, no. 86)
     HALL, H. R., *The early occurence of iron in Egypt* (Man V, 1905, no. 40)
108. CARTER, H., *The tomb of Tut-ankh-amun* (London, 1927, II. 248)
109. LANG, A. *Bronze and iron in Homer* (Rev. Arch. VII, 1906, 280)
110. HERODOTUS, II. 86 & 125
111. AAA, 1911/12, 45
112. LECLANT, J., *Le fer dans l'Egypte ancienne, le Soudan et l'Afrique* (Le Fer a travers les ages, Nancy, 1956, 83—91)
     WAINWRIGHT, G. A., *Early records of iron in Abyssynia* (Man, 42, 1942, no. 43)
     GARLAND, H. and BANNISTER J. O., *Ancient Egyptian metallurgy* (London, 1927)
113. HERODOTUS, VII. 69
114. REILL, TH. *Beiträge zur Kenntniss der Gewerbe im Hellenistischen Aegypten* (Diss. Leipzig, 1913, 59, 64, 68)
115. SYRIA, III, 286
116. SCHAEFFER, CL., *Ugaritica, études relatives aux découvertes de Ras Shamra*, I (Paris, 1939)
117. VIROLLEAUD, CH. *Les tablettes de Mishrifé-Qatna* (Syria IX, 1928, 90—96; XI, 1930, 311—342)
118. WISEMAN, D. J., *The Alalakh Tablets* (London, 1953, nos. 56 & 366)
119. ARM V. 5
120. MAISLER-MAZAR, B., *Excavations at Tell Qasila* (Jerusalem 1951) (Israel Explor. J. I, 1950/51, 61—73, 83; 125—140; 194—218)
     MAISLER-MAZAR, B., *Eretz Israel, Archaeological, Historical and Geographical Studies I* (Jerusalem 1951)
     VOGT, E., *Biblica* 33, 1952, 560—561
     NORTH, R., *Verbum Domini* 32, 1954, 44
121. TUFNELL, O. S., *Lachish III, The Iron Age* (Oxford, 1953)
122. LIGHTNER, M. W., *Analysis of iron implements from Tell Beit Mirsim* (BASOR no. 119, 1950, 22—23)
123. GORDON, CYRUS H., *The role of the Philistines* (Antiquity XXX, 1956, 22—26)
     MAYANI, Z., *Les Hyksos et le monde de la bible* (Paris, 1956)
     WITTER, W., *Die Philister und das Eisen* (Forschungen und Fortschritte XVII, 1941, 223—225)
124. ALBRIGHT, W. F., *The archaeology of Palestine and the Bible* (Chicago, 1932, 104—105)
125. 2. *Sam.* 12. 31; 1 *Ki.* 6. 7; 2 *Chron.* 26. 14; *Is.* 44. 12; 54. 16
126. II *Sam.* 19. 31
127. *Jos.* 8. 31
128. *Deut.* 4. 20; I *Ki.* 8. 51; *Jer.* 11. 4

129. *Job.* 20. 24; *Is.* 41. 7
130. DIETERICH, *Abraxas*, 191
131. *Jer.* 27. 19
132. JOSEPHUS, WARS VII. 8. 4
133. *Eccl.* 38. 28; 48. 17
134. I *Chron.* 29. 7; JOSEPHUS, *Ant.* VII. 14. 9
135. II *Ki.* 24. 14
136. BANERJEE, M. N., *Metals and metallurgy in Ancient India* (Indian Hist. Quart. III, 1927, pp. 121, 793)
    BANERJEE, M. N., *Iron and steel in the Rigvedic Age* (Indian Hist. Quart. V, 1929, pp. 432—440)
    BANERJEE, M. N., *A note on iron in the Rigvedic Age* (Indian Hist. Quart. VIII, 1932, pp. 364—366)
137. GORDON, D. H., *The early use of metals in India and Pakistan* (JRAI LXXIX, 1949/52, 55—78)
    SINGH, S. D., *Iron in ancient India* (J. Econ. Hist. Orient. V, 1962, 212—216)
138. BRITTON, S. C., *Ancient Indian Iron* (Nature 134, 1934, 238)
    DAEVS, K., *Ursachen der guten Erhaltung alter Eisensorten* (FuF XIII, 1937, p. 203)
139. URE, *Dictionary*, III, 1867, 764
    CRACROFT, W., *Smelting iron in the Khasya hills* (J. As. Soc. Bengal vol. I, 1832, p. 150)
140. PLINY, *Nat. Hist.* XXXIV. 150
141. HERODOTUS, VII. 65
142. QUINTIUS CURTIUS, IX. 24
143. WARMINGTON, E. H., *The commerce between the Roman Empire and India* (Cambridge, 1928)
144. SCHOFF, W. H., *The eastern iron trade of the Roman Empire* (JAOS XXXV, 1915, 224)
145. CLEMENS ALEX., *Paed.* II, 3. 189 P
146. PLINY, *Nat. Hist.* XXXIV. 145; OROSIUS VI. 13. 2, APULEIUS, *Flor.* 6; PERIPLUS 6, 39, 49, 56, 64
147. DUNBAR, G., *Other men's lives* (London, 1939, 259)
148. NEEDHAM, JOSEPH, *The development of iron and steel technology in China* (London, 1958)
149. READ, T. T., *Iron metallurgy in Shansi, China* (Trans. Amer. Inst. Min. Eng. XLIII, 1929, 3)
    READ, T. T., *The early casting of iron* (Geogr. Rev. XXIV, 1934, 54)
    READ, T. T., *Chinese Iron, a puzzle* (Harvard J. Asiat. Stud. II, 1937, 398)
150. PINEL, M. I., *Composition and microstructure of ancient iron castings* (Techn. Publ. no. 882, Amer. Inst. Min. Met. Eng., January 1938)
    DONO, Ts., *The chemical investigation of ancient metallic culture in the Orient* (J. Fac. Sci. Imp. Univ. Tokyo, sect. I, vol. III, 6, 1937, 287)

LAUFER, B., *The beginnings of Porcelain in China* (Chicago, 1927, 79)

WALEY, A., *Note on Iron and the Plough in Early China* (Bull. School Orient. Afric. Stud. London, XII, 1947/48, 803—804)

151. GALE, E. M., *Discourses on Salt and Iron* (Leiden, 1931)

152. SPENCE, M. and NEEDLER, W., *An iron dagger from Luristan* (Bull. R. Ontario Mus. Archaeol. 23, 1955, 14—23)

153. ROBERTSON, J., *An account of the iron mines of Caradogh* (Pract. Mechanic. Dec. 1843, 84—86)

DEGEN-KOVALEVSKY, B. E. *Sur l'histoire du fer en Transcaucasie d'après les données de fouilles d'une ancienne usine de fer exécutées en 1930 à Tchuber, Haute Svanie* (IGAIMK vol. 120, 1935, p. 238)

154. LAUFER, B., *Sino-Iranica*, 515

155. BECKER, H., *Leo Frobenius und die Brille des Islam* (Der Islam IV, 1913, 311)

156. HESS, J. J., *Die Bedeutung des Namens der Türken* (Der Islam IX, 1919, 160)

157. POLO, MARCO, *The Travels of...* (London, 1918, I, cap. 14 & 39)

158. DESCH, C. H., *Report Sumerian Copper Committee* (Brit. Assoc. Adv. Sci., Sect H, 1928/29)

PLENDERLEITH, H. J., *Metal Technique* (Ur Excavations, London, 134, II, 293—294)

159. MALLOWAN, M. E. L., *Excavation at Tall Chagar Bazar* (Iraq III, 1936, 26)

160. PARROT, *AfO* XII, 1938, 310

161. DESCH, C. H., *Letter on a hoard of copper objects found at Tell Asmar* (The Times, July 28th, 1939)

FRANKFORT, H., *Iraq Excavations of the Oriental Institute* 1932/1933 (Chicago, 1933, 59)

FRANKFORT, H., *Early Iron in Iraq* (Man 50, 1950, no. 160, 100)

162. MEISSNER, BR., *Babylonien und Assyrien* (Heidelberg, 1920/5, 2 vols.)

163. SCHEIL, V., *Pa-ar-zi-lu*, *"fer" sous la première dynastie* (RAss XXV, 1928, 42)

164. CT. VI. 25a

165. SMITH, S., *Early History of Assyria to* 1000 *B.C.* (London, 1928, 292)

166. ARL, I. 247

167. ARL, I. 405

168. ARL, I. 411

169. HERTZ, A., *Iron, prehistoric and ancient* (AJA, 1937, 441) .

170. ARL, I. 443

171. ARL, I. 476, 477

172. ARL, I. 492

173. ARL, I. 498, 501

174. ARL, I. 583, 585

175. ARL, I. 601

176. ARL, I. 740

177. ARL, II. 213

178. Wainwright, G. A., *The coming of iron* (Antiquity X, 1936, 5—25)
179. ARL, II. 178
180. Johns, no. 812, K. 954
181. Harper, 91, K. 620
182. Harper, 1317, K. 5397; Pfeiffer, R. H., *State Letters of Assyria* (New Haven, 1935, 108)
183. YOS, 6. 168
184. Strassmeier, Nab. 428
185. BIN, 1, 162
186. Herodotus, I. 186
187. Sayce, R. U., CAH, III, 19, 172
188. Brown, T. Burton, *Iron objects from Azerbaijan* (Ancient Mining and Metallurgy Committee, Secon Report (II) (Man 1950, 4)
189. Ehrich, R. W. (edit.), *Relative Chronologies in Old World Archaeology* (Chicago, 1954, 65—66)
190. Myres, CAH, I. 109
191. Soden, W. von, *Akkadisches Handwörterbuch* I, 1959, 47
192. KB, IV. 1
193. Richardson, H. C., *Iron, prehistoric and ancient* (AJA XXXVIII, 1934, 555; XLI, 1937, 447)
194. *Orientalní*, 1929, 281
195. BK, IV. 1. 35—40
196. BK, XII. 1; III. 8; XII. 24. I. 8; XV. 9. III. 3
197. KB, I. 14. 20—27
    Goetze, *Kizzuwatna* (Yale Orient. Ser. Researches XXI, 1940, 27—33)
198. Persson, A. W., *Eisen und Eisenbereitung in der ältesten Zeit* (Bull. Soc. R. des Lettres de Lund VI, 1933/34, 111)
    Goetze, A., *Kizzuwatna* (Yale Orient. Ser. Researches XXI, 1940, 27—33)
199. Smith, S., *Early History of Assyria* (London, 1928, 292)
200. Bittel, K., *Bogazköy* (APAW, 1935, no. 1, 13)
201. Herodotus, IV. 62
202. Aeschylus, *Prom. Vinc.* 714; Apollonius Rhod., *Argon.* II, 1002; Virgil, *Georg.* I, 58; Ammianus Marc. XXII. 8. 21; Dion. Per. 768; Avienus, *or. mar.* 947; Valerius Flaccus, 611
203. Peake, H., *The spread of iron-working* (Geogr. Rev. XIII, 1933, 63)
204. Theophrastus, *de natur. anim.* V. 14
205. Przeworski, St., *Die Metallindustrie Anatoliens...* (Leiden, 1939)
    Foltiny, S., *Athens and the East Hallstatt region* (Amer. J. Arch. LXV, 1961, 283—297)
206. Appian, *Mithr.* 96
207. Tacitus, *Hist.* II. 82
208. Strabo, 13. 4. 17; Cicero, *Fam.* 13. 21; Horace, *Epi.* I. 6. 33
209. Casson, St. *Ancient Cyprus* (London, 1937, 136)
210. Plutarch, Alex. 32; Demetr. 21; Clemens Alex., *Strom.* I.

16. 75; EUSEBIUS, *praep. evang.* X. 6. 5; PLINY, *Nat. Hist.* XXXIV. 121; XXXVI. 137

211. H. R. HALL, *The Civilisation of Greece in the Bronze Age* (London, 1928, 252)

212. PERSSON, A. W., *Eisen und Eisenbereitung in der ältesten Zeit* (Bull. Soc. R. Lettres de Lund VI, 1933/34, 111)

213. BROWN, T. BURTON, *The Coming of Iron to Greece* (London, 1956)
    FRÖDIN, *Asine* (1938), 371—373
    DESBOROUGH, *Protogeometric Pottery* (1952) 197, 271, 301
    COOK, JHS, 73, 1953, 120, 122
    COOK, JHS, 67, 1947, 42
    KARO, G., *Die Schachtgräber von Mykenai* (München, 1930, 318)
    COOK, JHS, 70, 1950, 2

214. HESIOD, *Days and Works* 151

215. HERODOTUS, I. 69

216. JEVONS, F. B., *Iron in Homer* (JHS XIII, 1892, 26—31)
    LANG, A., *Bronze and iron in Homer* (Revue Arch. VII, 1906, 280)
    HARLAND, J. PENROSE, *The use of iron in the Bronze Age* (AJA 34, 1930, 59)
    RICKARD, T. A., *The primitive smelting of iron* (AJA 43, 1939, 86—101)
    GRAY, D. H. F., *Metal-working in Homer* (JHS LXXIV, 1954, 1—15)
    HOPKINSON, G., *Prehistoric iron* (J. Iron Steel Inst. 168, 1951, 334)

217. HESIOD, *Theogony* 862—866

218. HERODOTUS, I. 68

219. CAMPBELL, W., and THUM, E. E., *Metal Progress*, Nov. 1931, 43

220. LIVADEFS, C. J., *The structural iron of the Parthenon* (J. Iron Steel Instit. 1982, I, 1956, 49—66)

221. NEUMANN, B. und KLEMM, H., *Metallographische Untersuchung von eisern Dübeln und Klammern aus der über 2200 Jahre alten Artemis-Tempel von Magnesia* (Arch. f. Metallkunde III, 1949, 333—335)

222. LIVY, 45. 29. 11

223. WITTER, W., *Ueber Metallgewinnung bei den Etruskern* (32. Ber. röm.-germ. Komm. 1942, 1—19)

224. VARRO, *de re rustica* I. 16. 4

225. PLINY, *Nat. Hist.* XXXIV. 139

226. LIVY, 28. 45. 13—21

227. CATO, *de agric.* X

228. DIODOR, V. 13

229. *Varro quoted by Servius on Aen.* X. 174; STRABO, 5. 2. 6

230. CICERO, *pro Rabir.* 20; *In Pis.* 87

231. C.I.L. VI, 892

232. C.I.L. VI. 9185

233. TACITUS, *Hist.* II. 82

234. STEPHAN. *Byz. sive Lakedaimon*

235. NEUMANN, B., *Römischer Damaststahl* (Arch. Eisenhüttenwesen I, 1927, 241)

236. LABORDE, M., *The part played by the region of Guipozcoa in the history of the Spanish iron and steel industry* (J. Iron Steel Inst. 164, 1950, 253)

TROJER, F., *Phase structure of a Roman iron-works slag* (Radex Rundschau 1952, 132—136)

QUIRING, H., *Vorrömische und römische Bergwerke in Nordmarokko* (Z. Berg-Hütten-, Salinenwesen 88; 1940, 213—218)

237. PLINY, *Nat. Hist.* III. 30; IV. 112; XXXIV. 149; STRABO 3. 2. 8; 3. 4. 6; MARTIAL IV. 56; XII. 18; JUSTIN 44. 3; SOLINUS 23. 2; SILIUS ITALICUS 1. 288

238. PLUTARCH, *de Garr.* 17

239. KERLEROUX, A. J., *Ancient exploitation de fer dans le Berry* (Techniques et Civilisations V. 1956, 2, 68—76)

MARÉCHAL, J., *Quelques considérations sur les objects trouvés dans la sépulture halstattienne de Vix* (Cote d'Or) (Techniques et Civilisations IV, 1955, 1—28)

MONTALEMBERT, R. DE TRYON-, *La sidérurgie en Gaule* (Techniques et Civilisations IV, 1955, 29—43; 153-172, 187—208; V, 1956, 21—34, 99—112)

PIJASSOU, H., *L'ancienne industrie du fer dans le Périgord septentrional* (Rev. géogr. H. Pyrenées S.O. 28, 1956, 243—268)

240. MARÉCHAL, J. *La nitruration du fer était utilisé par les anciens* (Métaux, no. 391, mars 1958, 133—137)

241. CAESAR, *de Bell. gal.* V. 12

242. TYLECOTE, R. F., *Metallurgy in archaeology* (London, 1962, 175)

SCHUBERT, H. R., *History of the British Iron and Steel Industry* (London, 1957)

STRAKER, E., *Wealden Iron* (London, 1931)

243. OHLHAVER, H., *Der germanische Schmied* (Leipzig, 1939)

244. WEIERSHAUSEN, P., *Vorgeschichtliche Eisenhütten Deutschlands* (Leipzig, 1939)

HINZ, H., *Eisenschmelzen in Bohmstedt und Goldebeck* (Germania 31, 1953, 241)

TÄCKHOLM, U. *Studiën über den Bergbau der römischen Kaiserzeit* (Uppsala, 1937)

KRASA, O., *Vorgeschichtliche Eisenschmelzen im Siegerlande* (Stahl und Eisen, 51, 1931, 1287)

SCHULZ, E. H., *Ueber die Ergebnisse neuer metallkundlicher Untersuchungen alter Eisenfunde...* (Arbeitsgem. Forsch. Landes Nordrhein-Westfalen, Heft 91, 1961, 73—106)

245. TACITUS, *Germania* 6

246. GILLES, J., *Vorgeschichtliche Eisenhüttenfunde des Siegerlandes* (Stahl und Eisen 56, 1936, 252—263)

247. MORTON, F., *Analyse von Eisenschlacken aus der römischen Niederlassung in der Lahn bei Hallstatt sowie von Eisenerzen aus der weiteren Umgebung von Hallstatt* (Germania XXX, 1952, 106—109)

248. MOERMAN, J. D., *Oude smeedijzerindustrie* (Bijdrage Meded. Ver. Gelre LVI, 1957, 3—32)

249. KOSSINA, G., *Die Anfänge der Eisengewinnung* (Mannus Erg. Bd. VIII, 1931, 1)

250. HINZ, H., *Eisenschmelzen in Bohmstedt und Goldebeck* (Germania 31, 1953, 241)

251. WITTER, W., *Ueber die Herkunft des Eisens* (Mannus 34, 1942, 78—81)

252. HANEMANN, H., *Metallographische Untersuchungen einiger altkeltischer Eisenfunden von der Steinsburg* (Sachsen) (Präh. Z. 13/14, 1921/2, 94—98)

HANEMANN, H., *Untersuchung von Rohstahl aus der vorrömischen Zeit* (Stahl und Eisen 51, 1931, 3, 67—68)

226. HAUTTMANN, H. und MORTON, F., *Metallographische Studie eines eisernen Hufeisendolches aus dem Hallstatt Gräberfeld* (Jahrb. Oberoesterr. Musealverb. 100, 1955, 261—262)

SCHMIDT, W., *Norisches Eisen* (Wien, 1932)

253. ZAPFE, CARL A., *A Viking nail 1100 years old* (Wire and Wire Products 30, 1955, 1500—1503)

254. OLDEBERG, A., *Metallteknik under Förhistorisk Tid* (Lund, 1943)

255. PLEINER, *Alteuropäisches Schmiedehandwerk, Stand der Metallkundlichen Forschung* (Československé Akademie, Praha, 1962)

PLEINER, R., *Etat des fouilles relatives à la production ancienne du fer en Tchécoslovaquie et autres pays slaves* (Techniques et Civilisations V, 1956, 113—128)

JARES, V., *Is the prehistoric ring of Byči Skala from cast iron?* (Hutnické Listy, II, 1947, 6, 128—129)

256. J. PIASKOWSKI, *Metallurgy in* G. PLINY's *Historia naturalis* (in Polish), *Archeologia*, Vol. 9 (1959), p. 99.

J. PIASKOWSKI and A. KRAWCZUK, *Metallurgy in works of Aristotle* (in Polish), *Kwartalnik Historii Kultury Materialnej*, Vol. 6 (1958), No. 3, p. 323.

J. PIASKOWSKI, *The technology of metals in XI—XII century based on the Diversarum artium schedula of the monk* THEOPHILUS (in Polish), *Etudia i materialy z dziejow nauki polskiej*, Vol. 3 (1955), p. 143.

257. PIASKOWSKI, J., *Le développement de la technologie de l'acier et du fer en Pologne d'après les examinations metallographiques des produits anciens* (Kwart. Hist. Nauki i Techniki, Num. spéc. 1957/58, 55—76)

PIASKOWSKI, J., *Cemetry from the Eleventh Century at Lutomiersk near Lodz* (Lodz, 1959)

PIASKOWSKI, J. and ROZYCKA, T., *The investigation of iron technology in Polish territory during the Hallstatt and La Tène periods* (in Polish), *Kwartalnik Historii Kultury Materialnej*, Vol. 7 (1959), No. 3, p. 379

PIASKOWSKI, J., *Metallographical examination of iron objects from cemeteries of Great Poland from the Hallstatt period* (in Polish), *Fontes Archaeologici Posnanienses*, Vol. 10 (1959), p. 202.

PIASKOWSKI, J., *Carburising of iron in Antiquity* (in Polish), *Przeglad Mechaniczny,* Vol. 19 (1960), No. 5, p. 130

PIASKOWSKI, J., *Metallographical examinations of iron objects from barrows at Szwajcaria* (Suwalki district) (in Polish), *Wiadomosci Archeologiczne*, Vol. 25 (1958), Nos. 1—2, p. 58

PIASKOWSKI, J., *The iron smelting and working technique in Gdansk* (Danzig) *from the tenth to fourteenth centuries on the basis of metallographical examinations* (in Polish), *Gdanskie Tow. Naukowe*, Prace Komisji Archeologicznej No. 2, Vol. 2 (1960)

PIASKOWSKI, J., *Metallographical examinations of medieval iron products made on archeological relics found in sites of Leczca, Czerchow and Buczek* (in Polish), *Studia z dziejow gornictwa i hutnictwa*, Vol. 3 (1959), p. 7

PIASKOWSKI, J., *Technique of medieval 'damsk' products on the basis of new investigations* (in Polish), *Przeglad Techniczny*, Vol. 80 (1959), No. 15, p. 49

PIASKOWSKI, J., *Development of the metallographic examinations of ancient iron objects in Poland* (Sibrium VI, 1961, 245—248)

PIASKOWSKI, J., *Report on metallurgical research on old iron objects in the years* 1955—1962 (Kwartalnik Hist. Nauki I Techniki VIII, 1963, 1, 77—86)

RADWAN, M. and BIELENIN, K., *La sidérurgie en Pologne centrale au premier millénaire de notre ère* (Rev. Hist. Sider. III, 1962, 163-178)

258. HEGEDÜS, Z., *Loupes de fer dans les Musées Hongrois* (Revue d'Histoire de la Sidérurgie III, 1962/3, 197—207)

259. GOURHAN, A. LEROI-, *Notes pour une historie des aciers* (Techniques et Civilisations II, 1951, 4—10)

SMITH, C. S., *A History of Metallography* (Chicago, 1960)

260. FRANKEL, J. P., *The origin of Indonesian "Pamor"* (Technology and Culture IV, 1963, 1, 14—21)

261. SALIN, E., *Etude physique, chimique et métallographique d'une épée de Luristan* (Rev. Hist. Sidérurgie III, 1962/63, 209—218)

MARYON, H., *Early Near Eastern steel swords* (Amer. J. Arch. LXV, 1961, 173—184)

262. COGHLAN, H. H., *A note upon iron as a material for the Celtic sword* (Sibrium III, 1956/7, 129—136)

263. PEARSON, C. E. and SMYTHE, J. A., *Examination of a Roman chisel from Chesterholm* (Proc. Univ. Durham IX, 1934, 141—145)

G. BECKER, *A cold-soldering process utilized in the manufacture of Roman sword-blades* (Umschau Wiss. und Technik, 63, 1963, 5, 143—144)

264. SALIN, E., *Sur les techniques de la métallurgie du fer de la préhistoire au temps des grandes invasions* (Revue de Métallurgie XLIX, 1952, 165—176)

FRANCE-LANORD, A., *La fabrication des fourreaux à épée à l'époque de la Tène* (Rev. Hist. Sidérurgie I, 1960, 1)

FRANCE-LANORD, A., *Examens métallographiques non-destructifs* (Rev. Hist. Sidérurgie III, 1962/63, 253—270)

FRANCE-LANORD, A., *Les lingots de fer protohistoriques* (Revue Hist. Sidérurgie vol. IV, 1963, 3, pags. 167—178)

C. Panseri, *L'acciaio di Damasco nella leggenda e nella realtà* (Boll. Accad. S. Marciano, Turin 1, 1962, 3—52)

Vaugiraud, S. de, *La cippe de Scarpone et les forgerons gallo-romains* (Rev. Arch. de l'Est X, 1959, 202—209)

265. Coghlan, H. H., *Etruscan and Spanish swords of iron* (Sibrium III, 1956/7, 167—171)

Panseri, C., Garino, C. and Leoni, M., *Richerche metallografiche sopra alcuni lame etrusche di acciaio* (Centro per la Storia delle Metallurgia, II, Milano)

Reggiori, A. and Garino, C., *Technical examination of a group of Gallic swords from northwest Lomarby* (Sibrium II, 1955, 43—55)

Storti, C. and Mariani, E., *Una spada gallica del III periodo de la Tène* (La metall. Ital. XLV, 1953, 141—144)

266. Maryon, H., *A sword of the Viking period from the river Witham* (Ant. J. 30, 1950, 175)

Klindt-Jensen, O., *Keltisk Tradition i Romersk Jernalder* (Aarbøger for Nordisk Oldkyndighed och Historie, 1952, 224—228)

Klindt-Jensen, O., *Denmark before the Vikings* (London, 1957, 81)

Oldeberg, A., *Ett märkligt järnsvärd fran Höganäs i Skane* (Ein bemerkenswertes eisernes Hallstatt Schwert aus Höganäs in Skane) (Vänersborgs Mus. Skriftserie 4, 1952, 27—70)

France-Lanord, A., *La fabrication des épées aux épqoues mérovingiennes et carolingiennes* (Pays gaumais X, 1949, 1—27)

267. Salin, E., *Les techniques métallurgiques après les grandes invasions* (Le Fer a Travers les Ages, Nancy, 1956, 45—56)

Salin, E., *La civilisation mérovingienne. III. Les techniques* (Paris, 1957, 1—115)

268. Kirsten, A., *Persson's Eisen und Eisenbereitung* (Gnomon XI, 1935, 43)

269. ZDMG, XLV, 1891, 340

270. CT, 18, 29, 51a; SL, 74, 316

271. OLZ, 1922, 19; AOF, 8, 1933, 310

272. *Nah.* 2. 4

273. Müller, M., *Lectures on the science of language* (London, 1882, II, 255)

274. Schrader, O., *Sprachvergleichung und Urgeschichte* (Jena, 1906, II. 1)

275. Pliny, *Nat. Hist.* XXXIV, 141

276. Pokorny, J., *Herkunft und Etymologie des Wortes "Eisen"* (Z. vergl. Sprachforschung 46, 1914, 292)

INDEX